First published in Great Britain in 2000
by Brignell Associates
in co-operation with
the European Science and Environment Forum.

ISBN: 0-9539108-0-6

Cover picture by Barry Diaper

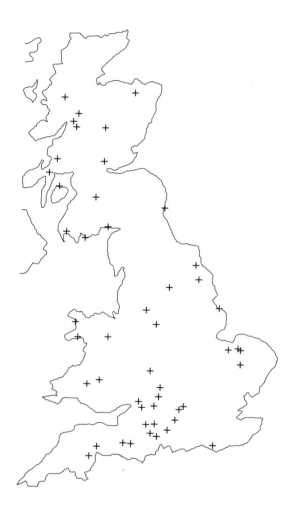

Frontispiece Fatal incidents of Pallacritis in Britain 1989-93.
Note the cluster centred on Harwell in the South of England.

Sorry, Wrong Number!
The abuse of measurement

By John Brignell

This book is dedicated to The Junkman.

All it takes is one voice.

The whole problem with the world is that fools and fanatics are always so certain of themselves, and wiser people so full of doubts.
Bertrand Russell

Contents

Chapter 1

Introduction

There is no safety in numbers, or in anything else.
James Thurber "The fairly intelligent fly"

A tale I have to tell of mice and men, potatoes and tomatoes, rabbits and nurses, cigareets and whuskey, lies and deceit and many other wonders. Unfortunately for the author, they are all linked by something that is an instant turn-off for most of the Anglo Saxon readership.

This, then, is a book of numbers – not the one sandwiched between Leviticus and Deuteronomy – but one about the abstract entities that rain down upon us from Government, the Civil Service, the Press, advertisers, academics, special interest groups and a host of others that seek to influence us. It is also about measurement, which is a process of assigning those abstract entities to events and entities in the real world. Are these entities friend or foe? In order to find out we have to challenge them – "Halt and be recognised!" Can we trust them? What is their provenance? The following is an informal guidebook intended to help navigate through a modern minefield.

Is all this of any importance? The fact is that people are lying to you (indeed, trying to frighten you) and they are using numbers to do it. They are lying for reasons of their own. Why do people want to tell you lies with numbers? Some want your money or your vote. Some want to control your life. Some want to gather power in their hands. Some need simply to justify their own existence (and salary). Unless you understand what they are up to, they are manipulating you without your knowledge. They are impoverishing you, both spiritually and financially.

A question that has to be addressed is whether it is justifiable to lie in a good cause. The answer has to be an emphatic NO, particularly for science (and I make no apologies for saying this more than once). There is an immediate practical reason in that most lies are eventually counterproductive, as the boy who cried "Wolf!" discovered. For science there is a deeper philosophical imperative – if it accepts but one lie it ceases to be science. Thus it is a basic tenet of this book that no cause is good enough to justify lying, especially using science to do so. Science either has integrity or it has nothing. Nevertheless, much of what I have to say will be regarded as blasphemy in some powerful circles.

Measurement may also be thought of as a process of comparison. When we need a new pane of glass we use a ruler to determine the required size, in the knowledge that the hardware shop will have a ruler of identical calibration (at least, as far as the eye can tell) and, though we are not aware of it at the time, that calibration is traceable through a series of sub-standards and standards to one source. At one time standards tended to be blocks of metal stored away in museums of measurement but, as science has advanced, they have been replaced by phenomena based on the universal properties of atoms. For measurement of human activity the process of comparison is more tenuous. There are no standard or substandard people, just vague notions of the Man in the Street or formerly the Man on the Clapham Omnibus. There is an even vaguer notion of "average". Averages are dangerous things, as the statistician found out when he drowned in a lake of average depth of 10 cm. A lot of people, perhaps a significant majority, believe in a "law of averages" as a means of predicting random events from past outcomes: so, if a tossed coin produces five heads in a row they think a tail is more likely on the next throw. As the man said "If you believe that, Sir, you will believe anything".

When I innocently started this project I set out to write a scientific book for the general reader with a few entertaining diversions from everyday life, but as soon as I started the research I found I had opened a can of worms reeking of the stench of corruption. To my surprise I discovered that the world gross polluters of science were to be found in the last institutions in the world that you would expect, but more of that later.

In what follows we are concerned with numerical results. There are many examples of bad science of a non-numerical nature. Dewdney for example cites the case of Freud, who produced a litany of untested hypotheses, seized upon by his followers to justify the infliction of the curse of psycho-analysis on their multitudinous credulous victims. Execrable though such perversions of science are, they are not the main concern here.

We all have a feel for numbers, though it is developed to a greater or lesser extent in individuals. For example, I could walk down my own stairs in the pitch dark and know when I have reached the bottom – yet if you had asked me how many stairs I have I would not have known. I knew that it is more than eight, say, or less than eighteen. In fact, after typing the previous sentence I went and counted – there are eleven. In the days when engineers used slide rules they had to calculate the magnitude of the numbers mentally and use the rule to give the precise numerals. Old-fashioned engineers, such as myself, get irate when students, using pocket calculators, come up with ludicrous orders of magnitude without realising it. They produce with bland innocence numbers that are the engineering equivalent of saying the average height of men is a thousand feet. Nevertheless, as with the stairs example, we all have some instinct as to whether numbers presented to us are reasonable. This is where the propagandists often go wrong. They exaggerate their numbers for effect and actually achieve the opposite effect to that intended, especially when haranguing the young. By the way, since I counted the stairs I have begun to stumble at the bottom.

Why have we lost our respect for the accuracy of numbers, and that at a time when they are more and more used by those who seek to influence us? It seems in part to have coincided with the rise in popularity of the "soft" sciences. Sociology boomed in the reaction against science and technology that accompanied the Vietnam War. In my early career I vividly recall a former tutee, who had taken up sociology after finding engineering too difficult, telling me "If a lecturer tries to put up a formula he is booed by the students." But the malaise is deeper and more established than that, particularly in the Anglo Saxon world, where innumeracy seems to be regarded as a badge of honour, a point to return to later.

By this stage you may ask "Is this all so important? Why is the old boy rattling on about it at such length?" I suppose my own unwarranted reverence for the accuracy of numbers stems from my upbringing. As a young apprentice at Standard Telephones and Cables my first serious job was working on aircraft navigation systems, an area where wrong numbers could mean lost lives. However, I hope to convince you that numbers are important in your own everyday life; that they are instruments of power, wielded by the few to enslave the many.

The ways in which the numbers are presented to us can be many and various – the position of a pointer on a scale, entries in a published table, a casual phrase half heard on the car radio, a quiet word in the confidentiality of the surgery, yelled at us from in front of a covered wagon (or behind a dispatch box), quietly insinuated as an aside in a public address or printed on the back of our corn flakes packet. In the toothpaste ad, the camera zooms in on the shining grin of the girl who has just got her man, when a caption flashes on the bottom of the screen "Contains 3% meta-hydroxy-preposterose" or some such informative message. What is this stuff? I've never heard of it, you've never heard of it. What will it do for us? Why not 2% or 4%?

No doubt this book will be dismissed by the in-crowd as the last bellow of a dinosaur facing extinction; one who has clung on to the old way of life regardless of the changing climate. The bygone foodstuffs of scholarship, service, integrity and accuracy have withered in the wintry conditions of the new age. Out with the old and bring in the new! Welcome to the Plasticine era, where everything is malleable. We live in the post-rational age. More people believe in ESP than in evolution. One in five Americans believe they have seen a ghost and twice that proportion believe in creationism. The wife of the British Prime Minister wears a magic medallion containing crystals to ward off dangerous radiation, reputedly on the advice of America's first lady. More people know their birth sign than know their blood group, which is a vital piece of information. Television, which promised the great enlightenment, holds the populace and in the darkness binds them in the grip of ignorance and superstition. This is all accepted as the norm. If you take a long hard look, however, you might just take a different view. Let's start with a look at the past.

1.1 A brief history of measurement

Measurement began our might: Forms a stark Egyptian thought,
W B Yeats "Under Ben Bulben"

Measurement is a necessary but not a sufficient condition for civilisation to exist. It is, of course, impossible to identify an exact moment in history when measurement suddenly came into being. Certainly the Babylonians in around 2440 BC had systems to measure land, weight and liquid volume. By 1500 BC they could calculate the area of a rectangle and a triangle. It was, however, the Egyptians who were the fathers of measurement. It is clear that by 3000 BC they had become practical engineers. The measurement of length in construction of the Great Pyramid was to better than an inch, or one part in ten thousand. All sorts of party games can be played with the shapes of the pyramids and they are still fertile ground for the pseudo-scientists. By the 12th Dynasty, in 1850 BC, effective measurement had allowed the development of extensive irrigation systems and the oldest instrument known dates from about 1800 BC. By 1500 BC they were solving linear algebraic equations and were measuring time by means of a sun clock. Measurement was taken up by the Greeks, and its servant, mathematics, began to develop an abstract life of its own. From about 500 BC schools of mathematics were developing all round the Mediterranean basin. Euclid and the School of Alexandria finally established mathematics and its applications as a central core of human activity. Archimedes, perhaps the greatest genius ever, applied mathematics to physics and real science began. The importance of these developments in today's world cannot be overstated. For example, many people using design packages on computers are unwittingly using the theorem wrongly attributed to Pythagorus hundreds of times a day. The new sciences of geodesy, astronomy, mechanics etc. were flourishing. As often happens, the rise of military power, this time under the Romans, caused intellectual progress to grind to a halt. Archimedes was killed by a Roman soldier because he would not move until he had completed the solution of an equation, but the Romans were great engineers and they exploited all the technology available. Julius Caesar was a sufficiently competent astronomer to be able to revise the calendar (46 BC). In the early centuries AD the likes of Ptolemy were refining astronomy and geography, so that realistic maps of the world came into being. Mathematics was being developed into refined forms in the lands of the East.

Alongside all this, pseudo-sciences held great sway over the people and their rulers. Star configurations were examined, entrails were stirred and oracles consulted. There were two cultures, one rigorous and logical the other meretricious and fantastical – *Plus ça change!* The Semitic monotheistic religion of the Middle East spread round the world, dividing and sub-dividing, producing a myriad of sects (Catholics, Sunnis, Calvinists, Orthodox, Shiites, Rabinists ....) they were all in the right and they devoted much of their lives to torturing and slaughtering each other. Every now and then they would turn their attention to the repression of science. Many of the great thinkers of the world suffered the ultimate form of censorship. In the 16th century Copernicus was forced to recant his heliocentric theory but in the 17th century Galileo revived it and survived (just) to sow the seed of the scientific revolution that was to reach its flowering with Isaac Newton.

Meanwhile, mathematics burgeoned throughout the middle ages and, abstract though it was in nature, it threw off baubles that were picked up by scientists and engineers. Measurement marched on; absorbing whatever was on offer. When science was in retreat, measurement grew through application and, when it advanced, measurement swallowed up its offerings. Newton and Leibnitz gave us the calculus and measurement expanded from the static to the dynamic. Science, however, did not really contribute substantially to technology until the 18th century. With the development of electricity and magnetism by the likes of Ampère, Kelvin and Faraday, measurement metamorphosed into the art of instrumentation. The Galvanometer reinforced the idea of reading numbers from a pointer, a facility that had been hitherto mainly restricted to clocks.

The final act began with the new 20th century when Lee de Forest invented the triode, giving the world its first amplifier and fast switch. A whole new raft of instruments became available. The invention of the cathode ray tube introduced the idea of a screen, new sensors were being developed and nothing in the world seemed immune from measurement. Brattain, Bardeen, and Shockley shared the 1956 Nobel Prize in physics for the invention of the transistor. The field effect transistor followed and suddenly photolithography was allowing thousands, then millions of transistors to be put on a chip, and cheaply. In the wake of all this, the computer developed from being a primitive lumbering giant into a midget of unconceived power. Measurement was moving out of human hands, the age of information had begun, and numbers began to assault humanity from all directions.

While all this was going on in the field of physical measurement, another form of assigning numbers was rising, albeit more slowly. This was the measurement of the activities of people. Accountancy is almost as old as numbers. Accountants were the servants of the powerful and wealthy from the foundations of civilisation, but it was only in the late twentieth century that they became a dominant caste. This was because the incompetence of legislators had produced a situation in which only these latter day necromancers could navigate successfully in the world of commerce and taxation, so the servants became the masters.

The Domesday Book, ordered by William the Conqueror in 1086 and completed by his son William Rufus, was designed to register systematically the landed wealth of the country, thus determining the revenues due to the king. It was a turning point in the history of measurement. Suddenly numbers had joined words as levers of power. It enabled William to strengthen his authority by exacting oaths of allegiance from all tenants on the land, as well as from the nobles and churchmen on whose land they lived. The idea of a census was not new (Jesus Christ was born at Bethlehem, where Joseph and Mary had gone to comply with the Roman edict of enrolment for the census) but with the Domesday Book it had reached new heights of effectiveness. The individual human being had begun to lose his anonymity and would be forever after impaled upon a record of words and numbers.

The invention of the digital computer was a cataclysmic event in the history of measurement, both physical and human. Gone were the days of depending on human beings, so susceptible to waywardness, fatigue and boredom. Here were the days of machines of infinite patience, stamina and dedication. You want to wade through fifty million records to find one errant taxpayer? Consider it done. The beneficial uses were, of course, immense – constant patient monitoring, space navigation, desktop publishing, design, simulation; the list is endless. But here we are concerned with the darker side.

First, computers are programmed by people, who are fallible; so, for example, frightened old widows are threatened with law suits over the non payment of £0.00 (I cannot count the number of program errors I have seen that arise from forgetting that a zero result might occur). Second, computers give numbers an unwarranted provenance, despite the constant repetition of the mantra GIGO (Garbage In – Garbage Out). Third, computers produce more numbers than human beings can digest, so they interpret them; and that's when the trouble starts. This book is not a tirade against computers. I have been computing longer than almost anybody; well, forty years anyway. I delight in their power and the insight it brings. Equally I despair at the abuse of that power, and it is despair that gives rise to much of this polemic.

1.2 Crossed Lines

> Let's find out what everyone is doing
> And then stop everyone from doing it.
> A P Herbert

One of the most important things we have to do in human life is draw the line. Whether it is eating, drinking, speed, sex or a thousand other things, we draw the line, consciously or unconsciously, move it one way or the other according to circumstances, and try to adhere to our decision. In nature the lines do not exist – everything is a continuum (at least at a level corresponding to our senses). They have no physical reality; any more than map contour lines are delineated on real hills. Moving a line slightly one way or the other makes little difference, but it is usually quite clear when it is grossly out of position. Some people are trying to draw our lines for us, which may be fair enough if the position of our line affects the well being of others, but often the interference is unwarranted. Bureaucrats of the Nanny State, zealots of all persuasions, fools, mountebanks, fraudsters and a host of others are trying to draw our lines to their own satisfaction. They try to inhibit our own line-drawing by withholding information or simply lying, and the most effective way of doing the latter is with numbers.

Sometimes we cross the line without noticing at the time. Under stress we might, for example, begin to drink too much and, if we are lucky, we get the warning signs before the damage is irretrievable (yes, I have been there myself) but we know the lines are there and in general we try to adhere to them. Some people, inevitably, lack this capacity for line-drawing (infants, psychopaths etc.) and it is society's business to protect them and others from the consequences. Often, however, the intervention of society in our lives is unnecessary busybodying and we have every right to resist it.

The new-born baby has no lines, just wants. In infancy they are gradually imposed on us. They seem to be so firm in childhood (*pace* Dr Spock) and it is the source of much teenage angst that they seem to shimmer and shiver like a desert mirage as maturity approaches. In adulthood we are very much preoccupied with the question of "my lines or theirs?" In all of this numbers predominate – speed limits, blood pressure, calories, AIDS statistics, IQ, dosage, examination marks, share values, insurance rates, opinion polls, atmospheric pressure, wind chill factor, crop yield, unemployment, hospital waiting lists, bank rate and on and on. The list is endless. Numbers fly at us from all directions, undigested, pre-digested, corrupted or simply invented. Decisions, decisions!

As an example of a line that is difficult to draw and a number that is hard to define consider the foetus and at what age it becomes a human being. Unless guided by religious dogma, most people would not recognise that the two undifferentiated cells after the first stage of mitosis constitute a human being. When it has developed recognisable features and limbs that it can move at will, however, most of us would accept that it is human and capable of being the victim of murder. At the other end of the scale there is also the matter of life and death when someone must make the decision to switch off the life support machine, taking into account the feelings of grieving relatives or those anxious to get at the inheritance. Nature draws no definite line between these states, but we humans have to frame a code of morals and laws, so the line must be drawn and, after it has been drawn, people will argue for ever that it should be pushed one way or the other.

1.3 Measurement, politicians and bureaucrats

A monster fearful and hideous, vast and eyeless.
Virgil, Aeneid

Readers will find this my treatment of the political aspect somewhat parochial, in that it is largely concerned with the British experience. Now, I could have done a great deal of paper research to widen the coverage, but, frankly, I do not believe a word I read in this area, mainly as a result of observing the discrepancy on my own patch between what I experience and what I read. I suspect, however, that the British experience is not unique, as modern communications send these trends flying round the world in no time; so, if you are American, for Thatcherism read Reaganism and so on.

In the late twentieth century politicians and bureaucrats have developed an obsession with measuring and tabulating and, unfortunately, they choose to do this in an area where measurement is, to say the least, a tenuous business, human affairs. There are two causes for concern in all this. First, the measures are considerably less trustworthy than their proponents assume and, secondly, the way you measure human beings controls the way they behave.

Politicians in Britain usually have experienced a narrow arts education and they have not been exposed to such truths as the Le Chatalier principle (a system in equilibrium will alter in such a way as to oppose any change imposed upon it) or another established scientific truth associated with Heisenberg – that you cannot measure something without changing it.

Take a simple example: if you make a measure of the goodness of a hospital the speed with which patients are first seen, that measure will immediately improve. If, however, you keep all other external factors (resources, bureaucratic overhead etc.) constant, the system will restore equilibrium; i.e. the total service will remain unchanged. This is an experiment in which observation has beautifully confirmed theory. The British National Health Service is the epitome of bureaucracy gone mad. The upper management is packed with political crony appointments, while the waste and inefficiency are killing people on a grand scale. As we shall see, wrong numbers have a great part to play in all this.

The appetite for numbers in our bureaucratic system is gross and growing. The enduring slogan that marks our age will be "Never mind the quality feel the width". In this giant house of horrors, more and more people spend more and more of their time feeding the monster. Schoolteachers, physicians, broadcasters, professors, policemen, business people and many others complain bitterly that they are allowed to follow their vocation for a decreasing proportion of their working day. At the other end of the social scale, barely numerate people (and elderly professors) struggle with gross impositions such as the self-assessment form for income tax. The computerised Moloch demands the sacrifice of human lives, though only in bits, so that they are available for its further gratification. The tentacles of bureaucracy grope and creep into the smallest corners of our lives. The monster thrives on numbers, gorging on them and disgorging them.

In order to appreciate the way in which bureaucrats achieve their ends, it is necessary to understand their mode of progression, which is crab-wise rather than straightforward. The first move in the bureaucrat's game plan is to identify a crisis and the way this is done is by using numbers. The actual nature of the crisis depends upon the particular murky pool in which the player swims, but the advanced gamesman will normally have little difficulty in employing one of the methods outlined later in this text. The next stage is more demanding, to stifle potential opposition, which requires a number of sub-ploys ranging from softening up to the recurrent quash. The finest tool in the armoury for this purpose is pliant journalists. They are always plentiful, desperate for copy and eager to save themselves thought or action. They are easily flattered and slaves to fashion. The final stage is a repeating cycle of cornering power and funding.

There is a bureaucratic technique that is important to understand, what might be termed The Ratchet. Successful bureaucrats are very patient. They achieve their ends by very small steps, but the major principle is that they never take a step backwards. The shining example of this is the nationalisation of the British university system, which was done over a couple of decades by small changes incorporated in successive education acts. By the time the *coup de grâce* was delivered in David Blunkett's bill of 1997 it was all over bar the shouting. Even then the death of autonomy was slipped in behind the row about student fees.

1.4 Number numbness – the great Anglo-Saxon plague

MENE, MENE, TEKEL, URPHARSIN.
Said to be Aramaic for numbered, numbered, weighed, divided.

I will not dwell on establishing the fact of number blindness in the Anglo-Saxon world. Dewdney, for example, has done so with greater wit and insight than I can muster. It is a truism that virtually the whole of science and mathematics is a closed book to vast swathes of the population, including significantly the ruling classes. Ever since the decline of the Victorian ideal the English Establishment has revelled in its ignorance of science. The great Victorian engineers, mill owners and entrepreneurs coveted the rôle of gentleman and, in pursuit of this, they sent their sons to Oxbridge for a liberal arts education. Thus the ownership of wealth and Industry passed into the hands of a self-sustaining unscientific establishment. In England, not a year goes by without some senior journalist writing an article that, overtly or covertly, celebrates his own innumeracy.

I wrote the above paragraph on August 15th 1997. On the 16th Simon Jenkins, good as gold, came up with an article in *The Times* headlined:

Power to the pupils
A level students rightly prefer 'soft'
subjects to dry and useless science.

Incidentally, before someone starts yelling telepathy, both our writings were triggered by the annual announcement of A level results. I wonder just in how many countries such a headline could appear without creating a furore, although it represents a world trend. To give Jenkins his due, before he laid down his quill and dusted off his parchment, he began his final paragraph thus:

"If I was a scientist I would plead with the Government to reverse its policy and cut science numbers drastically. I would not want to be the lame duck of education, my spokesmen special-pleading at every turn......"

If I were a journalist I would have discovered that this is precisely what many did. The treatment of scientists and engineers by the liberal arts establishment as an industrial resource, that can be switched on and off by a tap, is one of the most bitter sources of resentment. It is one thing having junk departments turning out junk sociologists, but quite another to be turning out junk engineers. If you think this is a point of no importance, imagine the next time you enter a lift or an aeroplane you see before you a brass plaque that announces:

The designer of this control system just scraped by with the lowest (E) grades at A level in Physics and Maths. He was admitted to a new university where, despite failing and repeating a number of subjects, he emerged with an honours degree in Engineering and is now devoting all his skill to your service.

"Your life in their hands" does not only apply to the medical profession.

The result of this blindness is that the abuse of numbers is carried out on a large scale and it seems that no one notices or even seems to care: again, see Dewdney for copious examples. The gullible majority are gulled on a daily basis. There will always be some people who are ready to believe that Elvis is still alive and living in a London bus on the moon, but the likelihood that they are reading a book such as this is rather remote. Even the less gullible, however, are being systematically misled by false or absent information.

Incidentally, I would not wish to put Simon Jenkins down as one of the bad guys. More often than not he is a goad to the establishment, and, not long after the above article, he was berating politicians for their innumeracy. In particular, he was the great chronicler of the recent disastrous trend to centralisation, which is a recurrent theme in what follows.

1.5 The Santa Claus question

When I was a child I asked my parents the awkward question "How could Santa Claus visit all those houses in all those countries in one night?" I cannot remember the answer, just my dissatisfaction with it. When I was a youth and read the account of a putative medical instrument called the De La Warr box I asked myself "How could he do all that research to assign numbers to all the different diseases in one lifetime?" The same question occurs with all these weird and wonderful diagnostic and therapeutic techniques. They appear to spring into being immaculate, like Aphrodite from the foam. Not for them the tortuous to and fro of argument in scientific journals, days and nights of observation and data gathering or pondering on levels of significance. Yet, how rarely does anyone ask the Santa Claus question! In the following we shall meet many cases where, if someone had asked the question, things could have been quite different, even to the extent of saving many lives.

1.6 The measurement of risk

Chaos umpire sits,
And by decision more embroils the fray
By which he reigns; next him high arbiter
Chance governs all.
Milton, Paradise Lost.

Much of this book will be concerned with the measurement of risk. This is an immensely important technological problem. Consider, for example, a manned space launch. The vehicle contains over a million components, and some of those (e.g. a microprocessor) have a million components inside them. Every one of those components has a failure rate attached to it, which the engineers have to do their best to estimate. A measure of this failure rate is the mean time between failures (MTBF). An MTBF of one million years is incredibly reliable, yet a system of a million such components could have an MTBF of only one year. Now this, of course, is a gross simplification, and we can enhance overall reliability by duplication, back-up systems etc., all beyond the scope of this book. Where it all becomes more contentious is in trying to measure the risks that you and I take every day. Every action carries risks, whether it is climbing into the gondola of a hot air balloon, lighting a cigarette, going to the doctor for a vaccination or deciding to stay in bed all day. The great problem for us all is to find out just what those risks are. As we shall see, there is a whole lot of lying going on. As in business the whole of life is a risk-benefit trade-off. Some very large risks are so commonplace that we discount them through familiarity, like getting into a car. Others can be so small that they are unmeasurable, like eating beef on the bone, yet because they are presented to us in an emotion packed way they assume an enormous significance.

The human perception of risk can be very strange. On March 10th 1997, when the idea of this book was beginning to gel from a long-considered vague plan into a definite project, 160 vehicles were involved in a pile-up on the M40 in thick fog. Drivers had been cruising along, some of them at 70 mph, seemingly oblivious of the danger they were in. Risk hardly seems an adequate word for it. We have all seen them. I don't know about you, but at the first sign of fog I always get off the motorway immediately, because the lunatics are always there. Yet I would be willing to wager that a large proportion of those involved go to great lengths to avoid risk in their everyday life — avoiding fatty foods, beef and, of course, tobacco and alcohol. Yet, cushioned in the unworldly isolation of their cars, like sleepwalkers on the edge of a cliff, they drive forward into the likelihood of terrible maiming and death. The fog adds to the unreality of the outside world. Likewise, every day you see pedestrians jaywalking through city traffic, mothers thrusting prams into the paths of oncoming lorries, oblivious of how much braking is required to nullify all that inertia, people jostling each other on a crowded underground platform. There is a plausible theory that people tend to maintain risks at a constant level, so that seat belts, for example, lose their safety value because people are lulled into a false sense of security and drive more carelessly. Physical risk is an area of human life in which the old cliché, that familiarity breeds contempt, always holds, as you can see every day watching drivers on the road. Yet those very same people will wax hysterical over a report that margarine (used in cakes) causes a twenty five percent increase in the probability of heart disease. As they say in Yorkshire "There's nowt so queer as folk."

1.7 Coincidence

> *"Wonderful!" I ejaculated. "Commonplace," said Holmes*
> Sir Arthur Conan Doyle, A study in Scarlet.

We have all had the experience of coming across a new rare word or name and then meeting it again almost immediately, but if you take into account all the occasions when this does not happen it is not quite so spooky.

When I started on this book I decided to have a real thrash during August 1997, which is the only month that gives UK academics any disposable time in reasonable chunks, and gave myself a target of 20,000 words. The coincidences were quite bizarre: no sooner had I written something than it seemed the next day an article would appear in *The Times* illustrating it. On analysis, however, many of the coincidences melted away, since it was clear that the thoughts of the journalists had been triggered by the same events as mine. This is illustrated in my remarks above on journalists celebrating their own innumeracy. In another case I wrote about the plight of air traffic controllers and, days later, there was a report of the third serious incident at Heathrow. I had known, however, of the overload in the system and air travel is in everybody's minds and newspapers at the height of the holiday season, when the overload is at its peak and the system starts to creak; so my unconscious had made a prediction that was not as spooky as I might have first thought.

Albert and Betty Cheetham from Derby met Albert and Betty Rivers from Swindon on holiday in Tunisia (*The Times*, 4th Feb 1998). They found that they had both celebrated 55 years of marriage, got married at the same time and date, had sons born in 1943 and 1945 and each had five grandchildren. However, tens of millions of Britons go on holiday every year. Some meet coincidences, but most do not. Imagine a headline "Two couples met on holiday and found that they had nothing in common at all". Someone gets the same numbers as the lottery machine most weeks, against odds worse than ten million to one. Ten million is a number so big that even professional mathematicians have difficulty in fully appreciating its magnitude. If you started counting once a second, eight hours a day, it would take you nearly a year to reach that total.

Many "coincidences" are not remarkable at all. For a 50% chance of two people in the same room having the same birthday you need only 23 people present. Our attitudes to coincidence are also conditioned by our exposure to fiction, where coincidence is exploited to a ridiculous extent. In many classic novels (John Buchan's *Mr Standfast* or the *House of Four Winds* come to mind) the coincidences invoked are on a quite ludicrous scale. Coincidences in science, particularly in health studies, are a more serious matter and will be the subject of much of our subsequent discussion.

1.8 Attitudes to numbers

I long ago came to the conclusion that life is 6 to 5 against.
Damon Runyon

It is always surprising and satisfying the way the old jokes sum up people's attitudes to things. This is my version of a chestnut about attitudes to numbers:

A group of professional candidates had applied for a lucrative post but were fazed to find that they had to sit an examination. The first question was "What is the value of π? Here are their answers:

The theologian
There are many different paths to the same truth. Just because I say it is one thing and you say it is another does not mean one of us is wrong. So let us leave unsaid those things that divide us and concentrate on those things that unite us.

The civil engineer
22/7, but adding a safety factor let's call it 4.

The physicist
3.1415927 plus or minus 0.00000005

The mathematician
Let the set of irrational numbers, S, be a subset of the set of real numbers N........

The statistician
Between 3.1 and 3.2, with a confidence level of 95%.

The advertising man
Not just one, not even two, but more than three!

The sociologist
It has no value at all to the deprived masses that dwell in our inner cities.

The politician
We put a value on all quantities and are fully committed to seeing that they are maintained. Our opponents may well reject this straightforward approach, seeking to obscure the issue in the eyes

of the electorate, but the electorate are not so easily deceived. I have travelled up and down the country, seeking the views of the person in the street on many matters of national, nay international, importance, as this very much is, and I can say, without fear or favour, that our policy on this question remains firm and unchanged and I am pledged to defend it against all attempts by mischief-makers to divert attention away from the substantive issues that are so important to us all in this modern world. So let us go forward together, hand in hand, secure in the knowledge that, while many things need to be changed, and changed drastically I might add, we hold on to the values that once made this nation great and will make it great again.

The accountant
What do you want it to be?

1.9 The author

> *behold, my desire is ....that mine adversary had written a book.*
> *Job*

This section is not an ego trip, but is included as a reflection of the author's views on subjectivity in measurement. In this book I have included facts about myself that I would rather have left unstated. The reason for this is that, after a lifetime of trying to prove otherwise, I have come to the conclusion that there is no such thing as objective measurement. Even in computer-aided measurement, of which I was one of the pioneers, human beings write the programs and choose the experiments. As the man said "everybody's got an angle." Usually, you can only work out the angle by reading between the lines. If there is no objective measurement it is even more so that any critique of measurement is subjective and I am fully aware that this text is laced with my own prejudices. I was tempted to go through and edit out some of the bile, but in the end chose the less comfortable path of honesty.

In short, I am an obscure, elderly, unreconstructed, politically-incorrect academic with strong industrial connections, also a chartered engineer and physicist. I have been involved in local Conservative politics for most of my life, probably devoting a total of about a year to it, including a few years as Branch Chairman. This arose from my upbringing in socialist Tottenham, which gave me a life-long abhorrence of socialism. Now, however, my aversion to Thatcherism, and particularly neo-Thatcherism, is even greater. I have watched the Neo-Thatcherites, under Major and Blair, marching on like soldier ants destroying everything in their path, with mounting horror. The Disraelian one-nation Conservatism that I once espoused seems to be dead and gone. All I achieved for my years of devotion was the demolition of almost everything I held dear. My dislike of current politics is not entirely detached. It is personal too. I found the job I loved turning into one I loathed. I was particularly distressed at the treatment of the younger colleagues, whom I had been responsible for recruiting into the profession, and whose job satisfaction and standard of living were falling year by year. Meanwhile, the politicians were quietly feathering their own nests year after year. I have a particular loathing for bureaucracy and the way it is taking control of our lives. I detest the way that urban politicians conduct a war of attrition on rural communities, the institution of marriage and the traditional way of life in general. Above all, if you will forgive the oxymoron, I cannot tolerate intolerance.

I smoke a pipe without inhaling but with great pleasure, having taken it up as a successful cure for a butterfly mind when I was a student. I happen to think that inhaling cigarette smoke is foolish, but that folly is a basic human right. I also drink moderate quantities of real ale and value the British pub as one of the last great institutions that *they* have not quite managed to destroy, though they are still trying. I would like to try to persuade you that it is not I who am obsessed with some of the issues that come up repeatedly in this text. It's just that they represent such an overwhelming source of wrong numbers that they dwarf anything else. I have cut them as much as possible in order to restore some balance, but I am painfully aware that they occupy a lot of these pages. I had enough material for several volumes.

Being old and unreformed I do not write in PC; so, if you expect the modern circumlocutions or standard PC mantras, stop reading now. You will not like the opinions and you will certainly not like the facts. I also adhere to the extremely unfashionable view that people ought to be allowed to live their own lives and, if they do not endanger others, take their own risks without being dictated to by self appointed know-alls. All that I ask is that they are given an honest account of what those risks are, in so far as they can be determined.

Previously I have written a couple of books and a hundred and something scientific papers and chapters, mostly on aspects of measurement and sensors. There is an element of self-indulgence in my need to write a book that is different in style from the million and more words of desiccated scientific prose that have characterised my métier until now. I have a pathological aversion to filling forms, which gets me into all sorts of trouble and colours my attitude to bureaucrats.

It is, of course, in the nature of things that men, when they reach a certain age, are wont to lament and cry *O tempora! O mores!* But even allowing for that, I contend that there is a more fundamental set of ills that have beset our society; in particular, the dislocation that occurred around 1982. These ills were accelerated by a burgeoning technology that amplified their effect beyond reason.

1.10 The book

> *The worth of a book is to be measured by what you can carry away from it.*
> James Bryce

I decided to apply the scientific method in writing this text. I had formed a hypothesis that the world was awash with false measurements. The way to test a hypothesis is to make predictions and see whether they are valid. The prediction I made was that all the various classes of abuse I believed I had identified would be amply revealed in news stories in a period of one year (which, of course, stretched into two) from the time I commenced writing, which was the early summer of 1997. Thus almost all my examples did not exist before that time and there was a risk that I would have no material at all, but I need not have worried. The few exceptions are where I wished to underline the historical development of some of these trends or quote some valuable opinions from the recent past. Because I happen to read *The Times* most of my examples come from its news coverage, but this in no way implies that it is uniquely prone to the sorts of abuse that are my theme, far from it. I concentrated on the information that reached me as an ordinary person and deliberately avoided the usual scientific literature search (which, I must admit, was something of a self-indulgence) though occasionally my curiosity got the better of me.

The moment a book is started it tends to assume a life of its own. I began by trying to put together a semi-technical treatise on pitfalls in measurement with a few illustrations from everyday life. When I started researching it I expected the usual cases of serendipity that make authorship less of a drudge than it might be. I was, however, in for a shock. I knew things were pretty bad out there but the sheer extent of deliberate cold-blooded abuse shook me. I now have a filing cabinet full of press cuttings and have been able to use only a tiny fraction of them.

In this book we are not very much concerned with the niceties of precise physical measurement. The abuses we are concerned with are so gross that any lack of physical precision is lost in the noise. In the worst cases we shall find that the act of comparison is between one human population and another and the potential errors are large and very much the subject of our debate. I have needed from time to time to include mathematical illustrations. In doing this I have largely restricted myself to simple methods that I can justify to the intelligent layman from first principles. This book is not just about the abuse, but also its consequences, be they political, economic, social or medical.

Never believe all you read. There are errors in this book, for example. I have done my best to eliminate them, but I have never yet produced a book or major paper without seeing an embarrassing error the moment it is published. My last book was checked by myself, several colleagues and the publishers' reviewers. Yet the moment I opened the first pristine copy I found a typo in equation 1. This time I am setting myself up as a sitting target by criticising the errors of others, so I am ready for the flak.

I do not write in the hope halting the process. Greater writers than I, Kafka and Orwell for example, have written and failed. The machine rolls on. The junk scientists cuddle up with the journalists, who cuddle up with the politicians. I wrote this book as an act of faith, not knowing whether it would ever see the light of day. I was made well aware at the beginning of my scientific career that challenging the prevailing orthodoxy was not the way to get published. If I had simply wanted to get published I would have written a book on alien abduction or the like.

The style of writing will be regarded as highly unorthodox in academic circles. I did some research into why people were not reading books written in defence of science. It was summed up by one bright young lady – "They are written by robots for robots; no emotions or opinions. I like books written by real people." I was anxious not to pepper this text with references, which would have made it look like a formidable technical publication, but I have included all my main sources in the bibliography and webography. I have relied heavily on them and am grateful for the stimulus and information they provided.

We are of course, dependent upon many other people in formulating the ideas that we ultimately espouse and the writing of this book is no exception. I apologise to anyone whose ideas I have adapted unwittingly, but there are people who made positive suggestions and I wish to acknowledge them with gratitude. They include Professors David Barron, Don McLean and Bob Grime; also Chris Swan and Penny Brignell.

Chapter 2

The causes of wrong numbers

All men are liable to error; and most men are, in many points,
by passion or interest, under temptation to do it.
John Locke

Measurement errors come about (sometimes) from equipment failure and (mostly) from human failure. There is thus a range of primary causes that act through a variety of mechanisms to produce wrong numbers. Let us set aside, for the moment, actual faults in equipment that are of non-human origin. The human causes of failure are:

Indolence
Carelessness
Incompetence
Subconscious motivation
Prejudice
Malice
Avarice
Zealotry
Politics
Fashion
Self-justification
Greed for power

2.1 The mechanisms for wrong numbers

O purblind race of miserable men,
How many among us at this very hour,
Do forge a lifelong trouble for ourselves,
By taking true for false, or false for true!
Tennyson, The Idylls of the King

How do these primary causes bring about wrong numbers? There is a number of possible mechanisms by which measurement errors are introduced. The items in the following list are not in any special order and are not mutually exclusive.

Inappropriate equipment
False observation – seeing what isn't there
Wishful thinking (self-deception)
Fabrication
Deception and Fraud
Out of date, partial or faulty data

Faulty processing of data
Sabotage
Politics and fashion
Displacement activity
Let us consider a simple example of each, chosen for variety as much as aptness.

Inappropriate equipment

I was consulted by a company who were having difficulties with their customers over an instrument within their equipment that was giving seriously faulty readings. The company was in legal dispute with the supplier of the instruments, who claimed that, when they were returned, they proved to be in perfect working order. I visited the client with two colleagues from my consultancy practice. When we opened the door of the cabinet the explanation was glaring. The instrument, which was not built to high standards of electromagnetic screening, shared its housing with large switchgear designed to control heavy machinery. Whenever a switch operated it induced large pulses of current within the instrument, causing it to misread. I advised that both parties were at fault in failing to communicate their specifications correctly and the case stayed out of court.

> Moral: it is a necessary but not sufficient condition for a system to work correctly that all its subsystems work correctly.

False observation - seeing what isn't there

The most famous case of false observation must be the canals on Mars. Percival Lowell was no mean astronomer (for example, he predicted the existence of Pluto) yet he described, and drew in some detail, canals he had observed on the red planet and believed that they were evidence of life. Advancing technology was to prove him wrong. People are still writing and selling books about such fancies as monuments on Mars. Incidentally, "canals" was a mistranslation of the Italian word for channels used by the original "discoverer" Giovanni Virginio Schiaparelli.

> Moral: Seeing is believing, but it ain't necessarily so.

Wishful thinking (self deception)

When I was a young lecturer I had a senior colleague who was seriously into study of the paranormal. I had come into the Department one Saturday morning to catch up on my work (a considerable sacrifice, as I was then commuting 40 miles into London). I was walking along a basement corridor when my colleague appeared from a door I had not noticed and dragged me in by my arm. I was astonished to find myself in a well-furnished and carpeted room, which appeared to house an audience, mostly, it seemed, little old ladies in long black dresses. They sat in front of an apparatus that seemed to comprise an infra red source and detector. In front was a large display meter with a pointer that swung randomly backwards and forwards. I recognised that they were observing a phenomenon that is the bane of the instrumentation engineer's life, $1/f$ noise. A young man was introduced to me as the medium. I was introduced as the independent witness. The young man was instructed to start, and he began to harangue the meter, yelling at it to "GO DOWN". Dear Reader, it went up.

"That's very strange," said my colleague "it has gone down every time so far." "It's because there is an unbeliever present" volunteered one of the ladies. I made my escape, and to this day I shudder to think what my position would have been if it had gone down.

Moral: Next time, run like hell.

Fabrication

At a time when the debate on drinking and driving was raging I heard a Single Issue Fanatic on my car radio claim that a driver on the legal limit was four times more likely to have an accident. The very next day another on the same channel claimed that it was nine times. Not only can they not both be right but observation proves them both wrong. Note, by the way, the use of the word *more* without the accompanying *than*. This is a mark of zealots, advertisers, politicians and others who practise to deceive.

Moral: sometimes one pinch of salt is not enough

Deception and Fraud

This is one of hundreds of such adverts on the Web. Note the impressive numbers.

SMALL FUEL IONIZER

Improved gas mileage
Better engine preformance (sic)

This small fuel ionizer is perfect for cars and pickup trucks. Tie this gold anodized aluminum tube to the outside of the fuel line on any internal combustion engine between the fuel pump and the carburetor. Properly installed, it ionizes the fuel prior to passing into the carburetor, making the fuel burn more completely and reducing emissions. Installations of this unit will usually increase mileage from 10 to 25%. It also improves performance by making starting easier, which saves wear on the battery and starter. All of this, of course, means less maintenance and more savings. This is an exceptional, environmentally friendly invention. There is also a large fuel ionizer available for large trucks, buses and heavy machinery.

SMALL FUEL IONIZER ... $20.00

I can't resist adding my favourite from the same manufacturer. It is the ease of installation that appeals.

WATER SOFTENER

Softens water!

Makes skin silky smooth!

This fish-shaped ionizer weighs approximately 5 pounds and is designed to soften hot water. Simply place the fish on top of your hot water heater. Within just a few days, you will enjoy soft, ionized hot water in your baths and showers, for washing clothes and dishes. (providing savings on soap, laundry detergent, dish soap, shampoo, etc.)! It works great in your spa, too. Remember to flush your hot water heater on a regular basis to remove hardened residue.

WATER SOFTENER ... $125.00.

Moral: P T Barnum grossly underestimated the birth-rate of suckers.

Out of date, partial or faulty data

I put on a demonstration for a group of students. It was an idea given to me by the incident with the medium referred to above. The apparatus had a meter whose pointer went up and down slowly at random. There was a steering wheel that allowed one to correct the deflection and keep the meter centred. A student volunteer was able to do this without difficulty. I announced that I was going to introduce a delay of five seconds, and without saying so I also switched off the random signal. The student's efforts at control resulted in the pointer oscillating more and more wildly until it hit the stops. "Don't laugh," I said, "the Chancellor of the Exchequer is doing this every day with data that are months out of date, not five seconds." Those were the days when Nigel Lawson was practising "one club" economics. Now the Bank of England is in charge of monetary instability.

> *Moral: "Better late than never" is somewhat an oversimplification.*

Faulty processing of data

I was external examiner to a PhD student who had written a thesis on the electronic nose. He plotted the resistance of his sensors against the detected variable and found that he obtained a non-linear descending curve. Having access to a computer he put the data through a range of logarithmic and other transformations and managed to convert the plots into straight lines, losing some precision in the process. Noting that the original curves were a familiar shape, the rectangular hyperbola, I plotted conductance (the reciprocal of resistance) instead of resistance from the same data and got a straight line.

> *Moral: Just occasionally, life is simple.*

Sabotage

A case of sabotage occurs in a true story related to me by Don McLean, Professor of Aeronautics. When he was a young RAF officer a colleague had acquired a new car, in fact an A40. He was so impressed with the fuel economy that he became the mess bore on the subject. Each evening he would regale the company in the bar with the latest figures of miles and gallons. One evening, in his absence, they decided to put a stop to this and plotted to extract fuel from the tank. A legal officer who was present pointed out that this would be an offence. After a moment's thought, however, he added "but, it would not be an offence to add fuel."

Each evening the hapless victim reported higher and higher fuel economy ratings. When it exceeded 80 mpg even he began to become suspicious. Eventually the steward put him out of his misery. There are more sinister cases.

> *Moral: If is seems to be too good to be true it is too good to be true.*

Politics and fashion

> *From the Washington Post Monday, August 10, 1998:*

> *Vice President Gore is scheduled to announce the new numbers today in the latest in a series of White House news conferences intended to call attention to the year's unusually hot weather. Both Gore and President Clinton also have made frequent reference to this year's killer heat waves in Texas and Florida in attempting to build congressional support for efforts to reduce emissions of greenhouse gases.*

This simple paragraph encapsulates so many of the different causes of wrong numbers – building up of hysteria by politicians, journalists and junk scientists for their mutual benefit, the missing link (*q.v.*) and the scramble for the tax payer's money.

Moral: Beware of deputy leaders bearing numbers.

Displacement activity

When animals and human beings are frustrated in response to some drive they often indulge in displacement activity (allochthonous behaviour) that has no relevance to the original drive. This occurs in measurement too. Desirous of measuring some unmeasurable quantity, such as the quality of teaching or research, people measure something else instead, such as procedures or publications. The mischief occurs when the resulting numbers are used to formulate policy.

In a *Discovery Channel* programme about ghosts an "expert" is seen wandering about a "haunted house" with a magnetometer, an instrument for measuring magnetic fields, and the numbers on his display move obligingly up and down. His thesis is that electromagnetic fields can cause levitation and, it is claimed, hallucinations. The fallacy here is that of orders of magnitude. It is like saying that because an elephant can lift a particular log then an amoeba will be capable of the same feat. Nevertheless, audiences are so impressed to see varying numbers produced that they fail to notice the missing link (of which more below). This is reinforced by fictional films such as *Ghostbusters* and *Star Trek*, in which hand held instruments reveal all sorts of vital information at the touch of a button.

Moral: Numbers without a provenance are just numbers.

2.2 Variations on a theme

The broad mass of a nation will more easily fall victim to a big lie than to a small one.
Adolph Hitler Mein Kampf.

The Big Lie

It is disturbingly frequent for the most blatant and gross falsehoods to be issued in press articles and broadcasts with no attempt at justification. A subject that will come up in this book with rather monotonous regularity is smoking. One of the most oft repeated numbers from the anti smoking campaign is that it causes 400,000 premature deaths in the USA each year. This number is a total fabrication – see, for example, the article *Lies, damned lies and 400,000 smoking-related deaths* by Levy and Marimont, *Regulation,* Vol 21 No 4 1988. The calculation, which was made by the Center for Disease Control and Prevention (CDC) involves almost every fiddle in the book. We shall discuss such methods in detail later, but they include unacceptable risk ratios, substantial confounding factors, unrepresentative sample populations and many others. Most startling of all is that 60% of the "premature" deaths occurred at ages over seventy and 17% of them at eighty-five and above. It has been pointed out that the same data can be used to "prove" that tobacco saves 200,000 lives a year.

There are, however, more subtle variations in the ways of producing wrong numbers. These tend to be practised by the Grandmasters of deception and should not be attempted by the novice.

The Missing Link

An increasingly popular ploy is to produce masses of convincing and usually correct evidence about some phenomenon and then use it to justify a theory that is only related by implication. The fact that the link is never established is hidden in a welter of indisputable facts. The classical example is Global Warming *(q.v.)* and its putative man-made origins. Some respectable journalists feel obliged to report this stuff, but it pays to examine their use of language. Typical is a BBC report on April 23rd 1998. The emphases and annotations in brackets are mine.

> *The world is getting warmer*
> *<Picture: image: [belching factory chimneys]>*
> *Caption: The greenhouse gases that warm the planet*
>
> *American scientists have examined the annual global temperature for the past 600 years and concluded that the years 1990, 1995 and 1997 were the warmest. Our science correspondent David Whitehouse reports.*

{We know it is getting warmer, thank goodness. 500 years ago was the depths of the little ice age. Who wants to go back to that? Only people who are nostalgic for ice skating on the Thames. Many scientists believe that the Quaternary Ice Age is not over yet.}

> *The research adds to the growing body of information that the Earth is being warmed by a man-made greenhouse effect.*
>
> {How does it do that?}
>
> *According to Herman Zimmerman of the United States National Science Foundation: "**The balance of evidence** now firmly supports an important human influence on the global climate system."*
>
> *The scientists, from the University of Massachusetts at Amherst, were able to estimate temperatures over more than half of the Earth. They say that variations in the brightness of the sun as well as gas and dust from volcanoes have played an important role in climate variation over the period studied.*
>
> {Well, that was nice of them.}
>
> *But **they believe that** the greatest recent effect comes from heat trapped in the lower atmosphere by the build up of carbon dioxide, a well-known 'greenhouse gas'.*
>
> {Some people believe in fairies.}
>
> ***Some believe that** if the amount of carbon dioxide in the atmosphere were to increase at its current rate the global effects would be severe.*
>
> {Some people believe in fairies.}
>
> *Rising sea level, more frequent extreme weather events, heat waves and droughts would be more common.*
>
> {Oh, yeah?}
>
> *The evidence that the Earth is getting warmer comes from many sources – the growth of tree-rings in Mongolia and Canada are getting wider showing that they are growing more each year; the growing season for crops in Australia is getting longer; permafrost*

in Siberia and Canada is melting.

> {Yes, but we knew all that. It has been happening for over 400 years.}

The distribution of climatic regions would change but scientists cannot predict how.

> {Why this sudden outbreak of modesty?}

*"We have **a sense of what might happen** to the planet as a whole but we don't really know what the regional impacts might be" said Herman Zimmerman.*

If you look at the original press release (NSF, April 22, 1998) you find that Whitehouse has left out nothing substantive. All the words tell us something we already knew and something they believe, without any logical link between them.

There are many other famous examples of the missing link in action. Perhaps the most long-established is the lie detector *(q.v.)* which monitors a number of physiological phenomena that have never been shown to be related to the activity of lying.

Moving the goalposts

This is known in the trade as the Carol Browner Gambit, among the less couth "doing a Browner" or among the uncouth simply "Browning". The basic technique is to determine whether you are heading for the desired outcome. If you are obviously going to miss it, you change the rules of the game and, if that does not work, you change them again and again until you are satisfied. An unforgivable sin among real scientists is to change the confidence levels part way through a study, but it does not faze the junk scientists to do so.

The Humpty Dumpty policy

If we substitute "number" for "word" in the famous quotation from *Through the Looking-glass* we get: "When I use a number it means just what I choose it to mean – neither more nor less." Like the original it has to be said in a rather scornful tone. H.D's next remark is also apposite "Impenetrability! That's what I say!" You have to establish great authority before you can use this one. A typical example is in the definition of "poverty". It is common to define it in terms the distribution of family income, say taking the lower quartile. This means that, however rich everybody gets, there will *always* be 25% who are poor. Naturally, pointing this out incurs a charge of being uncaring. An official definition of the poverty boundary used in the UK is half the national median income. If you doubled everybody's income, or even multiplied it by ten, you would still have exactly the same number of officially poor people.

The isolated statistic

This is also certainly not one for the amateur. It is based on the principle that, given enough statistics, there is always one that suits the purpose. What makes it problematic is the existence of another principle: for every isolated statistic there exists an equal and opposite isolated statistic. This leads to dialogues such as:

> Government spokesman: *"Unemployment fell by 1% only last month."*
> Opposition spokesman: *"But it is still 4% higher than this time last year."*

It takes a great deal of style to win such a debate, but it can be done, and frequently is.

The emotional non sequitur

The death of Diana, Princess of Wales, was used unashamedly by SIFs to try to force through a reduction of the drink drive limit from 80 units to 50. The driver in that case was well over the upper limit, so had no relevance and a change would have made no difference to that outcome. In this age of false sentimentality the opportunities for exploitation are increasingly frequent.

The Trojan Number

I was pondering how to illustrate this phenomenon when, lo and behold, a beautifully crafted example, generated by the Economic and Social Research Council, appeared on Teletext and subsequently in the Press (*The Times* 30 Oct 1997). The tag was a headline that smokers were gloomier about than their health than non-smokers. The Trojan number was that on average they estimated that they had a 41% chance of developing lung Cancer. The follow up was that in fact **only** 17% of male smokers and 11% of female smokers contracted the disease. This has all the hallmarks; a fairly boring statistic in line with the current political propaganda, followed by the punch line as an apparent afterthought. Announcements and press releases are often padded out with trivial new numbers as a means of recycling the old ones that carry the message.

The classical Trojan Number, however, is the total number of people claimed to be part of a survey. Thus the media story might begin "In a survey of 330, 000 patients it was found that they were twice as likely to die of X if they consumed Y." When you look at the original results, however, you find that only 30-odd of the patients actually died over the test period and of those only 20 risked the consumption of Y. The other 329970 were no part of the investigation and merely served as a make-weight to glorify the story.

Numerical monomania

Sometimes individuals or groups become obsessed with one number. This is often harmless, but it can be come extremely harmful when practised by those who exercise power. It often happens in health, where fashion is as at least as important as science. Suddenly everybody wants to know their one particular number, such as their cholesterol index. Where it is worst, however, is in politics where the adherents have control over the economy. Science can be of limited value in such applications and there is no substitute for common sense. When only one number is used as the measurand and one other as the control target in a multivariable system, the results can be disastrous.

A yachtsman who insists on using only the rudder and looking only at the finishing line will either capsize or collide. While a knowledge of the science of the wind and waves can be helpful to him, his multivariable problem can only be solved by behaviour learned through long experience. Sometimes politicians become obsessed with one number and the result is always catastrophic. At one moment in time they will be captivated by inflation and controlling it only by interest rates. A few years later the fixation will be currency conversion rates. In each case the end result is a massive price to be paid by individuals, including mounting bankruptcies among those who are innocent of any error on their own part.

Quantum leap

One of the tricks used by liars with numbers is to make their very small numbers of cases look like very big ones. A method of doing this is to use a multiplier, but they have a difficulty. Say they find that out of a sample of ten people they found that three that fulfilled their requirements. They could make it look bigger by extrapolating it to a "per 100,000 of the population" quantity. If they did that, however, they would get the round number 30,000 and even the simplest of punters would smell a rat. This is known to instrumentation engineers as the amplification of quantisation noise. The number 3 out of ten is highly quantised and even after amplification by 10,000 it is still highly quantised. Fear not! Our brave researchers have a way round this. They multiply by a number that is not round, hence disguising the quantisation. Let me illustrate.

One Professor Anne Charlton, leader of a team of Cancer Research Campaign Scientists reported that 9,314 boys between 12 and 13 who are motor racing fans are likely to take up smoking. This is more than twice the number of boys who do not take up the sport. Well that's pretty impressive; no obvious quantisation there. As a result of this sort of research the Government and the EU did one of their favourite things, imposed a ban, this time on cigarette advertising in motor sport (it all got a bit more murky than that, but that is another story).

The report in *The Times* (14th Nov, 98), however, gave a bit more information – in fact enough to enable us to work back and find out just what the good professor's figures actually were. We glean that there were 1,063 boys in the survey, 12% of whom were racing fans, and of these 12.8% became regular smokers. Ignoring the awkward 0.328 of a boy, that makes 16 boys. However, it is also revealed that 7% of the non-fans became smokers, so we can deduce that about 9 boys of our sixteen would have become smokers anyway, without the influence of motor racing. Thus we are left with just **7 boys** who were apparently influenced by motor racing. So, how did they get the impressive number? They took the number 16, divided it by the number in the sample and then multiplied it by the estimated number of boys of that age group in the UK (626,400). Yes, I know that comes to 9428, but the percentages are obviously rounded (unless they really did have 15.8 boys).

As it happens this is a statistically significant result, **but only** if you ignore possible confounding factors (*q.v.*). From my memories of schooldays, the boys who liked exciting sports were also likely to be the ones having a quick drag behind the bike sheds, the daredevils, while the swots were in Chess Club or the library. I was playing football. As far as I remember they did not have cigarette advertising on the cars then. On the basis of The Magnificent Seven, an editorial in The *Lancet* demanded ministerial resignations for failing to deliver an important blow to the tobacco industry.

Weasel words
Often numbers on their own are innocent and it is only when they are modified by accompanying words that they are transmogrified into lies.

Jargon
As soon as people form groups they begin to develop jargon. In itself it is harmless and helps to engender the feeling of togetherness. Sometimes jargon is unavoidable; a device that has not existed before has to be given some sort of name, the transistor for example, and such neologisms move easily into the general vocabulary and eventually the dictionary. Jargon also has other positive uses; the latinism of medicine helps its practitioners communicate across language barriers. More sinister is its use to keep others out of the closed circle, as with rhyming slang. At its worst jargon is used to mystify and deceive the gullible. A modern example occurs in the financial world, where deregulated banks are using their clients' money to back gigantic gambling syndicates. They are simply betting on whether certain numbers will go up or down, but disguise the fact by hiding behind the jargon of "derivatives" and "hedge-funds".

The hanging comparative

How often we see in the press and effusions of SIFs a comparative without anything to compare it with, e.g. *"More, better, greater etc."* without *than*. The classic case in marketing is chocolate bars, which the manufacturers periodically reduce and increase in size. The reductions are carried out gradually and quietly, while the increases are blazoned with "now bigger". The number that matters, price per gram, is carefully hidden behind all the razzmatazz.

The false limit

Another favourite is the quotation of an apparent maximum value, which is in fact way above the likely value, e.g. *up to*, which includes zero. Dewdney deals extensively with this form of cheating.

The absent provenance

Another ploy, beloved by advertisers, SIFs and politicians, is the number plucked out of the air without any attempt at justification. Again the standard weasel catch phrases give the game away – e.g. *recommended guidelines are, recent researches reveal, a well-known publisher states, exhaustive tests confirm, experts agree, 14% of deaths are attributed to, has been linked to etc.*

The borrowed technical term

This is one frequently practised by pseudo-scientists. Some words plucked from real science have a particular authority that can lend credibility to the most arrant nonsense, e.g. *resonance, frequency, vibration, ionisation, magnetisation etc.*

I could give you a one-hour extemporary lecture on, say, resonance; full of second order differential equations, mathematical transforms and diagrams. It would have no relevance to ESP, aromatherapy or any of the other inanities offered by pseudo-science.

In one day, an American TV Home Shopping Network sold more than a million dollars worth of "therapeutic" magnets. Another favourite, and the basis of many weird and wonderful products, is the *crystal*. This is a form of matter in which the atoms are arranged in a regular array. Crystals can be very beautiful and they can have a number of useful scientific properties, particularly in applied optics. Pseudo-science, however, endows them with much more than this. They have magical properties that can ward off dangerous radiation, "resonate" to pathological conditions in the human body and perform many other wonders.

The incredible shrinking forecast

The word "incredible" is one of those that has come into fashion among the chattering classes. In a late evening arts programme I saw while writing this section, among the hundreds of "likes", "sort ofs", "kind ofs" "I means" and "you knows", the words "incredibly" and "fantastically" modified almost every adjective and adverb. If it really is incredible why are they bothering to tell us about it? It is a strange thing that a word meaning "unbelievable" is used to introduce so many works of fiction, such as *The Incredible Hulk*. What is the point of a story if it is unbelievable? Yet when really incredible forecasts are made in the press the word is not used and nobody bats and eyelid. It is surprising how often such forecasts are made with dramatic results, normally the steering of billions of dollars of the good old American taxpayers' money in the appropriate direction. We are not supposed to notice that these forecasts are then gradually tempered over succeeding years until they are not dramatic at all. We shall see many examples in what follows –global warming, AIDS, CJD deaths and UK economic growth, to name but a few. The overriding principle behind all this is the belief that the public memory is short. Perhaps it would be a useful exercise to jog it occasionally.

Keeping an open mind

This is a lovely catch-all mainly used by those operating on the fringes between real science and pseudo-science (even international football managers justifying the employment of a faith healer). If I am measuring the value of a resistance in my laboratory, I do not record, for example, the humidity in Timbuktu. I have to make a subjective judgement as to what is relevant; otherwise my laboratory logbook would fill up in no time. This phrase, however, is used to justify almost any bizarre theory, regardless of whether it is compatible with the immutable laws of physics, which leads us on to the topic in the section below.

Déjà vu

They say that Christopher Columbus discovered America; but, of course, it was already there. When I was a small boy in the London of the late '40s, we used to catch the tube train to Cockfosters then the bus to Hadley Wood. For us it was a magic place, the pond most of all. We would fish with worms tied on to cotton thread, catching sticklebacks, frogs, toads and newts. Every now and then there was great excitement when someone caught an amphibian that was deformed (small boys are morbid that way). There was no agriculture for miles, let alone chemicals.

Forty years later in California (naturally) a naturalist discovered that deformed frogs occurred in the wild. In the intervening years Rachel Carson had published her jeremiad on the great ecological disaster. So a whole new branch of the ecological scare industry was born. There are probably many more examples of rediscovery. A correspondent to *The Times* pointed out that in the time of Henry VIII a butcher was fined for selling meat from a mad cow. There are probably many more cases where phenomena are only newly found because nobody bothered to look for them before.

More research is needed

This statement is one of the defining characteristics of junk science. Real scientists take it for granted that all research leads to more research. As GBS characteristically put it "Science is always wrong. It never solves a problem without creating ten more". It is one of the excitements of a life of science that research throws up more questions than it answers and the path leads ever onwards, who knows where? So this is a truism that real science does not bother to state. When junk scientists use it, however, it is a portmanteau sentence that carries the heart-felt message "I know these results aren't up to much. In fact, they're pretty insignificant. However, this is the way I make my living, and I call upon the generosity of the taxpayer to keep me in the style to which I am accustomed."

Tip of the iceberg

This is a rather more sinister version of "more research is needed." It is often used by professional alarmist to create a panic from a minimal amount of evidence. The classic case was the Cleveland child sexual abuse scandal of 1987. A team of paediatricians and social workers invented a plague of family child abuse and as a result 121 children were snatched from their families. Suddenly every parent in the country was a suspected abuser, since this could only be the tip of the iceberg. By the time the public inquiry started a year later 98 of the children has been returned home, scarred for life. The social workers resented the fact that they were (quite rightly in my opinion) pilloried for this catastrophe.

On the other hand, there are many aspects of the current parlous state of affairs that really might be the tip of the iceberg; as we shall see.

Precisely absurd

One of the instant give-aways for junk science is the use of totally unjustifiable levels of precision. Numbers that are produced by theoretical means, such as π, can often be quoted to any number of decimal places you like. Numbers produced by measurement cannot be treated in the same way. Accuracy to three significant figures (one part in a thousand) is reasonable for instrumentation, while four figures is pretty good going. There are areas of measurement where even one significant figure is hard to get – the measurement of risk being a prime example. Thus, if you see quoted a risk of 483 per million (as we shall), the alarm bells should start to ring. You will almost certainly find that such a number is accompanied by many other characteristics of junk science (q.v.).

2.3 The case of the missing mechanism

> *Doublethink means the power of holding two contradictory beliefs in one's mind simultaneously, and accepting both of them.*
> George Orwell, Nineteen Eighty Four

There is one problem that real scientists have with the fringe sciences and that is the inevitable absence of a mechanism to explain the claimed effects – "We don't know how it works, but it does."

If you consider any aspect of applied technology or scientific medicine, the phenomena on which it is based are governed by relatively simple and universal laws. If just one of these laws were convincingly demonstrated to have been broken, the whole basis of science and technology would collapse.

When in 1901 Marconi first communicated signals across the Atlantic Ocean between Poldhu, in Cornwall, and St John's, in Newfoundland, James Clerk Maxwell had already established the theory of this in a series of papers published in the 1860s, and the phenomena were completely understood. To those not versed in the vocabulary of vector differential equations Maxwell's formulation will appear extremely abstruse, but the ideas behind them are in fact very simple.

Consider, for example, what I call the Universal Law of Stuff, and I hope the lay reader will excuse a few simple equations. If we have a closed volume containing some stuff, as yet unspecified, there are only six things that could possibly happen to the stuff. Let us call the stuff Q and use subscripts to indicate each of those six possibilities. The stuff can:

Come into the volume, Q_i

Go out of the volume, Q_o

Be created within the volume, Q_c

Be destroyed in the volume, Q_d

Be stored in the volume, Q_s

Be unstored in the volume, Q_u

Now, as we have specified the only things that can change, it follows that if one of them increases by any amount, one or more of the others must decrease by the same total amount. Putting it mathematically:

$$Q_i - Q_o + Q_c - Q_d + Q_u - Q_s = \text{constant}$$

this constant being the amount of stuff in there when the volume was created. We can borrow from the mathematicians the notation of putting a dot over a term to indicate a rate of change with time, and since constants don't change with time:

$$\dot{Q}_i - \dot{Q}_o + \dot{Q}_c - \dot{Q}_d + \dot{Q}_u - \dot{Q}_s = 0$$

Now this law is absolutely immutable, besides being common sense. The stuff can be virtually any quantity you can identify and quantify. Examples are

Liquid
Gas
Electric flux
Heat
Information
Light
Electrons
People
Etc.

We can go further. If this stuff is created at a point, unless we have some means of directing the flow (e.g. focussing), it must spread out uniformly in all directions, so at a distance *r* from the source it has spread out evenly over a sphere whose surface area is

$$A = 4\pi r^2$$

and the density of the stuff at this distance must be

$$D = \frac{Q}{A} = \frac{Q}{4\pi r^2}$$

Thus, by pure common sense, we have established the famous inverse square law, which is obeyed by all stuff, unless we can focus it (e.g. by parabolic dish, lens, optical fibre or, for heat, a metal rod). In any particular field of science the general law of stuff will have a fancy name. In electrostatics, for example it is *Coulomb's law*. In particular, mass and energy are always conserved, though Einstein told us that one can be converted into the other.

Energy and mass cannot disappear from one location in space and pop up at another without passing through the intervening locations. If energy is not steerable, its density (the amount passing through a unit area) must diminish rapidly as it propagates. Its density at 100 metres from the source must be one ten thousandth of the density at one metre – neither more nor less.

The point is, then, that if just one instance is found where such laws are disobeyed, not only science but common sense itself collapse: Still, as my old physics master, Mr Baxenden, would often say "The trouble with common sense is that it isn't common."

Furthermore, the flow of all the stuff known to science can be detected, measured and blocked. Thus scientists, when they are confronted with an unfamiliar phenomenon always look for a mechanism, which is usually the flow of some detectable stuff or other: and that is why they get so irate when it is one of their own number who espouses some fringe science that ignores the vital question – Where is the Mechanism? A scientist cannot believe simultaneously in, say, Newton's Laws of Motion and, say, telekinesis. They are, in a word, incompossible.

Sorry, right number!

There are many groups of people who can be identified by their gullibility. One of the most prominent is the coterie of hi-fi enthusiasts. Their credulity often reaches truly Californian proportions. For example, they pay fortunes for bits of cable that are cored with oxygen-free copper in the belief that this will give them a higher quality of sound than ordinary copper. There is no known scientific mechanism by which any change in audio quality could be brought about in such a way. An advertisement in *The Gramophone*, however, produced an even more extraordinary example of mass naïveté.

The heading blared the "fact" that STATIC RUINS THE SOUND FROM YOUR CDs. There followed an impressive list of quotations from reviews of the new device that solves this "problem". Before we look at them, let us examine the science. Compact discs work in a completely different way from the old fashioned vinyl. They work purely with numbers – a series of noughts and ones burned into the surface of the material by laser. These are interrogated by another smaller laser in your player and converted back into continuous sound. About 15% of the surface of the disc is used for error correcting information. Even if damage does occur, this mechanism is sufficient to correct it, up to a point where the signal is completely disrupted and unintelligible. Furthermore, there is no way known to science that a static electric field could affect these numbers or their processing. The possible interactions between light and electricity (Pockels and Kerr effects) are tiny and only occur in certain special polar dielectric materials. This argument does not, of course, apply to old-fashioned vinyl discs, where dust particles attracted by the static charge cause clicks that add to the background noise, though they do not change the quality of the sound itself. Having established that the reviewers are examining a device that cannot possibly work, let us see what they have to say:

> "……..makes the spoken word more articulate and clearer in inflections (and therefore musical instruments too) and gives phrasing and timing in music a more natural, non-fatiguing character". H-Fi News and Record Review.

> "……..the sound isn't just smoother , sweeter or sharper. Rather the music itself seems to change, becoming rhythmically more cohesive and altogether more purposeful and coherent". Hi-Fi Choice.

> "…..improved the sound of every CD I played in every player I had, sometimes quite dramatically". Stereophile.

> "………the biggest change is in the treble, which becomes clearer and more detailed while the rest of the sound gets more dynamic. The base firms up a tad too and the sense of rhythm improves……the sonic changes are well worth the money". Hi-Fi World.

What can one say? Perhaps add a commentary on the power of faith or a quotation from Hans Christian Anderson's "The King's New Clothes."

2.4 Cause and Effect

> *It is the cause, it is the cause, my soul:*
> *Shakespeare, Othello*

Causality is one of those concepts that seem simple until you begin to examine it closely. Even in physics, where Newton's third law of motion rules (to every action there is an equal and opposite reaction), it is not always clear, or even useful, to distinguish between cause and effect. If you take a charged electrical capacitor and connect it by a wire with inductance and resistance to a similar uncharged one, the charge oscillates pendulum-like between one and the other until it reaches equilibrium (and, incidentally, exactly half the energy always disappears in dissipation or radiation). The voltages and currents in such a system can be precisely predicted by mathematical equations, but which is cause and which is effect? If the concept is difficult on physics it is orders of magnitude more difficult in human affairs.

We can establish relationships between phenomena, but that is not the same as determining causality. Just as the laws of electric circuits (Kirchhoff's laws) establish the relationships between voltages and currents so statistics can tell us about relationships in human and biological affairs. It is important, however, to understand what statistics can and cannot do Statistics can tell us that A is associated with B, not that A causes B or B causes A. Furthermore, statistics can only see through a glass darkly. Nevertheless, properly conducted statistics is a science precise in its imprecision. It can deliver confidence limits and levels of significance that are measures of the value of any particular result. It is important always to remember that, once we resort to statistics, there is always a probability, however small, that the result we achieve has occurred purely by chance.

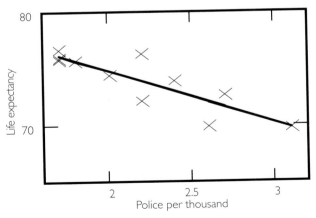

Figure 2.1 Life expectancy versus number of police per thousand of the population

Policemen can seriously damage your health

Two sets of data came my way on the same day. *The Times* (5th December, 1997) published data on the life expectancy for various areas in England and a friend gave me some figures on the level of policing by area. Eleven of the areas on the two lists were reasonably common, so I decided to plot one set of data against the other.

The figures range from the most healthy region (Cambridge) to the least healthy (Manchester). It is clear that there is a negative correlation. You can calculate your life expectancy by subtracting four and a half times the number of police per thousand of the population in your area from 83.8, which is the age you can expect to reach if you are lucky enough to live in an area with no policemen at all.

And if you think that is daft, you are not cut out to be an epidemiologist.

The web of causality

The example above is, of course, meant to be facetious, though it is no more bizarre than many theories that are published and publicised in all seriousness. The modest, though significant, correlation is quite valid (for the cognoscenti, $r = -0.858$) but we do not infer that policemen shorten life or, indeed, that long life causes a reduction in policemen. Our knowledge of the different circumstances in Cambridge and Manchester lead us to be unsurprised that one has longer life expectancy and needs fewer policemen than the other. We are also aware, however, that the factors involved are multitudinous and in a complex relationship. They include history, ancestry, prosperity, education and a host of other circumstances.

It is a popular misconception that causality is proven by priority in time. I used to have an office on the ground floor. Every day at about 9.50, birds would begin to gather in the trees and bushes outside my window. It was like a scene from Hichcock's film of the Daphne du Maurier story. At 10.00 a little old lady would appear and sit on the bench outside my window. I might have inferred that the presence of the birds caused the presence of the little old lady. She would open her capacious bag and bring out a box full of breadcrumbs, which she spread generously about on the grass. A silly example, you might think, but no sillier than some causations that are put forward in all seriousness by epidemiologists.

There is a correlation between blond hair and blue eyes. This does not mean that blond hair causes blue eyes or vice versa. On the other hand there is a correlation between grey hair and old age that is causative, but only in one direction. I probably mention this because I have experienced all four phenomena. In neither case does statistics have anything to say about causation; only physics, chemistry and biology can do that. We are bombarded daily with causal relationships that are nothing of the sort. Arthritis is associated with obesity, for example, or sunscreen is associated with skin cancer. More of these later.

Human behaviour is a complicated matter. There are all sorts of relationships that are conveniently ignored by those who are proponents of one particular simplistic theory or another. Heavy smokers and drinkers may well also tend to have a poorly balanced diet and stressful lives. Nurses who eat lots of margarine (used in cakes) or take diet pills may well tend to be obese and lie about their smoking habits to boot. Poor dental hygiene will correlate with a generally unhealthy life style. Urban populations will have a whole range of exposures that are different from those of rural populations and to isolate one of them (such as particulates from vehicle exhaust) is simply unreasonable. People tend to marry people much like themselves and therefore have similar life styles and case histories, which casts serious doubt on so-called spousal studies. Furthermore, human beings are highly suggestible, have faulty memories and go in for a lot of self-deception. These are all confounding factors (q.v.).

2.5 Numbers out of control – feedback and delay

"I can't hold her together much longer, Captain! She's breaking apart!"
Engineer Scott in Star Trek

The modern world relies heavily on applying processes to numbers, and the consequences of such processes can be anything from trivial to downright dangerous. If the processing is in a computer controlling a giant steel mill, a result of error could be death and destruction. If it is carried out by Government agencies trying to control the economy, there is potential for the lives and livelihoods of millions of citizens to be damaged irrevocably. There are two simple but momentous aspects of processing that contain the seeds of instability that can lead to such disasters; *feedback and delay.*

The case of the scalded chancellor

A nice everyday illustration of the sort of instability that can result from feedback and delay is given by Eastaway and Wyndham. You enter a shower in a cheap hotel and turn on the water, which is freezing cold. You then turn the control to hot and a few seconds later find yourself being scalded. You turn to cold and a few seconds later are freezing again, and so it goes on, with alternate scolding and freezing. This simple situation presents one of the most difficult control situations we face. The intelligent person soon learns two lessons – you must be very patient and you must not make sudden large changes. Unfortunately, the people in control of our lives do not always act in an intelligent manner. The above authors cite the case of the Chancellor of the Exchequer in 1989. The economy was looking on the cool side and, not realising that there was hot water in the pipe, the Chancellor turned the heat up by reducing taxes and interest rates. Soon the economy was out of control, with inflation roaring away and massive imports being sucked in, so he turned the control to cold by deflationary measures. After a delay there followed a sharp downturn in the economy with massive destruction of businesses and livelihoods. None of this was natural – it was all caused by the man with his hand on the control knob.

Some simple processes

It is a remarkable fact that all the problems of instability in the processing of numbers can be revealed by very simple processes. Consider a basic input/output process in which we take a sequence of numbers and multiply them by a constant. We can write this as:

$$y_i = a\,x_i$$

Thus if a is 2 and x_1, x_2 and x_3 are 5, 4 and 9, then y_1, y_2 and y_3 are 10, 8 and 18 respectively. All nice and simple; nothing can go wrong there. However, things change when we add some feedback and delay. In order to stop it all getting too verbose, let us write the above sequences as $x = 5, 4, 9$ and $y = 10, 8, 18$. We also use a simple input sequence engineers use to test processes, the unit pulse, which is the simplest input sequence we can think of, namely, $x = 1, 0, 0, 0, 0 \ldots\ldots$ and so on for as long as we like.

Now we can look at the simplest process with feedback and delay:

$$y_i = x_i + by_{i-1}$$

which is a mathematical way of saying "take the new input number and add to it b times the last output number". Consider the case where $b = \frac{1}{2}$ and apply our test sequence $x = 1, 0, 0, 0, 0, 0, \ldots$ The result we get is $y = 1, \frac{1}{2}, \frac{1}{4}, \frac{1}{8}$ a sequence that goes on for ever, regardless of the fact that we are adding no more inputs. However, as we go on the numbers get smaller and smaller, eventually approaching zero, which is known as an exponential decay. We also describe such a system as *stable*, since any disturbance to it, such as the first 1 we put in, will produce an output that eventually decays away to zero.

Now consider the case where $b = 2$. The result of putting our test sequence in is now the sequence $y = 1, 2, 4, 8, 16, \ldots$, which keeps growing for ever. This is an exponential growth and the system is described as *unstable*, since the output from a disturbance keeps growing, regardless of the fact that we are adding no more inputs.

So far, so good. It does not take a lot of brain power to work out that if b is greater than 1 the system is unstable and if b is less than 1 it is stable. However, when it gets really interesting and a bit less obvious is when we allow for the use of two delays in the output:

$$y_i = x_i + by_{i-1} + cy_{i-2}$$

which in words means, to get the new output, add to the new input b times the last output and c times the output before that. We now still have a very simple system, but one that is capable of all the complexities of behaviour that linear systems can exhibit. For example, choosing simple numbers for ease of calculation we get

$$y_i = x_i + y_{i-1} - 1.2y_{i-2}$$

and the results shown graphically are:

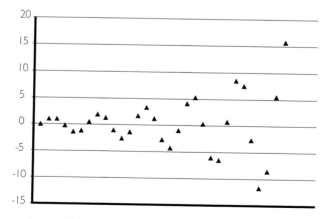

Figure 2.2 Progress of the sequence

36

We can see that the shape of the sequence is an increasing oscillation (an exponentially increasing sinusoid) and it will keep on increasing forever, regardless of the fact that we are adding no further inputs. In short, it is an unstable system. Quite a small change of the coefficients in the equation will alter the behaviour dramatically. For example, with a calculator try:

$$y_i = x_i + y_{i-1} - 0.8 y_{i-2}$$

These ultra-simple examples show the awesome power of feedback and delay. It is not difficult to predict the behaviour for any pair of coefficients, but as it involves complex numbers it is beyond our present scope. As it happens, this simple (second order) system with only two delays exhibits all the possible behaviours of any linear system, however many delays we have in it.

What can we learn from such simple illustrations? The main lesson is that the combination of feedback and delay can be deadly if handled without understanding. Our economic masters typically consider data that are three months old, relate them to data that are six months old and then try to adjust the input to produce a desired output. Is it any wonder that the results are usually disastrous? If only they had the honesty to come clean, apologise and say "Sorry, wrong number!"

Non-linearity

There is one further complication of numbers out of control that we need to consider. In the above we have used the term "linear". As used by mathematicians, this means more than just a straight-line graph. Very roughly speaking it means that if you double any input you double the corresponding output. Thus in all the above examples, if we had used the test sequence 2,0,0,0,0….. we would get the same shaped responses but with all the numbers doubled. Fortunately, we can often use the linear approximation, especially if we are careful to make only small changes, but in the real world there are no linear systems.

There is one special type of non-linearity that is nearly always present, and that is if the numbers get big enough they will break the system. If you keep turning up the volume of your powerful amplifier it will eventually tear the cone of your loudspeaker and the system will never work properly again. Incidentally, you can get the same effect by holding a microphone too close the speaker so that the combination of feedback and delay causes the familiar howl that plagues public address systems. If you make small changes to interest rates you can modify the behaviour of businesses and consumers in a desired direction, but if you overdo it, so that businesses are failing on a large scale, then the changes become irreversible and they are not there to respond to any further corrections.

The economy is an example of a system that is as complicated as you can get. It is not only large and multi-variable, with feedback and delay, it is also highly non-linear. One of the main reasons for this is that it involves the perceptions of large numbers of people. Again if you make small changes in interest rates or taxation people will adjust their behaviour accordingly. If, however, you make large changes their behaviour flips from one mode to another, a catastrophic change. Bankers stop lending, consumers stop spending, businesses disappear and you get what is called in the jargon a hard landing. Because of feedback and delay any attempt at correction is always in the time-honoured phrase "too little too late".

The economy is so complicated that nobody understands it, least of all the arrogant politicians and economists that presume to run our lives. The only reasonable strategy is, like the man in the shower, to make small changes over a long period, much as the Bundesbank or The Fed have done over the years with a few aberrations.

In these times of daily scares the complacency of people and governments towards the disastrous potential of numerical instability is truly remarkable. To a considerable extent, especially in Britain, real production has been replaced by illusory production (i.e. numbers). Transactions can wing their way round the world electronically, passing through half a dozen countries in seconds, each participant adding a percentage. Nothing is made and no real value is added. The players in the global casino are not only human, but are often simply computer programs. The potential for catastrophe is self-evident. Waves of selling could be triggered automatically, building into a financial tsunami that could engulf the world. It nearly happened once when a giant gambling syndicate collapsed, and only deft footwork by Alan Greenspan saved the day.

2.6 Some more laws

> *Irish stew in the name of the law.*
> *Spike Milligan*

In addition to the immutable physical laws there are some general laws that are relevant to the causation of wrong numbers.

Langmuir's Laws
These were identified by Nobel Laureate Irving Langmuir, who formulated them to provide a means of identifying bad science. It is truly astonishing how often they apply.

> *1. The maximum effect that is observed is produced by a causative agent of barely detectable intensity, and the magnitude of the effect is substantially independent of the intensity of the cause.*

> *2. The effect is of a magnitude that remains close to the limit of detectability, or many measurements are necessary because of the low level of significance of the results.*

> *3. There are claims of great accuracy.*

> *4. Fantastic theories contrary to experience are suggested.*

> *5. Criticisms are met by ad hoc excuses thought up on the spur of the moment.*

> *6. The ratio of supporters to critics rises to somewhere near 50% and then falls gradually to zero.*

Maier's Law
This is also adhered to by the practitioners of bad science.

> *If the facts don't conform to the theory, they must be disposed of.*

> ### *Corollaries:*
> *1) The bigger the theory, the better.*

> *2) The experiment may be considered a success if no more than 50% of the observed measurements must be discarded to obtain a correspondence with the theory.*

Hutber's Law

Patrick Hutber was a distinguished journalist who contributed trenchant columns to the *Daily Telegraph* for many years. His deceptively simple three-word law is remarkable for its consistent accuracy, which will be reiterated throughout this text:

> *"Improvement" means deterioration.*

Kingsley's Law

Formulated by Kingsley Amis to apply to universities, it is also applicable to many other areas, notably broadcasting:

> *More means worse.*

The Laws of Thermodynamics for laymen

> 1. You cannot win
> 2. You cannot break even
> 3. You cannot get out of the game

These are, of course, facetious, but they underline a severe restraint on what is possible in the use of energy. The real laws of thermodynamics are immutable and habitually ignored by junk scientists, pseudo-scientists and fraudsters.

Murphy's law

> *If anything can go wrong it will go wrong*

Particularly relevant here, as it was formulated by an engineer working on a measurement problem in a strain gauge bridge transducer. Again facetious, but disturbingly accurate in experience.

Brignell's law of league tables

> *All measures used as the basis of a league table always improve.*

> *Corollary 1*
> *All other measures get worse to compensate.*

> *Corollary 2*
> *What you measure is what you get.*

Moore's Law

This remarkable prediction, made in 1965 and based on only three data points, has held good ever since. It relates to the number of transistors that can be placed on a single chip and gives an exponential relationship, which can be stated verbally as:

> *The number of devices on a chip doubles every 18 months.*

What, you may ask, has these to do with the subject in hand? The answer is almost everything. It has produced incredibly cheap computers and data storage that have revolutionised science, bureaucracy, authorship and almost every aspect of modern life. The effects will be discussed at length in later chapters.

Le Chatelier-Braun Principle

> *If any change is imposed on a system in equilibrium, the system will change in such a way as to counteract the imposed change.*

This law, originally applied to chemistry, is remarkable for its wide range of application in fields as diverse as politics, economics and education. Nevertheless, as George Soros cogently pointed out, it can be a serious mistake to try to impose physical laws, such as equilibrium, to all human and economic affairs.

The Bureaucrat's credo

> I cause change therefore I am.

In bureaucracy there has been one of those cataclysmic changes that sometimes occur in nature, such as the sudden reversal of the earth's magnetic field. Before about 1982 they would resist change with all their might. After that time they saw it as the justification for their existence.

2.7 Who are the producers of wrong numbers?

> Man is a credulous animal and must believe in something;
> in the absence of good grounds for belief, he will be satisfied
> with bad ones.
> Bertrand Russell

Charlatans

One of the mysteries of our supposedly enlightened age is that charlatans are no less prevalent than they were in previous ages. Indeed, the more science explains, the more ordinary people seem to want to resort to magic. Half the population turns daily to "the stars" in the tabloid newspapers, despite the fact that the horoscopes are often mutually contradictory. Astrologers and mystics become national figures, waxing fat on television and appearance fees. Fringe medicine thrives and enjoys patronage in the highest social circles. Even the 1998 England World Cup football squad had a resident faith healer, though they signally fail to practice penalties, which sealed their fate. They also had a dietician who took away their baked beans and forced them to eat broccoli (not only junk science, but damned bad psychology). In any group of people you will find that virtually all know their birth sign, but few know their blood group, which could be a matter of life or death. Here is a list of services offered on one web page from the USA.

Acupuncture
aromatherapy
chelation therapy
chiropractic
holistic medicine
homeopathy
hypnosis
joy touch
massage therapy
naturopathy
psychic surgery
rolfing
therapeutic touch

Now, I personally have no doubts that some of these activities are effective. I have, for example, witnessed a totally convincing demonstration, on people I know, of hypnotism and I am inclined to accept its therapeutic value (and its dangers). For most of them, however, I have nothing but disdain. No, I do not have the evidence, and I am certainly not going to waste my time gathering it, but once again it is the case of the Missing Mechanism. As a scientist I am not prepared to accept "We don't know how, but it works." The best you can say of most of them is that they are harmless and give comfort to people. Where they are at their most dangerous is when they deflect patients from seeking proper care for serious medical conditions. Scientific medicine has its problems, and diagnosis is still an art, but it is still the only effective weapon we have in the permanent battle against disease.

What has all this to do with numbers? Here's an example from a book called Linda Goodman's Star Signs:

> "The number 1 vibrates to the Sun. It represents creativity, protection and benevolence. Number 2 vibrates to the moon. It represents imagination parenthood and sensitivity..."

If you know what all that means you are a greater man than I am, Gunga Din, but the good Linda does warn us "There are many ways the pied pipers of numbers distort the truth of numerology." That makes me feel a lot better.

Hucksters

An enduring image from the classical western films is the smooth talking salesman, standing on the back of his covered wagon, preaching the benefits of a snake oil that will cure all ills. Fear not, he is not a thing of the past. He is alive and well and living, among many other places, on the Web (to say nothing of Parliament), as we shall see later.

Admen

Now, according to the Advertising Standards Authority advertisements are not allowed to lie, but numbers are wonderful things when it comes to pulling the wool over people's eyes.

While taking a break from writing this section I was offered on TV a snack bar that is said to be 92% fat-free. Presumably this means that it contains 8% fat, but is that what it implies? Either it is fat-free or it isn't. You can't be 92% non-pregnant or 92% undead. Accusation of lying is not allowed in the British Parliament, so Winston Churchill came up with the expression "terminalogical inexactitude", which seems to fit the bill for many advertising slogans.

Journalists

> You cannot hope
> to bribe or twist
> thank God! the
> British Journalist.
> But, seeing what
> the man will do
> unbribed, there's
> no occasion to.
> Humbert Wolfe

Undoubtedly, the profession (if such it is) that has the least respect for accuracy is Journalism. I exclude politics and other forms of hucksterism from consideration in this context. I think I can honestly say that, where I have known the details, I have never read an accurate press report.

Apart from a general disregard for precision, they have the peculiar clichés of their calling. For example, they cannot bear to use the same form of number representation twice in the same sentence – "One third of children prefer red sweets, but over 66% like the yellow ones".

They have particular difficulties with fractions:

> One in three lecturers in higher education takes half or less of their holiday entitlement, rising to one in four on fixed term contracts, according to their union, Nafthe.
>
> The Guardian, 21 Oct 1997.

When it comes to risk and statistical significance virtually all journalists, including those who purport to specialise in science, are simply not interested. This despite the fact that, for example, The Foundation for American Communications (FACS) has provided a complete Risk Handbook on the Web specifically for their use. It is simply implausible that none of them knows the statistical truth, and the only explanation is that they are not prepared to let the truth stand in the way of a good story.

Just occasionally a journalist betrays some sign of conscience (see, for example, *Do we care about the truth?* By Nigel Hawkes, *The Times*, February 19, 1999) but it is indeed a rarity. Hawkes' article should be framed and hung above the desk of every science journalist.

Politicians

Now, I have to confess that my scientific detachment tends to come under considerable strain when I come to discuss politicians and I tend towards the e e cummings view:

> a politician is an arse upon
> which every one has sat except a man

In the present context, however, perhaps the dictum of Henry Brooks Adams is more appropriate:

> Practical politics consists in ignoring facts.

There is no point in elaborating at this stage, as there will be many examples in later pages.

Lawyers

The behaviour of lawyers is difficult to understand unless you bear in mind one fact – their major preoccupation is with the size of their fees. All their other activities, such as the courting of publicity, are geared to maximising them. In these pages you will see examples where lawyers have used scientific witnesses they must have known were perjured, presented cases they must have known were illogical and, worst of all, moved heaven and earth to prevent scientific fraud being uncovered. Away from the scientific context, some of the great fraudsters of the age have used their power to buy the law as a means of protection from investigation. One of the great evils in the law is that it allows itself to be bought as a willing accomplice of villains in the pursuit of their activities of fraud and deceit. Robert Maxwell, for example, by issuing an endless stream of writs, was able to prevent his crimes from even being discussed in the open. His case demonstrates that you don't even have to be rich, just in control of enough of other people's money. Thousands of people are financially ruined and the politicians stand by, offering a token wringing of hands. In particular, the corrupt state of the US legal system, with scumbag lawyers raking in millions of dollars, is creating a major world problem. In theory, barratry (the ·stirring up of vexatious litigation) is illegal in Britain, but we seem intent on copying everything that is worst in America. The prurient Kenneth Starr was able to spend forty million dollars (good old American taxpayer) to establish that the President had dropped his trousers in the White House and had lied about it (quite properly in my opinion; it is a rule of civilised society that a gentlemen never tells). Yet that President's crimes against scientific truth went without comment. For myself, I can forgive him for Monica Lewinsky, but not for Carol Browner. An excellent little book by Frank Furedi *Courting Mistrust: the hidden growth of a culture of litigation in Britain* tells a disturbing tale of the trends.

Bureaucrats

Not a day goes by without bureaucracy extending its hegemony. Never underestimate the appetite for power in bureaucrats. It is a hunger that feeds on itself and grows with success. Their life is a game of monopoly in which the winner accumulates as much power as possible. We shall see many examples in later pages. Opposition to pointless change is easily combated by bureaucracy. They use ridicule. Natural conservatives, such as myself, who object to unnecessary change for its own sake, become inured to mockery. Typical is the *Times* leader, which guys them as people who think that nothing should ever happen for the first time. The current neo-Maoist atmosphere of permanent revolution is paradise for the ambitious bureaucrat.

Scientists

It is a sad fact that scientists are among the most prolific of generators of wrong numbers. There are many famous examples of bad science, some of which will be mentioned later, but it appears likely that many more go undetected.

There are more scientists alive and working today than total number in previous history. This has been the case since the dawn of science. In other words it is an exponential growth. With a few notable exceptions, each one of them, like this author, is a jobbing craftsman – one that will do to swell a conference, start a seminar or two. Some, however, are not content with being deferential, glad to be of use, politic, cautious and meticulous. They seek a higher glory. This manifests itself first in their choice of area in which to work. They seek results that are politically correct or headline-grabbing, charged with human emotion. They dream of providing the X in the sub-editors' template *Times* headline **"Thousands will die of X, by Nigel Hawkes"**.

Furthermore, this exponentially growing cohort needs resources. Even Britain, noted for its parsimony in this area and the only country in the world to reduce its research in the eighties, spends £6 billion a year on research. At one time a few flatterers at court could wield all the influence that was available, but in the age of democracy the majority had to be got at or, to be more accurate, the new princes who dispensed the wealth torn from the suffering taxpayer. These disciples of Machiavelli in their turn need results to justify their own burgeoning empires. Thus Science and Truth are exposed to inexorable pressure to bend themselves to the exigencies of *realpolitik*.

For some the temptations of the glory of appearing in the national media are simply irresistible. These publicity hungry professors, once they have caught the bug, have to go on to the next fix then the next. They gear their research towards results that will hit the headlines. When the results turn out to be statistically insignificant they simply abandon the elementary constraints of statistics. They produce half-baked results that are popular, scary or politically correct and so can rely on the bureaucratic establishment to steer more and more of the taxpayers' money in their direction. We see them regularly on our TV screens, eyes aglow with the thrill of fame, egos puffed up with self-importance, usually declaiming of some threat to humanity. Let's face it, it's fun to see yourself on TV. I've done it myself a few times, but I would not sell my soul for the pleasure.

SIFs and Puritans

Single Issue Fanatics (or SIFs) were first identified, I believe, by Bernard Levin. SIFs have always been with us, but until recent times their activities were largely confined to religion or politics. Being a SIF is not confined to holding strong views on a matter. Adolph Hitler and James the First, for example, were violently anti-smoking, but they were largely concerned with other things. With the SIF the object of his hatred (and they are never FOR anything, which differentiates them from fans) consumes his whole existence.

Why do people become SIFs? It can happen through a terrible tragedy in their lives — a child lost through the criminality of a drunken driver or a much-loved parent dying of lung cancer after a lifetime's cigarette smoking. A respectable scientist might lose a loved companion through early death and turn in desperation to the occult in a vain attempt to get in touch with the other side, thence getting further and further sucked in to things that are an offence to all his training.

On the other hand, some people are born as SIFs waiting for a cause. The exact nature of the cause is almost immaterial. It just has to be something that they can sink themselves in to the exclusion of all else. When I got involved in the students' union a cynical tutor told me that it would experience a crisis in January or February, since it always did. The crisis duly arrived, and great fun it was, with late night meetings full of urgency and passion. It was all part of growing up, but some people never do, and to repeat the same buzz they become SIFs. In the extreme this syndrome can be sinister and frightening. There are people who have a need for violence, but they have a sufficient veneer of civilisation to require a cause to justify it. Killing and maiming human beings is sanctified in their minds by being associated with the rights of our fluffy friends or the re-drawing of a national boundary.

One of the problems for ordinary, sane people is that they cannot come near to penetrating the mind of such a person. They might accept the old saw that "A fanatic is one who can't change his mind and won't change the subject", but, until the bombs start to detonate, they see nothing more sinister.

It is the same with Puritans. Again, the jokey definition of Puritanism "The haunting fear that someone, somewhere may be happy" may be largely accepted, but the reality can be more sinister. Whether it is Cromwell's "Godly", McCarthy's Subcommittee or the New Left in the Anglo Saxon universities, the urge that drives the Puritans is their need to run other peoples lives. They invariably initiate witch hunts that lead to other people losing their livelihoods, their freedom and even their lives. Even as I write there are people languishing in US gaols as a result of farcical trials for "Satanic Abuse".

What, you may well ask, has all this to do with numbers? The answer is that SIFs and Puritans lie, and one of the most effective ways to lie is with numbers, as we shall see in later chapters. There is a fundamental question in all of this — is it permissible to tell a lie in a good cause? For science, as we have stated in the previous chapter, the answer must be an emphatic **No!** There are two further important reasons for this. The first is that Science is a house of cards in which each part of the structure depends on all the rest. Take one away and the whole edifice collapses. The second is that one person's good cause may be another's anathema. Official good causes in the past have included the elimination of witches, Yorkists, Lollards, infidels of all varieties and any form of opposition to the ruling clique. Theories that were violently enforced include the geocentric cosmology, creationism, racial superiority, polytheism etc. In modern times SIFs and Puritans have created a climate of fear, in which anyone challenging their numerical claims on, say, passive smoking or drink-drive, is condemned for promoting infanticide. There seems to be a real fear of writing or publishing the truth about the subjects. Even the most respectable authors either shy away or obediently toe the party line.

The big problem that SIFs create is that they take society's eye off the ball. One of the greatest health problems of today is the rate of increase of asthma. In response the SIFs yell "passive smoking", yet the exposure to tobacco smoke in the UK and USA has fallen by at least an order of magnitude over the last decade or so (I did more passive smoking as a child in one visit to the cinema than most modern kids do in their whole childhood). Many children never experience exposure. Meanwhile the number of asthma cases rises inexorably (doubling about every nine years) and we do precious little about it.

Another mark of the SIF is the resorting to intemperate language, especially about those who dare to voice a dissenting opinion. A former ASH official described critics such as myself as "a handful of crooks, has-beens and corrupt rogues dragged out of the bars by the tobacco industry." For the record my sole contact with the tobacco industry was a visit to a factory about fifteen years ago to observe the automation techniques.

The level of abuse hurled at renowned scholars by non-entities sometimes has to be seen to be believed. Frederick Sietz, a distinguished physicist, President Emeritus, Rockefeller University, and former president of the National Academy of Sciences, dared to side with the doubters on global warming. He was harangued in the columns of *The New York Times* (May 2, 1998) by one Robert L Park, a Professor of Physics at the University of Maryland, and gratuitously accused of being in the pay of the petroleum industry. Park reveals his credentials by stating that "Most climatologists agree that as a result of increased burning of fossil fuels, the temperature of the earth has gone up perhaps 0.7 degrees Fahrenheit..........many of the world's great cities, may be flooded in the next century by rising sea levels as the polar caps melt. Drastic changes in rainfall patterns could wreak havoc on food production." In fact, even some of the most committed adherents of the Global Warming scam agree nothing of the sort. The attack on Seitz is a continuation of one in Environmental Health Perspectives Volume 106, Number 4, April 1998, in which his stand is likened to "the denials offered by the tobacco industry which were disingenuous and resulted in untold human misery". Untold? Hardly! As we shall see later.

The great claim of the SIFs and Puritans is that they are motivated purely by concern for others. If so, why are they so selective? Here's a number from a headline in *The Times* (July 30, 1997) —**Climber tenth victim of the Alps in two days**. I wonder why we had no comment from the lobbyists who are so concerned with human health and welfare.

What has to be remembered about these pressure groups is that they are now big businesses, with turnovers measured in millions, mostly extracted from ordinary concerned citizens. All enterprises, once started, are on a cash flow treadmill. Just in order to keep going businesses need to keep pushing their product, which in this case is anxiety.

2.8 A little bit of modelling

*I am never content until I have constructed a mechanical
model of the subject I am studying. If I succeed in making one, I
understand; otherwise I do not.*
Lord Kelvin

I wish to avoid getting too technical, but we have got to the point where we need an illustration of some of these principles. One of the best ways of testing statistical methods is by modelling. If we know the answer before we pose the question then we have a means of measuring the goodness of any method purporting to arrive at that answer. The method can then be trusted in future when we do not know the answer *a priori*. Modern computer packages give us the means of generating random numbers with any of a range of pre-set properties. In the following I have used only the simplest of ideas based on the fact that if we know the probability, *p*, of an event and hence the probability, *1-p*, of it not happening, we can determine the probability of any outcome of any number of trials. This is the binomial distribution, based on a theorem known to Omar Khayyam in 1100 AD. In the following I have used solely a software generator of random numbers from this distribution. We shall justify the model later.

The question we pose is – Why do real scientists insist on such apparently strict criteria? If you are using statistics you are already dealing with events of low probability, since highly probable events do not need such support. Thus the probability of your getting a certain type of cancer (let's call it toe-nail cancer) in the next year might be of the order of one in ten thousand. If that probability is increased by 50% it is still of the order of one in ten thousand. A few numbers will illustrate the point.

The case of the ten scientists

What if ten different scientists took different groups of 100,000 people in order to measure this probability? How would their numbers vary?

I used Mathcad to generate one possible set of such numbers taken for populations of 100,000 and a probability of 0.0001, getting:

8,10,6,10,11,10,16,11,7,13

I then increased the probability by 50% and repeated the process, getting:

18,17,20,6,15,12,23,14,21,14

Now, we can clearly see that the numbers have gone up, which is not surprising as there is a total of one million people in each line, but what can each scientist deduce? Let us say that the ten scientists were looking at two groups of people and recording the number with, say, toe-nail cancer. The first group are from the general population and the second group are from those who use toothpaste with 3% meta-hydroxy-preposterose. Each scientist, unaware of the work of the others, publishes his conclusions and the ten conclusions are that meta-hydroxy-preposterose has the following effect on toe-nail cancer:

An increase of 125%
An increase of 70%
An increase of 233%
A **decrease** of 40%

An increase of 36%
An increase of 20%
An increase of 44%
An increase of 27%
An increase of 200%
An increase of 8%

Converting these percentages we get **risk ratios** of:

2.25,1.7,3.33,0.6,1.36,1.2,1.44,1.27,3,1.08

Now we, of course, know the correct answer, which is 1.5, and on average they are not badly out at 1.72, which again is not surprising over a total of a million people, but the result is that scientist number 3 makes his fame and fortune with scare stories in all the national papers, while scientist number 4 is consigned to oblivion.

That's all very well you may ask, but what if there were no genuine effect at all? Well, I generated another set of numbers from the same distribution but with the original probability unchanged and, to cut a long story short, we get the following results:

An increase of 37.5%
An increase of 30%
An increase of 33.3%
An increase of 10%
An increase of 22.3%
An increase of 20%
A decrease of 31.3%
A decrease of 18.2%
No change
A decrease of 23.1%

It does not look very random, with the decreases coming last, but that's statistics for you.

Now comes the subtle bit – almost nobody publishes negative results, and if they do they are disregarded (this is known as *publication bia*s and has been extensively verified, as we shall see). So we now have from our studies we now have.

An increase of 37.5%
An increase of 30%
An increase of 33.3%
An increase of 10%
An increase of 22.3%
An increase of 20%

At this stage somebody from an American government agency will combine them into a meta-analysis and the headline emerges:

Meta-hydroxy-preposterose causes a 30% increase in toe-nail cancer

Remember all this is generated from a model in which there is, in fact, zero effect, the numbers in each trial are enormous compared with many published ones and there has been no selection or massaging of the figures.

I trust that all this illustrates why real scientists are reluctant to accept risk ratios of less than three and never accept them less that two (that is a 200% and 100% risk increase respectively). There are other reasons, such as *confounding factors*, which we will meet later. However, if you are now convinced that the methods implied in the above are scandalous, hold on to your seat. If you are not convinced, why not throw this book away and pick up a nice *Mills and Boon?*

As a rule it is difficult to get access to the records of such large numbers of people so our scientists are reduced to looking at it another way. They call it a control study. Let us run another simulation, again using generated random numbers. From the State Hospital they get access to records of all the people who have contracted toe-nail cancer in the past year and question them about their use of meta-hydroxy-preposterose. Let us assume that each of our scientists lives in a state with a population of 1 million and for simplicity that 10% of the population use meta-hydroxyy-preposterose.

The ten scientists go to their state hospitals and find the following numbers of cases of toe-nail cancer:

100,105,98,87,94,110,108,111,96,100.

On average they would expect to find one tenth of each of these numbers use the stuff, but what they actually find is respectively:

9,8,12,7,8,5,20,13,12,8

which in turn lead to risk ratios of:

0.9,0.76,1.22,1.24,0.85,0.45,1.85,1.17,1.25,0.8

At first sight scientist number 6 has drawn the short straw, but he sells his results to the toothpaste manufacturers, who put out an advertisement headed:

Research shows meta-hydroxy-preposterose halves toe-nail cancer

But the winner is scientist number 7, who gets all the chat show fees after the newspapers publish headlines:

Meta-hydroxy-preposterose causes an 85% increase in toe-nail cancer

The others get a consolation prize by being included in a meta-study by an American Government Agency that shows a 35% increase in cancer risk and are awarded large grants by the ever generous American taxpayer to continue their research. At the risk of being inordinately repetitious, this is all based on no effect at all.

Headline Man

You might think our scientists have done pretty well for themselves. Not a bit! They are rank amateurs. They have not optimised the use of their data at all, but along comes **Headline Man** to show them how to do it. In order to model his activities let us make some further simple assumptions. He has access to the State Hospital where they specialise in toe-nail cancer, which has an annual probability of occurrence of 0.0001. The population covered by the hospital is 1 million, so you would expect about 100 patients, and the people of this State have very regular habits – they all tend to like one of the ten foods that he chooses to investigate, and detest the other nine in equal proportions. Thus you would expect about 10 patients to like each of the ten foods and none of the others. Of course, because of the random nature of such things we don't get exact numbers.

Our epidemiologist, for such he is, has luck from the outset – he has 105 patients (it must be right because the computer says so). He does not know what we know, that the distribution of preferences in the patients is exactly the same as for the rest of the State. He gets for the ten foods the following numbers:

10,8,13,8,14,8,18,16,8,12.

Now in order to make a comparison he does a control study of the preferences of 1000 average citizens and gets the following numbers:

91,104,102,104,86,85,128,93,103,84.

From these numbers he is able to predict how many of the 105 should have been in each category if the population with cancer were the same as the general population. So he is able to build up a table:

Food	per 1000 of general population	Cancer patients	Predicted from general population	Difference	%
Fish	91	10	9.555	0.445	4.657
Tomatoes	104	8	10.92	-2.92	-26.74
Red Meat	102	13	10.71	2.29	21.382
Asparagus	104	8	10.92	-2.92	-26.74
Margarine	86	14	9.03	4.97	55.039
Apple Pie	85	8	8.925	-0.925	-10.364
Coffee	128	18	13.44	4.56	33.929
Alcohol	93	16	9.765	6.235	63.85
Watercress	103	8	10.815	-2.815	-26.029
Red Meat	84	12	8.82	3.18	36.054

Now he is really cooking with gas. He writes a number of press releases and a few scientific papers that are accepted by International Journal of Cancer and finds that he has generated headlines in the press all around the world:

Tomatoes, Watercress and Asparagus reduce toe-nail cancer by 27%
Margarine (used in cakes) increases toe-nail cancer by 55%
Drinkers face 64% higher risk of toe-nail cancer
Leave out the Coffee and go for the Apple Pie to avoid toe-nail cancer
etc, etc

Remember, again, all these headlines derive from an effect that does not exist at all. It is all just natural statistical variation. The numbers have been generated in my lap-top computer using the stated probabilities and distributions (for the technically minded, the function *rbinom* in Mathcad 8). I would like to emphasise that for each of these simulations I took the first set of numbers that appeared and made no attempt to optimise the selection for my purposes. I did, however, cheat on inserting the names of the foods, taking into account the predilections of real epidemiologists. If you think that Headline Man is an exaggerated fable, wait till you meet the Harvard Nurses Health Study. The technique used by Headline Man is known as data dredging, a wonderful tool for publicity seekers, because the more factors you trawl for the more likely you are to get some positive results at random.

One of the lessons of these simulations is that a problem with an implicit risk ratio of, say, 1.5 might exist; but the fact is that it is beyond the reach of scientific statistical methodology (nothing, of course, is beyond the reach of junk science), which is not a difficult concept for scientists, who are used to such ideas as the uncertainty principle. It is, however, not so easily acceptable to the layman, a fact that is ruthlessly exploited by the villains of our piece. One of the most difficult things to get over to non-mathematicians, including most journalists, is that 90% is NOT a large number. It is less than one. What causes difficulties for the innumerate is that 90% is a large proportion (nearly all) but it not a large increase (less than a doubling). What are examples of really significant risk ratios? Well, heavy cigarette smoking has an association with lung cancer with a risk ratio of about 20, while aspirin produces a relative risk of 35 for Reye's syndrome in children. This is where epidemiology *can* be effective – for large risks of comparatively rare diseases.

Our two forms of simulation have illustrated two problems in the application of statistical methods to identifying effects. They can fail to find an effect that is actually there and they can identify an effect that is not there. This is why real science is so circumspect in its use of such methods. Nevertheless, you may well think, surely respectable journals will not accept results that can so easily be ascribed to random chance. In fact, attempts are usually made to filter out such misleading data, and this is where the plot really begins to thicken. Most papers submitted for publication will contain the magic formula $P<0.05$, which is such a powerful talisman that it virtually guarantees publication. Before we examine its credentials, let us give emphasis to two other major sources of wrong numbers.

Confounding factors

One Dr Erwin, a psychologist at Nene University College, Northampton reported that students with old fashioned names, such as Doris or Norman, do better in their examinations (by about 4%) than those with more attractive names, such as Alison or John (*The Times*, December 17th 1998). His findings were based on a survey of 68 psychology students at a British university. Names were based for their attractiveness on their popularity in a survey of just 20 volunteers.

So far, so junky! It is, however, the conclusions drawn from these data that merit comment. The explanation was that people with unusual old-fashioned names learn to adapt to the extra attention that their name brings, becoming more resourceful. "It toughens them up and spurs them on to higher levels of achievement than otherwise might have been the case" claims the good doctor.

You might, nevertheless, wish to consider that Charles and Fiona on average could have a different cultural experience throughout their early life than Darren and Tracey. If you did, you would be introducing a confounding factor. As for the twenty electors, they might contain a duke's children called Elvis and Kylie and a meat porter's children called Gervase and Hermione. Would they regard each other's names as popular? As we shall see in these pages, ignoring such factors is one of the mainstays of junk science.

Publication bias

We have mentioned this source of wrong numbers above, and it is important not to let it slip by without emphasising its significance. The fact is that negative results simply do not get published. Editors of journals do not like them, as they are dull and will turn off the readership. Referees of articles tend to reject negative results as being of little interest. Above all, authors are reluctant to submit such articles because they are unlikely to be accepted and do not enhance their reputation. I have been guilty of it myself, and many of my negative results have got no further in publication than the theses of my students. The lack of publication of negative results is particularly important in the health field.

The existence of publication bias has been widely researched and verified (see, for example, special issue *BMJ*, Sept 1997). There is not only the censoring aspect; covert duplication of research results also occurs. Publication bias is one of the important criticisms levelled against so-called meta-analyses, which combine the results of several studies. There are claims that it can be detected by such things as "funnel plots" but these are all a bit too esoteric to be included here. The safest thing to do with meta-analyses is take them with a large pinch of salt.

2.9 What is this thing called P?

There is a simple mathematical statement that is common to many of the studies referred to in this book — **P<0.05**. Sometimes it appears in the form of a confidence limit of 95%. What this means is that there is a one in twenty chance that the results proclaimed occurred purely by accident. Now you might, with some justification, think that this is not a very stringent sort of test. How did it come about?

The idea of P was introduced by R A Fisher, one of the giants of statistical theory. One of his aims was to introduce a statistical test that was purely objective. It has remained a matter of vigorous debate ever since whether such a goal was even possible. The argument involves something called Bayes' theorem. I do not propose to go into this, for two main reasons. First, the argument is too abstruse to be included in the present context. Second, though I understand the mathematics of the theorem, I do not understand the philosophy of its application; and the more I read the less I understand it. I am not therefore he right person to guide others in this respect. For an interesting and stimulating polemic on this subject read the ESEF pamphlet by Robert Matthews — *Statistical Snake-oil; the use and abuse of significance tests in science*. The essence of the argument is that, unless you take the prior plausibility of the study into account, reliance on P alone will produce results that are hopelessly optimistic. Now where scientists, including myself, become uncomfortable with such arguments is that they introduce a measure of subjectivity, something we always try to exclude. Nevertheless, the proof of the pudding is in the eating, and there is no doubt that an unacceptable number of spurious results are entering the scientific literature. Apart from the regular scares that we have dealt with at length there is what Matthews calls —

The case of the vanishing breakthrough

Have you ever wondered what happened to all the wonder drugs that you read about, which then disappear from the scene? Anastripase and magnesium injections were both miracle treatments for heart attacks. A small dose of aspirin prevented the development of fatal pre-eclampsia. There were many others.

A team from the Queens Medical Centre in Nottingham compared death rates from heart attacks around 1990 with those in the clinical "Dark Ages" a decade before. They found that there was no difference. It was 20% and it remained 20%. The effect of all those wonder drugs we were told about was precisely **nil**. This is more than sufficient evidence to cause us to question the significance tests used in the clinical trials that made those drugs seem so promising.

Even without such doubts there are still further matters of concern in the use of P<0.05 with such tenacity.

Why 0.05?

Here is a disturbing quotation from Matthews' pamphlet:

> So just what was the profound logic that led Fisher to choose that talismanic figure of 0.05, on which so much scientific research has stood or fallen? Incredibly, as Fisher himself admitted, there weren't any. He simply decided on 0.05 because it was mathematically convenient.

It is now quite clear that the choice was a very bad one. It means that many supposedly significant scientific results are entirely spurious. This number has become an icon throughout science. It is the determinant of whether research is submitted or accepted for publication. Throughout the world scientists sieve their numbers, looking for the magic breakthrough. If P is greater than 0.05 they abandon the line of research and go on to something else. If it is less, they throw their hats in the air and start writing. In this I have been as guilty as the next man. There are important consequences in all this:

1. One in twenty of all scientific tests on non-existent effects and using accepted statistical significance is wrong.

2. There is a massive tendency to *publication bias*. Not only was the one wrong positive result published, but the nineteen negative results were not published.

3. As soon as the researchers get their 0.05 they stop taking measurements to avoid reducing the publishability of their results, for nowadays researchers are measured by their publications.

4. Researchers plug their results into a statistical package, turn the electronic handle and see whether they have won the prize on the statistical fruit machine. They do this without attempting to understand the theory behind the statistics they are using.

5. There is a powerful motivation towards cheating, even sub-consciously. This is exacerbated by the publish-or-perish attitude arising from modern auditing.

Confidence intervals

It is often considered more impressive to quote a confidence interval than a simple probability, but here effectively the same criterion is used — a one in twenty chance of being wrong. For example, I plugged Headline Man's values from our simulation for alcohol and toe-nail cancer into a statistical package available on the web and obtained the 95% confidence interval for the risk ratio as 1.0038 to 2.6746.

This does not quite include what we know to be the correct risk ratio of 1.0, but the range, with its centre at 1.8382, emphasises the impression that our calculated risk ratio of 1.6385 is highly significant, whereas we know it is entirely spurious.

For the most successful of our ten scientists I got an even more impressive 95% confidence interval of 1.1947 to 2.8704. Without doubt his paper would be accepted by a respectable scientific journal as representing a significant finding. It is not surprising that one of our scientists achieved such success, since with ten of them we had a 40% chance of it happening at this probability level.

It is interesting to work out just how many different workers, groups or studies it requires to make it almost certain that at least one spurious result will be obtained and hence a paper published under the one in twenty regime. This is illustrated in the graph. Clearly, by the time we get over fifty, it is a virtual certainty that there will be at least one publishable spurious result. Now, on a world scale in some popular areas of study, those that are politically correct for example, 50 is not a large number. Thus it follows that, regardless of the truth of the matter, there will always be at least one publication that supports any politically correct or SIF viewpoint.

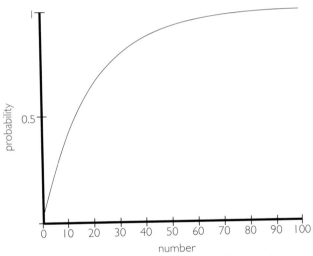

Figure 2.3 The probability of the publishing of a spurious result for any given number of workers.

At the risk of labouring the point, which is absolutely crucial to our argument, I made a calculation, for the conditions of our simulation, of the most likely maximum risk ratio that would be achieved for a given number of studies on a non-existent effect. To do this I used the theory of the statistics of extremes, which is important in the study of such things as floods and the failure of materials, but is not appropriate to present in detail here. The results are summarised in the following table.

Number of scientists	Most likely maximum risk ratio
10	1.4
100	1.8
1,000	2.1
10,000	2.4

This table is of limited value, as the risk ratio itself is a random number, which in the statistics of extremes is skewed to higher values, but the table illustrates just how wise is the choice of 3 for a safe risk ratio and how 2 is a barely acceptable limit. Below this limit, spurious results can be forced through by sheer weight of numbers Furthermore, this is without considering the important effects of confounding factors.

It may seem that I have exaggerated the effects in the above. In fact I have understated them. Our ten scientists, in calculating their risk ratios, have divided a random number by another random number with the same statistical spread. The effect on the risk ratio is to double the relative statistical spread. In fact it is quite possible for one of them to get a risk ratio of infinity, which happens if the denominator is zero. It would only happen in about one out of 100,000 cases, but it is a pretty impressive result when you think it is based on no effect at all.

Headline Man revisited

How does all this statistical significance stuff affect Headline Man? At first sight, it's a bit of a blow. He might make a splash in the popular press with some of his claims, but only one of his results is significant according to the talismanic one in twenty, so he only gets one published scientific paper out of it. Fear not! He sticks with the ten foods, but simply looks for twenty diseases rather than just one. He now has 200 combinations of food and disease. If one in twenty come up trumps by accident then he still has his ten headlines.

Of course, ten headlines is pretty good going, but you can't make a career out of it. So the next move is to identify a cohort of people and monitor them long term for as many foods as you can identify and all known diseases. You give it a portentous name, such as the Harvard Nurses Health Study, and then you can generate headlines at a rate of once a month for a lifetime. That is what they call data dredging. It is like a fruit machine that comes up with the jackpot every twentieth play. The real beauty of it is that, even though it is all based on no real effect at all, a regular flow of results is guaranteed, as is the press coverage of all the scares and breakthroughs you can generate.

2.10 Who are the forces of right?

> In every generation there has to be some fool who will
> speak the truth as he sees it.
> Boris Pasternak

One of my hobbies is growing things in my greenhouse, particularly tomatoes, which, as every right thinking person knows, are spectacularly good for my health. One of the perennial problems is red spider mite (*Tetranychus urticae*) which each summer seems to infest my plants and slowly destroy them. In order to control them I introduce as a biological control a predatory mite (*Phytoseiulus persimilis*). Each day I go into the greenhouse with my magnifying glass and come back to my wife with an account of whether the good guys or the bad guys are prevailing. It is often a close run thing but, given time, the good guys seem to win against overwhelming odds. I feel like that about real science and pseudo-science. As I write the bad guys have the upper hand. They monopolise the press, have the ear of powerful politicians and seem to breed like rabbits. Real scientists are in retreat, treated as out of date irrelevancies, some sort of throwback to an unenlightened past. I know from personal experience that it is virtually impossible to get a letter of rebuttal published in the press.

On seeing the above question, you may well ask "Who is this guy, to tell us who is right and who is wrong?" A fair question, and the only answer I can give is that I make the judgement in the light of what I deem to be the Scientific Method. Whether I am qualified to be such a dempster must remain within the judgement of the reader. I do not, however, wish to produce a book solely about the bad guys and I have leaned heavily upon the following for facts and opinions. They are not the only ones on the side of right, but they are the first of the few and the leaders of the resistance movement

The Junkman

This is the cognomen of public health specialist, Steven J. Milloy, the executive director of *The Advancement of Sound Science Coalition* (TASSC) and publisher of the *Junk Science Home Page* on the Web, which should be compulsory reading for all science and engineering students, not to say (without much hope) politicians and lawyers. Unfortunately, he is cursed with a sense of humour, which causes his opponents to dismiss him, as one of their prime characteristics is that they never laugh. He has written numerous books and editorials on the parlous state of science in the public health domain in the USA. Despite the apparent levity, his approach to science is absolutely rigorous and his swingeing attacks on the bigots and bureaucrats of the establishment are guided missiles of absolute precision. I am extremely grateful to Steve for generously giving me permission to quote his material, which I have done copiously.

Roger Bate

Bate is Director of the **Environment Unit at the Institute for Economic Affairs**. He writes regularly for papers such as *The Financial Times, Sunday Times and Wall Street Journal*. He is also Director of **ESEF** and as such a leader is in the fight against the pollution of science. He has been involved in a number of valuable books, such as *Environmental Health: Third World Problems — First World Preoccupations*.

Robert T. Carroll

This Professor of Philosophy at Sacramento City College publishes on the Web **The Skeptic's Dictionary**, containing over 250 sceptical definitions, essays and references from acupuncture to zombies. These fully justify his motto — *the only thing infinite is our capacity for self-deception*. Another efficacious antidote to the lunacies of our times, these pages are further compulsory reading for seekers after truth. Bob was also generous in allowing me to use his writings, of which I have availed myself to a considerable extent.

Alan Caruba

A business and science writer, he founded the National Anxiety Centre is a response to all the "Earth is Doomed!" stories in the media. Every April the Centre gives "Chicken Little Awards" to those individuals and groups who have scared the daylights out of millions of people and, each December, the Centre takes a look back at "The Most Dubious News Stories of the Year." Throughout the year the Centre works to inform the press so it can avoid being a part of the "Anxiety Industry", government agencies and non-governmental organisations that deliberately mislead the public. Its home page is well worth a regular visit.

S. Fred Singer

Singer is an atmospheric physicist who has received many awards for his distinguished research work. The **Science & Environmental Policy Project** was founded in 1990 by Singer on the premise that sound, credible science must form the basis for health and environmental decisions that affect millions of people and cost tens of billions of dollars every year. A non-profit educational group, its mission was to clarify the diverse problems facing the planet and, where necessary, arrive at effective, cost-conscious solutions. This has been an important source of facts for this book and its web pages an island of calm in a sea of hysteria.

A K Dewdney

The Associate Professor of Mathematics at the University of Western Ontario is the scourge of the modern plagues of innumeracy and bad science. His book *200% of Nothing* is an entertaining account of the parlous state of numeracy in the western world. In *Yes, we have no Neutrons* he provides a sharp exposé of bad science. Always entertaining and a joy to read, he deserves to find a place on everybody's bookshelves.

Alvan R Feinstein

This is a rarity – an epidemiologist who adheres strictly to the scientific method. He is Professor of Medicine and Epidemiology at the School of Medicine, Yale University. His exposure of the errors introduced by biases and confounding in *What Risk* is a startling exposure of just how bad things are in the world of epidemiology.

James Randi

is a professional magician (The Amazing Randi), author, lecturer, amateur archaeologist and amateur astronomer. A tireless campaigner against pseudo-science and quackery, he has received a wide range of highly justified awards and citations for his trenchant debunking of some of the most egregious fraudsters of our age. Read and enjoy his home page on the web.

Bernard Levin

A prolific book writer, broadcaster and columnist, (Henry) Bernard Levin has reached the stage at which he has become an institution. Sometimes irritating, always entertaining and informative, he is one of a dying breed of great intellects who illuminate the world for the rest of us ordinary mortals. I cannot remember how long ago I first read his writings about the new phenomenon of Single Issue Fanatics. Like most people I did not take this particularly seriously, thinking he was describing a bunch of harmless eccentrics. Little did we know that these monomaniacs would, through their sheer persistence and determination, come to rule our lives. An example of his disinterest is the way he has always spoken up in the defence of smokers, though a life-long non-smoker himself. Now in his seventies, the familiar bristly hair turned to a badger-like creation in black and white, he is still one of the few remaining rational and humane voices on the subject. His article *When non-smokers are a drag* (*The Times Weekend*, November 22, 1997) is glorious condemnation of man's inhumanity to man in this new age of politically correct oppression and a reminder of when the world was a kinder place.

Dr James Le Fanu

There are many medical journalists who write excellent articles on aspects of health, but Dr Lefanu is almost unique in his avoidance of the pitfalls of junk science. His articles in *The Daily Telegraph, The Times* and other papers are distinguished by their clear, panic-free advice. His books are equally wise and beneficent. In particular, his book *The rise and fall of modern medicine* is a landmark, powerfully illustrating many of the points made here.

Brenda Maddox

I do not know much about this journalist, but when I go through my filing cabinet drawer overflowing with turgid press cuttings gathered for this book, her few articles stand out for their clarity, disinterest and sheer good writing.

Frank Furedi

is a sociologist at the University of Kent in Canterbury and author of *Culture of Fear: Risk Taking and the Morality of Low Expectations*. He is another rarity – a sociologist who always talks sense. His scathing attacks on the Nanny State are excellent and to the point. He has contributed important chapters (in *Environmental Health*, for example) about the sociology of health panics. His little book *Courting Mistrust* is a devastating indictment of the compensation culture.

Michael Fumento

A science writer and lawyer specialising in economics and science for the Investors Business Daily, Fumento is one of the major voices for rationality. His books *Science under Siege: Balancing Technology and the Environment* and *The Myth of Heterosexual AIDS* are salients in the war against junk.

Woodrow Wyatt

It is a great irony that Lord Wyatt of Weeford died the very week of the most ludicrous piece of Nannyism in the history of politics – the ban on beef on the bone. What fun he, and we, would have had. His writing and television reporting on everything from communist ballot rigging in the unions to the excesses of the anti-smoking lobby justified his appellation as "The Voice of Reason". A great entertainer as well as an informer, he will be sadly missed.

I would have liked to have included Dr Stephen Barrett in my list of good guys. His Quackwatch home page comprises a thorough indictment of almost every from of quackery and is well worth reading. When it comes to the treatment of smoking, however, his disinterest dissolves under the pressure of political correctness. In particular, he quotes without demur the study by Kawachi *et al* on passive smoking and heart disease. This is one of the most egregious examples of junk science in the canon (see the Junkman's article "Second hand smoke and mirrors" for a comprehensive demolition) and is based on a notorious data set from the survey of nurses' health, from Harvard of course.

Chapter 3
A gallery of fallacies

We have already met informally a number of fallacious arguments that lead inevitably to the generation of wrong numbers and we shall meet them many more times. It is useful at this stage to categorise them a little more formally. There are two main classes of common fallacy, which we may call fallacies of logic and fallacies of number.

3.1 Fallacies of logic

Time was when school children and university students automatically studied logic. They miss a lot by not doing it now, if only the entertainment of picking the fallacies out of the speeches of politicians. Many of the most common fallacies were catalogued by the Greeks and Romans. The first group of fallacies mentioned below are from the classical list, but are restricted to those that are most important in the modern generation of wrong numbers. See, for example, *Stephen's guide to the logical fallacies* in the webography for a more detailed coverage.

False dilemma

Alternatives are offered when in fact there are more than two options. This is a favourite ploy by SIFs, who typically will employ the words of Jesus "He that is not with me is against me". Most people will adopt the Rhett Butler option: "Frankly, my dear, I don't give a damn." In most areas of human life there is a whole range of options, but the propagandist will try to convince you that it has to be black or white, with no shades of grey. Thus they will claim that the only alternatives are a complete ban on something they don't like or total anarchy and disaster. This can be applied to almost anything – guns, GM foods, tobacco, alcohol, cars etc.

Argument from ignorance (Argumentum ad ignorantiam)

This is often used as a last resort when the evidence put forward has been effectively refuted. "Ah!" say the claimants, "but you cannot prove that it is not true, so it probably is." It is applied from everything from astrology to the GM food scare. Taken to its extreme we would not eat anything, because it is impossible to prove that any food is entirely safe.

Post hoc fallacy

Post hoc, ergo propter hoc means "after this, therefore because of this". It describes the common fallacy of assuming that because one thing follows another that the one thing was caused by the other.

In the discussion of clusters *(q.v.)*, for example, we will mention the John Travolta film *A Civil Action*, which is based on the assertion that trichloroethylene, which might have entered the water supply from nearby factories, caused an "excessive" number of leukaemia cases in Woburn, Massachusetts. Since there is no evidence as to what actually causes leukaemia, the fact that the contaminant entered the water before the leukaemia cases appeared does not prove that it caused them.

Personal attacks (argumentum ad hominem)

It is a characteristic of people taking weak logical positions that they attack the person presenting an argument rather than argument itself. Typically SIFs will dismiss all critics of their position as being in the pay of the tobacco/chemical/alcohol or fuel industries.

There are variations and it is easy for the rest of us to fall into this trap. An American politician lives on a large estate but denounces urban sprawl, or a British minister runs two Jaguars but takes steps to ensure that ordinary rural people cannot afford to drive the old banger that is their only protection against total isolation, both on environmental grounds. The fact that they do not practise what they preach might make them unsavoury, but it does not prove them wrong (the fallacy *ad hominem tu quoque*). It does not prove them right either, and I for one will not feel constrained to avoiding comment on such behaviour.

Appeal to Authority (argumentum ad verecundiam)

It is quite proper for scientists and other specialists to cite an authority to support a point, but often it is not. It might, for example, be a point on which experts in the field genuinely disagree. The person quoted might not be qualified to have an expert opinion on the subject. An example incorporating both variations is "Global Warming is affirmed by Al Gore, George Bush and John Prescott."

Anonymous Authority

This very common fallacy, popular with SIFs, was mentioned in our discussion of weasel words (*q.v.*). There is an appeal to authority but as that authority is not named it is impossible to confirm that the authority (if such exists) is an expert or has even made the statement claimed.

Complex Question

Two otherwise unrelated points are conjoined and treated as a single proposition. The victim is invited to accept or reject both together, when in reality one is acceptable while the other might not be; for example "Do you want your children to grow up healthy and free from man-made chemicals?"

Non sequitur

The next two fallacies are examples the *non sequitur* (it does not follow)

Affirming the Consequent

This is any argument of the following form:

> *If A then B*
> *B*
> *Therefore, A*

For example: If teaching improves, more students will pass their exams. More students are passing their exams. Therefore teaching has improved.

A cynic might take the view that the exams have become easier.

Denying the Antecedent

This is any argument of the following form:

> *If A then B*
> *Not A*
> *Therefore, Not B*

Example: "If you come into contact with carcinogenic chemicals you will get cancer. California has banned carcinogenic chemicals. Therefore Californians do not get cancer."

Fundamental food fallacy

Orchis teprosanthes, the monkey orchid, has been valued by herbalists over the years as a treatment for sexual problems, on the grounds that its tubers resemble human testes. The EU precipitated a potentially dangerous trade war with the USA by announcing a ban on hormone treated beef. What do these two statements have in common? The answer is that they are both examples of one of the most prevalent fallacies in junk science.

The digestive system is designed to reduce the complex molecules that make up the plants and animals in our diet to very small building blocks. It must do this so that they can diffuse through the walls of the intestines. The shape of food, such as the orchid, has no relevance to what it contributes to the chemicals in the blood that the body uses to create the complex molecules it supplies. The cattle growth hormone, *bovine somatotrophin*, is reduced to its constituent amino acids, which the body then uses as building blocks to create its own complex proteins. Even if it were injected directly into the human bloodstream it would have no effect as *human somatotrophin* quite a different molecule.

Likewise, saturated fat in the diet has no relation to saturated fat in the bloodstream. That it has was merely a hypothesis put forward by one Hugh Sinclair in 1951 (see letter by his student Dr Alan Shrank, *The Times* December 28th 1998). It was adopted as fact by the food scare industry and subsequently decimated the dairy industry. Thus we have people purchasing absurdly named products, such as *I can't believe it's not butter*, when they would be far better off sticking to the natural diet. The young generation in the Netherlands, for example, has been raised on dairy products and is fitter and a foot taller than its parents. As in many facets of life, moderation and variety are the only things that matter in diet.

Fats are an important group of naturally occurring substances that are the *glycerides* of the higher fatty acids, such as *palmitic, stearic* and *oleic acids*. They are broken down and used to repair wastage of human fat, which is oxidised in the body to contribute to the energy requirement. The fat that the food faddists carefully remove from their juicy steak was once pure grass (unless some idiot forced cannibalism on the unfortunate cow). *Cholesterol*, a complex alcohol, is a large molecule ($C_{27}H_{45}OH$) which is broken down by the digestive system to make important substances, such as the *steroids*, vital substances that include the sex hormones. The body manufactures its own cholesterol, which is an important component of nerves and other tissues. It is only when the metabolism becomes disordered that excess cholesterol is produced, leading to potentially serious cardiovascular disease. Tobacco consumption is said to be one of the many factors contributing to this condition.

Reification

Dewdney points out that Binet, the inventor of IQ tests, greatly (and rightly) feared they would come to be abused. In particular, he feared the process of reification: if we can give it a name it exists. Many people seem to think that if they can think up a name for something it **must** exist, even some trained scientists and engineers. They devote their lives to searching for phenomena such as psychokinesis, regardless of the fact that no one has ever demonstrated a breach of such fundamental principles of science as the conservation of energy.

3.2 Fallacies of number

Linear extrapolation

Much of what we have to discuss in this book is related to cause and effect. We may consider them in the form of a simple graph of one plotted against the other. A problem that often arises is that we only have one point on that graph. The question is — what do we assume about the points on the rest of the graph? We do, in fact have one other point on the graph. Most people know that if we have zero cause we also have zero effect. I say most people, because there are some who do not know this. Practitioners of homeopathic medicine, for example, believe that they can dilute an active material infinitely, so that there is effectively none left, but it will still have an effect.

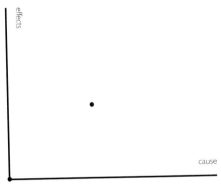

Figure 3.1 the extrapolation problem

The linear extrapolation fallacy is based on the assumption that all the other points on the graph lie on a straight line joining the two points and infinitely extended. A reasonable assumption you might think. It certainly has the merit of simplicity, and we are properly enjoined to make the simplest assumption possible (Occam's razor). Indeed, linear behaviour is often found in nature; for example, the electromagnetic properties of free space. It so happens, though, that in the properties of matter, and particularly living matter, linear behaviour is rather rare.

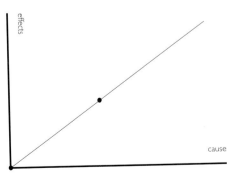

Figure 3.2 Linear extrapolation

In fact, a much more common form of behaviour is in the form of what is called a sigmoid curve (because it is roughly S-shaped). This curve may be roughly divided into three important regions.

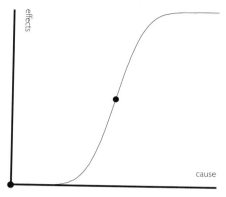

Figure 3.3 Sigmoid extrapolation

Threshold

This is a value of the cause below which there is no appreciable effect. It is often rather ill defined, since the curve only gradually becomes tangential to the horizontal axis as the cause is reduced.

Active region

This is the area in which a given change in the cause produces the biggest change in the effect.

Saturation

This term arises by analogy with a bath sponge. It will continue to take up water until it is full and can take no more, i.e. it is saturated. In the saturation region the effect has reached its possible maximum, and no further increase in the cause can change it.

Because of the widespread occurrence of the sigmoid type of behaviour the reasonable sounding idea of linear extrapolation is a major cause of wrong numbers. There are two very important variations of the linear extrapolation fallacy, as follows.

The concentration fallacy

The effect of chemicals depends greatly on their degree of concentration. Even the most potent acid is often ineffective when highly diluted. Aqua Regia (a mixture of concentrated nitric and hydrochloric acid) is so powerful that it can dissolve gold. Dilute it sufficiently, however, and you can drink it with impunity. Many experiments are performed at high concentrations to ensure that the effect is large enough (or probable enough) to be observable. Such research goes wrong when the results are used to predict the effect of low concentrations by assuming that proportionality applies right down to zero.

There is a brown patch on my lawn – an area of dead grass. When I was preparing to cast Growmore fertiliser pellets onto my vegetable patch, I accidentally knocked the bag over. I scooped up as many of the spilled pellets as I could, but enough remained to kill the grass. Perversely, though I have "proved" that Growmore is deadly poisonous to plant life, I still use it on my vegetables. As we shall see, thousands of piteous rodents are obliged to sacrifice their lives to provide equally convincing proof.

The dosage fallacy

Dosage is not the same as concentration. You can have a high dose at low concentration or a low dose at high concentration. The recommended dosage for most medicines is calculated to be high up in the active region. A higher dose than that will offer no medical advantage. Of course a very high dose can have other effects, such as killing you, and this is an important limitation to our argument. For reasons of simplicity, we have only considered one cause and one effect, whereas in real life the effects can be multitudinous.

Vitamins provide an excellent example of the dosage fallacy and the extension of the linear extrapolation fallacy in the upward direction. There are thirteen known so far and they are all essential in very small quantities for correct functioning of the metabolism.

Vitamins, apart from C, are aromatic compounds like hormones. The threshold and saturation doses are very low. If the regular dose is below the threshold, deficiency diseases of various degrees of severity occur. They include acne, anaemia, beriberi, scurvy, pellagra, night blindness and rickets. A person with a normal metabolism on a balanced diet obtains from it more than enough of every vitamin. Further doses are above the saturation level and produce no beneficial effect. A substantial proportion of the population regularly overdose on vitamins; such is the power of advertising. At best this causes no harm. At worst it can cause severe poisoning. Excess vitamin A, for example, can suppress growth; stop menstruation; damage red blood corpuscles; and cause skin rashes, headaches, nausea, and jaundice.

The independence fallacy

Consider a loaded die for which the probabilities for the numbers one to five are all 0.1. The probability of a six must then be exactly 0.5, neither more nor less, since the probabilities of all events must add up to one. In scientific jargon this is a system of five degrees of freedom; i.e. five number are sufficient wholly to describe the state of the system. If you change just one of the probabilities you automatically change all of the others. It is entirely fallacious to suppose otherwise.

The most notorious occurrence of the independence fallacy is in the discussion of causes of death. Since the Middle Ages, for example, the probability of dying of an infectious disease has fallen by more than a hundred-fold. Since the probability of dying is one, all other causes must increase to compensate. Even in our own lifetime this trend has continued unabated. It is therefore inevitable that more people will die from non-infectious causes such as cancer and heart disease. Nevertheless, vast areas of the media are taken up with the "mystery" of why these diseases are increasing, and whole industries are set up to exploit the fact. More of this later.

Gamblers' fallacy

A great deal of human effort goes into developing fool-proof systems for winning at games of chance, such as roulette, horse-racing or lotteries. This is largely based on the gamblers' fallacy that past events affect the probabilities of future events. Unless the wheel is fixed, the probability of any number arising at roulette is the same as any other, no matter what has appeared in the recent past.

There are, however, variations that the persistent gambler might wish to take into consideration. An important quantity in this respect is the mathematical expectation. If you enter the British National Lottery, your basic mathematical expectation for a one pound wager is about 50 pence. This is because the other fifty are taken by the government, the charities supported and the profits and administration costs of the lottery company. Now, this mathematical expectation could be anything from a certainty of getting fifty pence per pound, which you would realise if you bought enough tickets to cover all the available numbers, to a one millionth chance of getting half a million pounds. It is possible, however, to increase the mathematical expectation. It has been discovered, for example, that people prefer numbers in the middle of the ticket to numbers on the periphery. Therefore, if you choose numbers from the outside, though you do not increase your chance of winning, you increase your chance of a larger prize, since there will be fewer people with whom to share it.

There are also other factors, such the psychological skills that favour the expert at poker, or the reading of form that is better than that of the bookmakers. It is very difficult to obtain useful information in the latter respect, as one of the characteristics of gamblers is that they have very selective memories. The salient fact is that there are very few poor bookmakers.

Mathematical distance

If you start of at some point in space and move, say, 12 metres forward, 3 right and 4 up, then you have reached a new point that can be defined with respect to your origin by an array of co-ordinates (12,3,4). You can also easily determine by Pythagorus that you have travelled precisely 13 metres from the starting point. Furthermore you can see that another point, say (13, 2, 5), is close, in fact 1.73 metres away. This idea of distance is extended by mathematicians to more abstract arrays of numbers of any number of dimensions; yielding one of the most powerful tools is mathematics.

Ordinary people also have this concept of distance between arrays of numbers, but there is a trap. Sometimes numbers are not really numbers at all, but merely labels. The most celebrated instance of this is in the lottery. How often do you hear people say "I was so close; three numbers were only one out." You could, however, label the balls in any way. It would not be so impressive to say "I was so close, a pink triangle instead of a blue circle". This is the essential genius of the 6/49 lottery. After each draw, thousands of people are left thinking that they were so close to the big prize, when in fact they were no closer than any other loser. This trap occurs in all sorts of ways when numbers are used as labels rather than numerical values. Even more confusing are cases where there might be numerical ranking but there is not. When looking for number 13 in the High Street, we might expect it to be next to number 14, or perhaps opposite, but there are cases where for historical reasons it is at the other end of the street.

3.3 The loaded example

Before we leave the subject of fallacies, there is one further important comment to make. In my example of *denying the antecedent* above I have used the example of Californians and cancer. Stephen on his fallacies home page uses "Since scientists cannot prove that global warming will occur, it probably won't." Each of us, in selecting our example, has done so in such a way as to lend weight to a particular viewpoint. Since I am engaged in a polemic to try to counter a powerful prevailing orthodoxy I do not apologise for this. If, however, I were to do the same thing in a paper purporting to establish a scientific truth it would be a different matter. Selective examples are a potent form of persuasion and one should always be on guard from them.

In what follows I will not attempt to point out and name all the fallacies involved in the wrong numbers we shall discuss. It would all become far too repetitive. Readers who have followed the above definitions should be able to identify them, often in multiples, among the claims of the various generators of wrong numbers.

Chapter 4
Scares

Have you heard it's in the stars,
Next July we collide with Mars
Cole Porter

I mentioned in the introduction that numbers are often used to frighten us. The classic format for this is the **Scare Story**, which seems to come up with monotonous regularity. Why do scares happen? There are five basic reasons

1. They sell newspapers and books and fill TV screens

2. They confirm the power and jobs of bureaucrats

3. Lawyers make even more money

4. They create vast and lucrative industries

5. People enjoy being frightened, as long as it is in the comfort and security of their own homes (hence the huge market in horror videos).

The trouble with scares, as with SIFs, is that they take our eye of the ball and we neglect possible serious long-term problems. In most of the cases enumerated below there is a potential problem for society that needs a cool hard look. Instead, they are subjected to short term mass hysteria. Much of what we have to say about scares also applies to their antithesis, breakthroughs.

4.1 The doomsayers

That a lie which is all a lie may be met and fought with outright,
But a lie which is part a truth is a harder matter to fight.
Tennyson – The Grandmother.

There is a coterie of authors whose names come up over and over again in the annals of scaremongering. They achieve world fame, widespread publication and the concomitant wealth. They appear on TV and before committees of the US Senate or the UK House of Commons. There is an even larger number of candidates for the coterie, hammering on the door, seeking admission. These doomsayers have a common mode of operation, taking a small truth and embellishing it with hyperbole and extrapolation until it is a large nightmare. The problem they create is that, when the nightmare proves to be untrue, the small truth buried within tends to get lost with it. Here are just a few of the big players.

Rachel Carson

Carson was, without doubt, the doyenne of the alarmists. In fact, she could be said to have created the genre. When she published her first serious success, *The Sea Around* Us in 1951 it was unfashionable to gainsay the prevalent orthodoxy of the inevitable and beneficial march of science and technology, but it was taken up by the *New Yorker*, which guaranteed her fame and fortune. She began work on her magnum opus, *Silent Spring*, which by the time it was published in 1964 had a receptive public waiting for it. The Vietnam War was beginning to escalate, the hippie movement was forming in California; perhaps science and technology did not have all the answers.

Theo Colburn, Dianne Dumanoski and John Peterson Myers

This triumvirate sought to regain the throne vacated by Rachel Carson. Their book *Our Stolen Future: Are We Threatening Our Fertility, Intelligence and Survival A Scientific Detective Story* (Dutton Publishing, March 1996) is a farrago of pseudo-science, which does not even merit elevating to junk science. See The Junkman for a comprehensive demolition. The Foreword is by:

Vice President Al Gore.

This ambitious politician has nailed his colours firmly to the mast of Junk Science, which he saw as the key to the White House. A demagogue and zealot, he achieved his apotheosis at the Kyoto Conference on Global Warming, where he committed the USA to an economically crippling programme of reduced carbon emissions, while letting much of the world of the hook. His apocalyptic vision is that, if his treaty isn't passed, the world will see "more record floods and droughts, diseases and pests spreading to new areas, crop failures and famine." And that is only one of his essays into Junk Science. As somebody said "The trouble with political jokes is that they get elected."

Paul Ehrlich

You have to admire someone who makes himself rich and famous by being consistently wrong. Of course, the doomsayers rely on the fact that people buy their books for a quick thrill and then forget the predictions. Unfortunately, occasionally some cad comes along and reminds everybody of what they actually said in the past. The rotter who queered Ehrlich's pitch was Michael Fumento of the Investor's Business Daily, who listed some of the gems of Paul's epistles to the Americans:

> *"The battle to feed humanity is over. In the 1970s the world will undergo famines . . . hundreds of millions of people (including Americans) are going to starve to death."* *(1968)*

> *"Smog disasters" in 1973 might kill 200,000 people in New York and Los Angeles. (1969)*

> *"I would take even money that England will not exist in the year 2000." (1969)*

> *"Before 1985, mankind will enter a genuine age of scarcity . . . in which the accessible supplies of many key minerals will be facing depletion." (1976)*

In a rational world you would expect someone with this sort of track record to disappear from view. Far from it! Not only does he find more and more mugs to buy his dafter and dafter books, he keeps winning lucrative prizes. His preposterous *"Population Explosion,"* received the MacArthur Foundation's famous "genius award" with a $345,000 cheque, and he shared a Swedish Royal Academy of Science prize worth $120,000. It's a mad, mad, mad, mad world. It is far more important to be politically correct than to be factually correct.

Devra Lee Davis

This woman and her gang do not bother with trivial numbers. Just in time for the Kyoto Junkfest they came up with a prediction that eight million people would die from particulate air pollution associated with fossil fuel, unless the world limits greenhouse gas emissions to levels advocated by European nations. This was a result of a study based on two classic examples of junk science, the second of which establishes some sort of record with dire predictions from a risk ratio of just 1.04 (as ever, see the Junkman for a debunk). That, however, was nothing compared with her next pronouncement, issued on April Fool's day, 1998. This concerned a frightening prediction of a decline in the proportion of male births (as a result, of course, of pollution by man-made chemicals). When you look at her impressive numbers you find that they all reduce to a massive 0.02% of extra female births over a 44 year period. Now, if you really need something to worry about, I suggest you find something better than an extra three and a half girls a year in the whole of the UK.

Carol Browner

The EPA Administrator is, without doubt, the Queen of Junk. Her sibylline pronouncements are so horrific that she scares the US Government into parting with billions of dollars of the good old American taxpayers' money. For example, pending the implementation of her new rules on air quality seven years from their announcement (how can she wait that long?) there would be 105,000 more premature deaths; 1.75 million more aggravated asthma episodes; 1.75 million more acute respiratory problems in children (including aggravated coughing and painful breathing); 420,000 more cases of chronic bronchitis and 63,000 more hospital admissions for respiratory problems. She merits the title of The Most Expensive Woman in the World; for, not only does she steer billions of dollars through the EPA, she also imposes costs of hundreds of billions on US industry and ordinary people. Talk of the egregious Carol leads to the next topic.

4.2 The body-count politic

> A single death is a tragedy. A million deaths is a statistic.
> Joseph Stalin

Body counts became an emotive issue in the Vietnam War. These numbers made a significant contribution to the defeat of the USA. They cannot be ignored in a democracy as they can in a dictatorship; a point not lost on Saddam Hussein, who was relying on them to turn the Mother of all Battles. Neither was it lost on the SIFs, who invented the virtual body count as a potent weapon. They soon learned that sub editors cannot resist a headline of the form "Thousands to die of ...." or ".........kills babies". As we shall see in these pages, however, theoretical thousands are inadequate for the purpose. Even Carol Browner's hundreds of thousands pale into insignificance in comparison with some of the virtual body counts, which have been known to reach numbers as high as 58 MILLION, but more of that later.

4.3 Diet and health

> We have left undone those things which we ought to have done; And we have done those things which we ought not to have done; And there is no health in us.
> The Book of Common Prayer

The diet industry

This was one of the most extraordinary phenomena of the twentieth century. Obesity has been elevated to the status of one of the deadly sins. Much of the blame must be laid at the door of the medical profession. As a writer in the *New York Times* stated: "A reason for the medical campaign against obesity may have to do with a tendency to medicalise behaviour we do not approve of." They tell us that half the UK population is overweight – compared with what? Diet books outweigh all others in the popular book shops and their authors are making a mint. It is not only about obesity; people have become obsessed with their innards. One Australian doctor wrote a whole book about a diet for the liver and thousands of people actually bought it.

Anorexia and bulimia are new diseases unique to our age. Their existence is an appalling indictment of the pressures that our culture puts on individuals and women in particular. The fashion industry has a lot to answer for. In earlier centuries the so-called super-models would have been considered fit only for the freak show. Many surveys show that men actually prefer a more normal shape in their women, but the pressure continues. The hypothesis that homosexual dress designers want their models to look like boys seems a believable explanation.

Before I sat down to write this bit I walked down to the village pub for my evening pint. A man standing next to me ordered a bacon sandwich – "And if I am going to be this wicked, I will go the whole hog and have it on White Bread!" What have we come to, when a grown man sees the consumption of a small, simple, nutritious food item as flirtation with depravity? The remark might have been semi-jocular, but behind it lay a real fear that has been instilled by the endless pronouncements of a self appointed gang of food gurus. Some people call them the *food fascists;* a hyperbole, I once thought. Now I am not so sure. The word fascist derives from the Latin *fasces,* a symbol of authority, which is what these people gratuitously bestow upon themselves.

Food Scares

The sheer scale and intensity of the food scare industry is illustrated by the MOREOVER column in *The Economist* of April 25th 1998. The heading is **The Literature of Food Scares** and the sub-headings **San Francisco** (where else?). **Books about health scares are now appearing as frequently as food scares themselves**. Just savour the titles of the books reviewed:

TOXIN.

SPOILED: THE DANGEROUS TRUTH ABOUT THE FOOD CHAIN GONE HAYWIRE.

DEADLY FEAST: TRACKING THE SECRETS OF THE TERRIFYING NEW PLAGUE.

MAD COW USA: COULD THE NIGHTMARE HAPPEN HERE.

SLAUGHTERHOUSE: THE SHOCKING TRUTH OF GREED, NEGLECT AND INHUMAN TREATMENT INSIDE THE US MEAT INDUSTRY.

E.COLI 0157: THE TRUE STORY OF A MOTHER'S BATTLE WITH A KILLER MICROBE.

The odd one out is the last book, a slim volume by an English doctor, Theodore Dalrymple, MASS LISTERIA: THE MEANING OF HEALTH SCARES. The few lines quoted from this provide the most magnificent, succinct and accurate summary of the whole phenomenon:

> *Health scares play an important part in the mental economy of modern man. They allow him to believe that, were it not for this or that pollutant, he might be immortal, while explaining the anomaly of death. And they do something more: they provide him with that most indispensable of creatures, a scapegoat.*

Common Salt

Informed people have refrained from adding salt to food for a couple of decades. When you think that this commodity was once so important that Roman soldiers were paid in it (hence the word salary) this is a remarkable change of practice. Why should this happen? It is because "medical research" had linked dietary salt with high blood pressure (hypertension). Recently, however, a review of 56 clinical trials of hypertensive and normotensive individuals, have concluded that this was nonsense. There is even evidence from a study of hypertensive men that a low sodium diet actually *increases* risk of heart attack. *(Hypertension.* 1995;25:1144-1152).

Sodium chloride is one of the most essential compounds for the existence of life on earth. It makes up about three percent of the mass of the sea. The trick by which animals were able to leave the sea was to carry it around inside them in the form of blood plasma. Without salt in your diet you will die. You can get a sufficient dosage from a natural diet, as it is also essential to other life forms, but it adds a harmless piquancy to many dishes. Of course, if you overdose, you will also die.

Red Meat

This is one that will run and run. It is promoted by the vegetarian lobby, who seek to blame meat for everything from (of course) cancer to (can you believe it?) broken forearms. It appears with monotonous regularity in the headlines, e.g. "Big meat eaters cancer warning" (*Daily Mail,* 13 September, 1997). Despite frequent rebuttals in the medical research it keeps resurfacing. One gang of epidemiologists, who looked at a bunch of old women and did a data dredge for associations between all sorts of diseases and foods, were thrilled to discover a link between Hamburgers and Non-Hodgkin Lymphoma, relative risk 2.35 (95% confidence interval 1.23 - 4.48). If you look at enough associations you are bound to come up with a good one eventually, as **headline man** demonstrated.

When it comes to lying with numbers the pasty-faced brigade are among the extremists. In 1997 The Vegetarian Society was reprimanded by the Advertising Standards Authority for a series of advertisements showing people with horrifying scars and the slogan "It's much easier to cut out meat". They went on to suggest that meat eaters were 40% more likely to develop cancer; a claim, of course, totally without scientific foundation.

Homo Sapiens has been around since the later Pleistocene, about 300,000 years. He is an omnivore, the dentition (your teeth) tells you that, and he has been eating red meat throughout that period. If red meat were poisonous then the inevitable attrition of survival of the fittest would have turned him into a herbivore, but it hasn't. Man evolved as a hunter-gatherer. The diet he is optimised for is a mixed one of meat and vegetables. Any deviation from such a diet is likely to be sub-optimal. Meat is, for example, one of the most efficient sources of iron. You can get it from parsley and other vegetation, but not so effectively.

Women who eat more than five servings of red meat per week are reported to have 23 percent increased risk of forearm fracture (95% confidence interval 1.01-1.5). Not only did three authors bother to research and write this junk, but the American Journal of Epidemiology (who else?) bothered to publish it

Fats

Worknote to myself, Friday August 29th, 1997 — Wait for the next food scare and look into it.

Headline in *The Times* Friday September 5, 1997:

> **Margarine Linked to breast cancer**
> **Women with high levels of trans-fatty acids, which are found in cakes, have a**
> **40 per cent higher risk of developing the disease, Nigel Hawkes reports**

Don't you just love it? All these women have been giving up butter and putting up with revolting margarine because of the urging of the health fanatics and up comes one Dr Kohlmeier of the University of North Carolina to tell them that it is giving them breast cancer; and what a bonus the good doctor has given the journalists by enabling them to link it to cakes! The poor loves, having long put aside their cigarettes and dry Martinis, were probably indulging in the odd little cake to brighten up their grey lives, when along come the wild-eyed epidemiologists to snatch it from their trembling fingers.

I trust that the reader by this stage will have immediately spotted the junk science element in the sub-heading. 40% increase means a risk ratio of 1.4, which in real science is negligible. **Headline Man** did better than that when there was *a priori* no effect at all. I hope you don't mind, but I don't think I will bother to look into it after all.

Incidentally, a few weeks later Bart's Hospital (of all places) climbed on to the same junk science bandwagon – another of my idols bites the dust. There is no real scientific evidence that saturated fats in the diet affect blood fat levels or the incidence of heart disease.

Frankenstein Foods

What a wonderful example of scary hype this term is! It is used by the opponents of all genetically modified foods. Genetic modification is simply another tool. Like a carving knife it can be used for good or ill. You could make tomatoes or potatoes toxic by selective breeding if that was your desire; after all, they do come from the same family as deadly nightshade (*solanaceae*, the source of the alkaloid atropine) and all green parts of the potato are poisonous anyway. It is difficult to see how improving growth rates, frost resistance or longevity in storage can be harmful. Inducing insecticidal or antibiotic action in plants, however, is potentially another story, with possibilities of generating resistant strains and damaging other species. There would seem to be a compelling case for monitoring and controlling such activities. Meanwhile it is all fertile ground for publicity hungry professors and food activists.

I had originally drafted a paragraph welcoming the forced retirement of an Aberdeen scientist who in August 1998 had prematurely published the results of a botched experiment by way of a scare story on a television programme. It seemed a small victory in the battle against of junk science. I had, however, reckoned without the combined power of SIFs and the media. Quite suddenly in February 1999 the scientist in question, one Dr Pusztai, became an overnight star and one of the most spectacular media feeding frenzies ever occurred. It is an exemplar of the whole genre. The trigger was a presentation by a group of twenty scientists made a presentation at the House of Commons. We suddenly had the junk scientist as hero. No fewer than twenty nine separate SIF groups combined to exploit the resulting furore. Politicians who tried to ride the storm were overwhelmed and panic legislation ensued. It was probably the most successful generated scare ever.

Some of the variants that "scientists" came up with were quite extraordinary. One of the most extreme was that genes could "jump species", something they cannot do by definition. A species is defined as a group of closely allied mutually fertile individuals. Thus by definition if they are different species they cannot interbreed and therefore exchange genes. Unfazed by real science our heroes went on to warn that gene hopping could unleash potentially fatal new strains of meningitis and other diseases. The even more basic illogicality of their position is that, if the genes were present in GM foods, they must have already been available in the world gene pool and therefore according to the junk theory able to hop anywhere the fancy takes them. Let us not, however, let logic get in the way of a really good scare.

Are GM foods safe? yell the headlines. What a stupid question! You might as well ask *Are purple foods safe?* If it is an aubergine it is safe: if it is deadly nightshade it is not. If it is a cow it is purely poetic.

As usual, the SIFs clouded the real issue. All vegetables should be labelled with their variety, including whether they are genetically modified. Then we would not have foisted on us all that supermarket junk, such as tomatoes that look wonderful but have leathery skins and flesh tasting like wet cardboard.

What a war the Frankenstein Food farce is! It has a large collection of SIF groups ranged against the giant monopolistic chemical multi-nationals – the unedifying in full pursuit of the unprincipled. The media harangue from the touchlines, to keep the pot boiling and sell more of their own products. The losers, as usual, are the ordinary people. Organisations like Greenpeace, the modern equivalent of the Luddites and bookburners, accountable to nobody, use their mangled logic to justify overturning democracy and committing acts of extreme vandalism. The great absurdity is that genetic modification offers some of the things that these people have been demanding for years, such as a reduction in the use of pesticides and nitrogen.

4.4 Chlorine

"Since its creation, chlorine has been a chemical catastrophe. It is either chlorine or us." Thus spake Greenpeace activist Christine Houghton in 1991. Even by Greenpeace standards this is a pretty remarkable piece of ignorant, hysterical nonsense. Chlorine was created at the beginnings of the universe. It is essential to life on earth, not only in the form of its sodium salt, but as a constituent of more than more than 1500 vital compounds in plants and animals, including our digestive juices.

The chlorination of drinking water has saved more human lives than any other hygienic measure. When chlorination was stopped in Peru in 1991 as a result of pressure from the EPA and Greenpeace, the largest epidemic of the twentieth century occurred. 800,000 people became ill with cholera and 6,000 people died. Millions of people are still dying all over the world because of dirty water. The anti-chlorine movement was one of the many legacies of Rachel Carson. It was intensified by an EPA study in the mid 1980s that purported to show that one of the by-products of chlorination (trihalomethanes) was carcinogenic. This involved subjecting hapless rodents to very high concentrations. More of which later.

4.5 The Pill

It was inevitable that the scaremongers would latch onto the birth control pill. This was one of the most beneficial inventions of all time and did more than anything else to liberate women from their servitude. There might be a tiny extra risk of heart disease or breast cancer, but the pill is at least twenty times less dangerous than pregnancy. At the height of the scare, women were abandoning the pill and the number of abortions soared. Then in 1999 the results of a study of 46,000 women were reported and the risks were shown to be minimal.

All this was not good enough for one Kim McPherson of the London School of Hygiene and Tropical Medicine on the basis that there was not any evidence about those who were taking oral contraceptives for a long time before having a child. There is no evidence of a lot of things, like the long term use of corn flakes before having ones ears pierced, but let that not stand in the way of a good scare. Women seem to be the favourite target of scaremongers; even their tampons are not immune.

4.6 Asthma

When I was a child almost every household contained a heavy smoker. The cinemas we attended at least once a week were so thick with tobacco smoke that the projector beam struggled to reach the screen. There were fewer vehicles, but those there were belched out clouds of unregulated smoke. At certain times of the year we would have to walk to school in fog so thick and yellow that visibility was less than a yard. At other times we would wake up to find ice on the inside of the bedroom window. There was no central heating and no fitted carpets.

Despite all this asthma was a rarity. As there were no inhalers containing preventives and broncho-dilators, when it did occur it was a disabling disease. Those few children who were unfortunate enough to succumb to it were like the permanent invalids of Victorian fiction.

Since that time asthma has increased steadily in frequency. A recent survey in Britain showed that up to a third of all children had experienced the symptoms of the disease. There is no significant regional variation, but the incidence in non-metropolitan areas was higher. In the USA occurrence of the disease has doubled in the last decade. 5,000 Americans die of it every year. Most children almost never experience environmental tobacco smoke, almost none have ever seen a "pea-souper" fog and vehicle exhaust is highly regulated. Yet to what do the SIFs attribute the increase? It is so inevitable it is hardly worth repeating.

4.7 Clusters

I trust you were impressed by the diagram forming the frontispiece. It was constructed in the following manner. I used a random number generator – Mathcad rnd(x) – to produce the x and y coordinates of 100 points and plotted them as a scatter diagram. I then used Microsoft Paint to superimpose them on a Clip Art map of Britain and erased all the points in the sea. There is no such disease as Pallacritis. It is an invention of mine (in fact, an anagram). There is no pattern and the distribution is purely random. We see clusters and lines because the human eye is trained to look for patterns. In many areas of activity this facility provides a powerful short cut, but it often leads to grotesque errors (as in optical illusions) and, of course, some wonderful scare stories.

I have to confess that I took the best for my purposes of six such scatter diagrams and then turned it upside down, since a cluster in the sparsely populated highlands of Scotland would not have the same impact as round Harwell, a nuclear research centre. I was also worried about the possibility of the Linkwood distillery on Speyside being affected by Pallacritis.

It is a sad fact that people in the extremes of distress look round for causes and are somehow comforted by finding one. This is understandable. What is offensive is that there are others who exploit this for their own ends. The one in ten thousand who get lung cancer without cigarette smoking find it hard to accept that they have just drawn the short straw in life, so they leap on the bandwagon of the anti-smoking lobby and blame passive smoking. The tragic figure of Roy Castle is a case in point. Lung cancer is largely a disease of smokers, but about five percent of cases represent the natural background. The randomness of disease seems to be harder to accept in our Godless age. Families with children who are leukaemia victims look round for a cause, such as power lines and nuclear power plants. Somehow, finding a scapegoat makes it easier to accept.

The Junkman identifies one of the best techniques of cluster fabrication as the Texas Sharpshooter method. It goes something like this: The Texas Sharpshooter sprays the side of an abandoned barn with gunfire. He then draws a bull's eye target around a cluster of bullet holes that occurred randomly. He then can say, "See what a good shot I am!"

Nevertheless, clusters make a good story. In Disney's *A Civil Action*, John Travolta stars as a personal injury lawyer crusading for "justice", naturally in the form of millions of dollars, against two companies accused of dumping chemicals in Woburn, Massachusetts in the 1970s. Allegedly, the chemicals contaminated drinking water, causing eight children's deaths from leukaemia; four times the "average" rate. It is in the nature of statistical distributions that some areas will have four time the average rate and some a quarter of the average rate. The chances of it happening by accident are, in fact, pretty small (on the numbers given about one in five thousand) but Woburn represents only about one in 7,500 of the population of the USA. So it might well have drawn the short straw at random. Who knows? There was a 13.5% chance that it would have no deaths at all. The important factor, however, is that no one has established the missing link, that the chemicals involved are capable of causing leukaemia.

4.8 Skin Cancer

For skin melanoma there is a believable mechanism, since the UV component of solar radiation is an ionising agent. I, for one, would like to know more about it as I am a high-risk subject (fair skin, blue eyes with lots of body moles) but the literature on the subject is, to say the least, confusing. Sunscreen ointments represent a massive world-wide industry, but there seems to be no agreement as to whether they are effective, or even make the situation worse. We are told that only one incident of sunburn in a lifetime is likely to produce skin cancer, but everyone who is sensitive to the sun has been burned once in their lifetime. That is how they discover that they are sensitive. We are told that there is a positive association between the use of sunscreen and developing skin cancer. Hardly surprising, when those at risk are the most likely to seek protection.

4.9 AIDS

The first HIV virus probably crossed species from chimpanzee to man in about 1950. It had everything going for it as unlike, say, the Ebola virus, it killed its victims very slowly and so had time to spread. Ironically, the smallpox vaccination campaign might have contributed to its early expansion, but that is something for the epidemiologists to argue about.

AIDS gave the doomsayers a whale of a time (e.g. US Health and Human Services Secretary Donna Shalala " *Soon because of AIDS we might not have any Americans left.*"). The behaviour of AIDS, however, was unacceptable because it was politically incorrect. Not only did it differentially affect sexual groups; it also favoured the wrong races. So the myth of the Universal AIDS epidemic had to be conjured up, even though white heterosexuals provided all of four percent of the total cases and Asians virtually none at all. Hence the slogans and headlines were generated: **AIDS is an Equal Opportunity Destroyer; AIDS Runs Wild Among Teen-agers** etc – the latter based on a dramatic increase of ten cases in the whole of the USA during 1996.

Le Fanu summed up the realities of the AIDS scare:

> *The epidemic did not materialise but this had nothing to do with "safe sex" – rather, the principles on which the epidemic were predicted turn out to be misconceived. The proposed scenario was that the HIV virus would cross over from the recognised "at risk" groups to the "heterosexual population" in whom it would spread by the multiplier effect. There are several reasons why this was highly unlikely but now Dr David Barlow of St Thomas's Hospital, London, has provided another scenario - "assortative sexual mating". People don't sleep around with anyone but within well-defined social groupings – they stick to their own kind – and as a result the disease remained ghettoised. So, though it is certainly biologically possible (if difficult) to be infected with the HIV virus following heterosexual intercourse, sociologically it is a most unlikely event.*

As I write, AIDS is No. 8 on the list of causes of death in the USA and dropping rapidly. First is heart disease, with 2.3 million deaths. Second is cancer, with 734,000 deaths. AIDS caused fewer than 33,000 deaths in 1996. AIDS, like global warming, seems to exhibit the phenomenon of the incredible shrinking forecast. In 1986, the U.S. Public Health Service (PHS) estimated that the number of U.S. residents infected with human immunodeficiency virus (HIV) ranged between 1.0 million to 1.5 million. By 1990, presumably while the AIDS epidemic was on the rise, the PHS estimated that 800,000 to 1.2 million US residents were infected. In 1996, researchers at the Centers for Disease Control and Prevention (CDC) estimated the number of U.S. residents infected with HIV, as of 1992, to be actually between 650,000 to 900,000. More than twice as many Britons die from falling out of bed than die of AIDs.

Now Africa is another story.

4.10 BSE and CJD

> It is worse than a crime, it is a blunder.
> Boulay de la Meurthe

What a saga this has been! It has everything from low farce to appalling human tragedy. This is something that should never have happened. It is axiomatic in disease prevention that you do not create cycles of consumption. For example, if you allow drinking water to be contaminated with human excreta you create the conditions in which disease can spread alarmingly. I could hardly contain my disgust when I heard that for years the animal feed industry had for years, with the encouragement of Government, been feeding bovine and ovine remains to cows and sheep. They are herbivores, for heaven's sake. My sense of outrage at hearing the news that farmers had been feeding the remains of cattle and sheep to their own kind was only equalled by my abhorrence on learning that they were still feeding antibiotics to farm stock. The fact that this appalling practice was exacerbated by a gradual relaxation of the standards on treatment of the animal remains only serves to underline the dangerous folly of the officials involved. It must rank as one of the scientific crimes of the century that an anonymous MAFF official, as long ago as 1987, censored a report on the new syndrome, removing the words "scrapie-like". Why did he do that? What did he have to hide? It is easy to be wise after the event and, as they say, hindsight is always 20/20 vision; but the tale of official prevarication, procrastination and deceit would fill a book (and no doubt will do so many times over).

However, *revenons à nos moutons*. I do not intend to revisit the whole sorry imbroglio. Enough ink, paper and magnetic oxide have been and will be expended on it, and as I write one of those interminable Government inquiries has begun its work. Our theme is wrong numbers, and particularly their use in junk science.

Headline in *The Times* 23rd August, 1997:

New CJD strain threatens thousands

In fact, the patient in question had been a vegetarian for eleven years, when BSE in cattle had only been known for ten. The immediate deduction was that the incubation period for the disease was longer than had been thought, so the number of cases to be expected would have to be inflated substantially.

A spokesman: "It is an unusual case, but I do not think it destroys our hypothesis that the most probable route for infection with the new strain of CJD is food containing contaminated beef."

Now, this guy's hypothesis may well turn out to be correct in the long run, but that does not stop me from getting an uncomfortable feeling that I have seen this scenario somewhere before. Could it be in Langmuir's laws *(q.v.)*?

What also worries me is that I had thought of at least one alternative hypothesis that was certainly not damaged by this new observation: that the "new" strain of CJD was always there, but nobody thought of looking for it.

There is no denying that the new variant of CJD is a terrible disease. The accounts of the families involved are harrowing to read. Yet it is still extremely rare in comparison with many other appalling diseases that are killing thousands of people but receive no press coverage at all. Again, far more people die of falling out of bed than die of new variant CJD.

The end result of the panic, however, is that the bureaucrats have managed the mindless destruction of an entire industry and rural communities have received yet another savage blow.

4.11 EMF

This is one of those scares cause real scientists to ask – where is the mechanism? Electromagnetic fields from power lines have been accused of causing various diseases, such as brain tumours and leukaemia. There is all sorts of epidemiological "evidence", most of it contradictory and inconclusive. Unlike sunlight, these sources are not ionising in nature. Two things matter in this respect, frequency and field strength. This makes mobile phones, for example, millions of times more suspect, but still rather unlikely. Power lines have been accused of promoting clusters of disease, but we know all about clusters.

Oddly enough there is a much more plausible mechanism that the scaremongers appear to have neglected. Because of the high electric fields close to the lines a phenomenon called corona can occur, particularly in damp weather, and this can produce very reactive gases, such as ozone and the oxides of nitrogen. Perhaps I could start my own scare a make a bit of money as a chat show guest. Meanwhile, the legal sharks in the US are circling, looking for the opportunity of a nice little earner. One woman was awarded a million dollars by a jury for "losing her psychic powers" after a CAT scan, but a judge subsequently reduced it to one dollar. What's the matter with the man, doesn't he appreciate the value of psychic powers? One bunch of epidemiologists even came up with electric razors as a cause of leukaemia (risk ratio 1.3). You have to admire their ingenuity.

Some of the effusions on the web about EMF are quite extraordinary. One David Yarrow, for example, publishes pages and pages of this sort of stuff:

> Magnetism affects water in odd ways. Normally water's pH is neutral due to its balance of acid (H+) to alkaline (OH-) ions. But south pole magnetism causes water to become slightly alkaline, while a north pole shifts pH a tad acid. This subtle shift is critical in biological systems such as cell membranes.

4.12 Mobile phones

A wonderful scare story appeared in the Sunday Mirror (March 7, 1999). The headline, in 3cm capitals announced THIS IS HOW A MOBILE PHONE HEATS YOUR BRAIN. Adjacent was what looked like a brain scan, with a vast red zone occupying most of the area. There is, of course, no calibration. Looking inside the paper we find that it is, in fact, a model (which cost £40,000) and the image has been constructed from the outputs of an unstated number of sensors. These results are said to be from a project called "Cephos" which apparently involves scientists in 13 different European countries. The article tells us "Only when scientists know how much radiation is absorbed will they be able to know the effect the build-up of energy has on the brain."

What on earth are they on about? It is a first year student experiment to find out how much energy is absorbed by an object. You measure the field strength at a given distance from the transmitter, then you interpose the object, in this case a real human brain, and measure it again. The difference indicates the proportion of energy absorbed by the object. First, however, we would require our student to make an order of magnitude calculation.

Let us say the human brain is the equivalent of about one Litre of water. A mobile phone battery holds less than one ampere hour of charge at less than five volts, so let's be pessimistic and call it about five watt-hours, which is less than 20 kilo-joules. Four joules will raise one gram of water through one degree Celsius, so our 20,000 will raise our 1000 grams through 5°C. Thus, if the *whole* of the battery power were instantaneously absorbed in the brain the average rise in temperature would be of the order of five degrees. Hence, even if the heat had no means of escape, the temperature rise would be 5°C over the talk time available, say an hour. The total rate of energy consumption of the brain, however, is about 25 watts, which amount of heat is very efficiently removed.

Furthermore, we know that the brain absorbs only a small portion of the energy, otherwise the phone would not work if our head were between it and the transmitter. It would be remarkable if the brain managed to absorb 1% of the energy, which would make the temperature rise with no heat loss 0.05°C. To give our scare-mongers their due, we have neglected our old friend the inverse square law, so most of the heating would be concentrated near the ear in use, but it would still be unmeasurable. Going out in the sun without a hat would have a much greater effect than our phone.

"Ah!" respond the scaremongers "It is not the heat that matters but the scrambling of our brains." Just how is that done? There are, of course, numerous studies involving rounding up the usual suspects, such as tumour-prone mice. Colin Blakemore, physiology professor at Oxford University, has gone public with his fear that cellphones are affecting our brain functions.

4.13 Global warming

It is a capital mistake to theorise before one has data
Sherlock Holmes.

The earth has been warming up and there is little that the puny efforts of mankind can do about it. The controlling factor is probably periodic changes in solar activity as reflected in the sunspot cycle. However, you don't corner any taxpayers' money making that observation; hence man-made global warming.

Don't the media and the politicians just love this one? An American Vice President has made a whole second career out of it and a British Deputy Prime Minister seeks to emulate him. Is there such a thing as man-made global warming? I don't know, I very much doubt it and I am pretty sure it is insignificant, but here are some embarrassing numbers – the earth is about one degree cooler than it was at the time William the Conqueror was compiling the Doomsday Book. Oceanographic studies suggest that the earth went through a temperature minimum about 400 years ago, the so-called Little Ice Age. Go back a bit further (say about four hundred million years) and there was ten times as much atmospheric carbon dioxide. According to Global Warming Pundits, the temperature should have been between at least 5°C warmer than today. Yet, geologists say the earth was then in the grip of a major ice age, with temperatures at least 5°C colder than today. Recent history also suggests that carbon dioxide levels have little effect on global temperatures. Average temperatures have increased 1.5°C since the mid 19th century, and 0.5°C since 1940, when carbon dioxide emissions from human activities began to take off.

The Global Warming Cassandras have generated so many myths that commenting on them would require a whole book. Take just one: Global Warming will cause increased storm intensity and frequency. In fact, severe storms are more closely associated with cold weather than warm weather. The worst in the North Sea, for example, occurred during the Little Ice Age. Half a million lives were lost in storms in 1421, 1446 and 1570. Only two of the top 20 deadliest storms have occurred since 1963 and none in the 1980s or 1990s, when the earth supposedly had its hottest temperatures on record. The worst storm in British history occurred in 1703, when 8,000 people died.

The Kyoto junk-fest on Global Warming in December, 1997, brought all the environmental SIFs out of the woodwork. Half a dozen of the leaders of the Friends of the Earth, Greenpeace and the rest, wrote to *The Times* on the first of the month telling us "the scientists" are right about the increase in global temperatures due to human interference. They pilloried "single issue groups" such as the US fuel lobby for attempting to derail the negotiations. Remember this is the same bunch of scaremongers who told us in the sixties that all the fuel and minerals would have run out by the end of the century, i.e. now. In 1971 "scientists" were warning of an oncoming ice age due to industrial pollution. That was before they thought up the greenhouse gas scam. My God, how the money rolls in! More than 500 real physicians and scientists (from The Advancement of Sound Science Coalition, TASSC, and the European Science and Environment Forum, ESEF) signed an open letter to world leaders opposing the climate change treaty negotiated in Kyoto, within a few months the number of signatories had risen to 15,000 of whom 10,000 held higher degrees. It was completely ignored by the media. Meanwhile the handful of scaremongers continue to grab the headlines.

As with all such liars the tragedy is that, by crying wolf, they are obscuring the real issues. It is a fact that the resources of the planet are finite. Waste is a bad thing *per se*. Pouring pollution into finite volume, such as the North Sea, is inherently stupid, as is cutting down and burning the rain forests or concreting over a small and beautiful island like Great Britain. We do not need phoney calculations to tell us that. Nevertheless, at the end of the century there is still plenty of fuel and minerals are cheaper than ever. The known reserves of almost everything are greater now than they ever were. The television reports of the Kyoto summit all spoke as though man-made global warming were an incontrovertible fact agreed to by all scientists. World leaders were actually debating whether the greenhouse effect existed. If it did not we would all be dead, as would the rest of life on earth.

One of the most remarkable things about the doomsayers is the consistency with which they are wrong. In the mid-seventies they were forecasting a new ice age because of pollution: by the mid-eighties they were forecasting global warming for the same reason. Arch doom-merchant, Paul Ehrlich, wagered arch sceptic, Julian Simon, that scarcity would drive resource prices up between 1980 and 1990. Simon won the bet easily. Why don't they just give up and go away? Because there is money and fame in doom.

As the George C. Marshall Institute reports, global warming is a fading crisis. Consider the trend in predictions from the United Nations Intergovernmental Panel on Climate Change (IPCC):

In 1990, the IPCC predicted 3.3 degrees centigrade of global warming by 2100.

In 1992, the IPCC predicted 2.8 degrees centigrade of global warming by 2100.

In 1995, the IPCC predicted 1-2 degrees centigrade of global warming by 2100.

By now they should be predicting global cooling. Yet another incredible shrinking forecast.

Why do climatologists persist with their fanciful disaster theories? Could it be something to do with their two billion dollars of annual funding? Good old American taxpayer!

Am I worried about Global Warming? No – the fossil fuels are not going to last that long for a start. This will eventually become the serious issue, though it has been shrouded by lies and obfuscation from the green lobby. When the time comes our descendants might need a bit of warmth. Man-made greenhouse gases represent, at most, 0.2% of the total. Agriculture and forestry are far more important in this context than combustion. Carbon dioxide is on the increase. To be accurate carbon dioxide is now about 360 parts per million of the atmosphere, compared with 290 at the beginning of the 20th century. Reasonable estimates indicate that it may eventually rise as high as 600 parts per million. Oceans and land hold some 50 times as much carbon dioxide as the atmosphere, and movement between these reservoirs of carbon dioxide is poorly understood. The observed rise in atmospheric carbon dioxide does correspond with the time of human release and equals about half of the amount released. Greenhouse gases were all once plants and will return to plants, i.e. food. Atmospheric temperatures have been rising from the low of the little ice age for the past 400 years or so, but still remain below the 3,000-year average.

Have you ever wondered how Greenland got its name? When Eric the Red and the settlers arrived in Greenland in 986, the climate supported the Viking way of life based upon cattle, hay, grain and herring. It remained that way for 300 years until after the end of the Republic in 1261. But substantial climate changes occurred later, with each year growing colder and colder. When the last ship left in 1410 the Nordic settlement was extinct and the Inuit, with their ice-adapted lifestyle, took over.

Much of the global warming data are generated by computer models. They are appallingly crude, neglecting for example the facts that clouds have shape and the sea is salty. I have been computer modelling for longer than most people (well, forty years anyway) and would not dream of putting forward such claims on such a tenuous basis. Headlines around the world proclaim that the world's most powerful computer confirms global warming. I could program it to say that two plus two make five.

I cannot say that some of the language used by the global warming promoters inspires me with confidence. "The climate system is an angry beast and we are poking it with sticks," says Dr. Wallace Broecker, of Columbia University. What on earth does that mean? I can see that the weather might be described as an angry beast, but the climate? It is claimed that there is evidence of abrupt changes in the climate in the distant past. This may well be so; a volcano, a large meteor or a major solar storm are quite capable of giving it a good poke, but I have seen nothing to convince me that current human activities are anywhere near that potential.

The Junkman, as always, has a succinct summary of the modelling situation:

> The National Weather Service failed to provide warnings about a tornado in Georgia that killed thirteen. But although the National Weather Service can't tell us what type of weather we're having now, we can be assured that it can predict global warming 100 years from now? Maybe we should nail down the immediate forecast first. How about spending taxpayer dollars on protecting existing taxpayers?

The key number to bear in mind is that the US budget for global warming studies is about $2 billion and some of the top executives in the racket earn salaries that would make many industrialists envious. The US Secretary of the Interior, Bruce Babbit, has his eye on the ball

> Climate change is underway. We have already changed the atmosphere through fossil fuel emissions. That's a scientific fact beyond denial. The effects are starting to show up. And there's going to be a treaty negotiation in Kyoto, in Japan, at the end of this year to try to set national plans to control global warming.

> But it's an unhappy fact that the oil companies and the coal companies in the United States have joined in a conspiracy to hire pseudo scientists to deny the facts, and then begin raising political arguments that are essentially fraudulent, that we can do this without damaging the economy, the same kind of arguments they used against acid rain, they used against the Clean Air Act, the Clean Water Act. This time I think it's especially unfortunate, and I think that the energy companies need to be called to account because what they're doing is un-American in the most basic sense. They are

compromising our future by misrepresenting the facts by suborning scientists onto their payrolls and attempting to mislead the American people.

Move over Joe McCarthy.

What a wonderful excuse global warming provides! The free advertising newspaper that comes through my letter box, the *Andover Midweek Advertiser*, bore the headline, 17th March, 1998, **Water levels blamed on global warming**. Peter Jeffs, described as the boss of the Environmental Agency, said of chronically low water levels "This may be a random change in rainfall rate, but could also, understandably, be ascribed to global warming effects." And we all thought it was excessive abstraction near the aquifers feeding our chalk streams! Every little deviation from expected weather is seized upon by the media. Not only the drought, but also the floods that swept the Midlands in mid-April 1998 were ascribed by the media to global warming. These *were* unusual, of a magnitude to have a return period (i.e. likely recurrence) of 150 years, but unusual things happen most years. Among those who declined to be trapped into the general hysteria by television interviewers was the climber, Chris Bonnington, who pointed out the unheralded fact that Tibet had had the coldest winter ever recorded, leading to the deaths of thousands of people and yaks.

Instead of moaning about the climate, we should be counting our blessings: not only are we privileged to live during a period in which the earth is relatively warm and welcoming, we also have the advantage of a quiet period of vulcanism, which renders unlikely (but not impossible) the sort of icy catastrophe that overwhelmed the people of the sixth century.

4.14 Malaria

Another one from the Global Warming crowd – warmer climates will cause the spread of tropical diseases, such as Malaria, to a wider area (i.e. Europe and the USA). "I am concerned because our environment is becoming more unstable." says Dr. Paul Epstein, from the Harvard Medical School, of course. "I'm suggesting that some of these disease issues are symptoms of that instability." Here's an actual number – Britain once had 60,000 cases, when the climate was little different from now. Indeed, in the early 1920s 16.5 million people suffered from malaria in regions reaching the Arctic Circle. 100,000 men died of Malaria during the building of St Petersburg. It became known as the city built on bones.

Here's what a real expert (Paul Reiter, Dengue Branch, Division of Vector-Borne Infectious Diseases, National Center for Infectious Diseases, Centers for Disease Control and Prevention, Dengue Branch, San Juan, Puerto Rico, USA had to say in a letter to *The Lancet* (March 14, 1998):

Sir – In your news item on the Kyoto Summit (Dec 20/27, p 1825), Justin McCurry reports on warnings that man-made climate change may unleash a public-health disaster. Specifically he mentions "adamant" claims by Paul Epstein and Andrew Haines that global warming has already caused malaria, dengue, and yellow fever to invade higher latitudes in the temperate regions and higher altitudes in the tropics.

Such claims, oft repeated, plainly ignore the past. Until the 20th century, malaria was a common disease throughout much of the USA, and it remained endemic until the 1950s. Yellow fever played a major part in US history. Widespread epidemics of dengue were also common, and continued until the 1940s. In Europe, malaria was probably present in neolithic times. In ancient Greece, Hippocrates clearly distinguished between the symptoms of vivax and falciparum malaria. Throughout history, nearly all countries of that continent were affected. Even in the present century, devastating epidemics occurred as far north as Archangel on the Arctic Circle, and the disease remained endemic in such un-tropical countries as Holland, Poland, and Finland until after World War II. Yellow fever also killed tens of thousands in many European countries until the end of the 19th century, and a devastating epidemic of dengue, with an estimated 1 million cases and 1000 deaths, occurred in Greece in 1927-28...

The distortion of science to make predictions of unlikely public-health disasters diverts attention from the true reasons for the recrudescence of vector-borne diseases. These include the large-scale resettlement of people (often associated with major ecological change), rampant urbanisation without adequate infrastructure, high mobility through air travel, resistance to antimalarial drugs, insecticide resistance, and the deterioration of vector-control operations and other public-health practices.

Fortunately, a century ago a Briton, Ronald Ross, discovered the rôle of the *Anopheles* mosquito in the life cycle of the malaria parasite, *Plasmodium*. It is a nasty beast, with an ability to mutate almost equal to that of the flu virus. Unfortunately, the real tragedy is that malaria is now killing millions of people, and infecting hundreds of millions every year. One reason for this is that the West has imposed on the rest of the world a ban on DDT insecticide spraying. If you had to choose between death and DDT which would you choose? Yes, I know this is all an oversimplification, but the point about imposing Western fetishes on the unfortunate world is a valid one; which brings us to the next topic.

Meanwhile malaria *is* on the increase with hundreds of millions of cases. Yet, according to *Nature* (26 September 1996) in a report entitled *Malaria Research: An Audit of the International Activity* (Wellcome Trust, London 1996) it is estimated that global spending on malaria research in 1993 was $84 million — $42 for each of the 1.5 million to 2.7 million people who die from the disease each year. In contrast, the researchers estimated that $3,274 is spent for every AIDS death and $789 for every asthma death.

4.15 Man-made chemicals

This [book] is not to be tossed lightly aside, but to be hurled with great force.
Dorothy Parker

Here are rich pickings for authors of money spinning books. For a really good scare, read *Our Stolen Future: Are We Threatening Our Fertility, Intelligence and Survival A Scientific Detective Story* (Dutton Publishing1996) by Theo Colburn, Dianne Dumanoski and John Peterson Myers, foreword by Vice President Al Gore. I won't comment in detail — see the Junkman for a comprehensive demolition.

Don't worry, though. According to these authors you will be perfectly all right as long as you drink no tap water, bottled water or breast milk and eat no meat or vegetables.

I must admit that I have a slight worry that all this junk might be obscuring a genuine problem. A report that male fish downstream of a sewage outlet are changing their sex, if genuine, is something I find rather disturbing. On the whole I am glad I live in an area where the drinking water does not contain recycled human waste.

Another worry I have about water is that, living as I do near the world's most famous fly fishing river, I have noticed that the clarity of the water has continuously deteriorated over the last couple of decades. This is probably due to leeching out of excessive nitrogenous fertilisers from agricultural land and the proliferation of trout farms. Bad news for fly fishers like me, but it isn't going to kill anybody.

Talking of water, Roger Bate, editor of *What Risk*, asked 123 people outside underground stations the following question:

> The chemical industry routinely uses a chemical 'dihydrogen monoxide' in its processes. It is used in significant ways and often leads to spillages and other leaks and it regularly finds its way into our food supply. It is a major component of acid rain. It contributes to erosion.
>
> It decreases the effectiveness of automobile brakes. In its vapour state it is a major greenhouse gas. It can cause excessive sweating and vomiting. Accidental inhalation can kill you. It has been found in tumours of terminal cancer patients. Should this chemical be strictly regulated or even banned by an authority such as the British Government or the EU?

Five percent said "No".
19 percent said "Don't know"
The rest said "Yes".

Of course H_2O is not a man made chemical, but the fact that an appropriately posed question can persuade three quarters of a sample of the population to approve its banning is a telling commentary on how the scaremongers are able to operate so freely and on so little evidence. Just to reinforce the point, Idaho student, 14 year old Nathan Zohner, made the same experiment and persuaded a startling 86% of his classmates to demand a ban on water.

There is only one essential difference between man-made and natural chemicals – the former are purer. Aspirin, for example, is a synthetic chemical compound, acetylsalicylic acid. It takes its name from the willow tree (*Salix*) whose bark was used by the ancient Greeks to control fever and pain, but the natural form is a cocktail of chemicals of unknown total effect, whereas the man-made form is pure and has many beneficial properties. It also has known problems (I, for example, cannot take it, on medical advice) and in children it increases the risk of contracting the rare and frequently fatal Reye's syndrome, a disease of the brain and some abdominal organs.

DDT

Dichlorodiphenyltrichloroethane has probably save billions of people from the most terrible of insect borne diseases; not only malaria but also yellow fever, typhus, elephantiasis and many others. It has been a miracle of science that has alleviated more misery than any other discovery apart from the chlorination of water. It is a powerful specific insecticide that is harmless to humans and most other organisms. In India alone, DDT reduced malaria from 75 million cases to fewer than 5 million cases in a decade. There was a sound scientific reason for reducing the use of this chemical, as many harmful insects were developing resistance to it. However, in the panic induced by Rachel Carson's *Silent Spring* and a campaign orchestrated by the EPA this beneficent chemical has been banned in western countries and they have pressured others to follow suit. The USA has imposed this ban on the rest of the world by threatening to boycott food products. Mexico, which reduced its incidence of malaria from 2.4 million cases to 5,000, is now implementing a programme to phase out the chemical largely responsible. The widespread use of chemicals merely to increase agricultural production is rightly condemned, but that does not justify throwing the baby out with the bath water.

The indictment against DDT was based on three typical fabrications by the EPA:

1. It was a danger to bird-life, particularly raptors.

2. It was carcinogenic to humans.

3. It had an indefinite lifetime in soil and would pose a permanent threat to insects and other organisms.

In fact, throughout the period for which DDT was in use the number of raptors in the USA increased. DDT is **not** a human carcinogen, a fact that was declared by the US National Cancer Institute in 1978. The dose for human poisoning is so high (about 100 grams) that all deaths due to it are either accidental or suicide. DDT breaks down in the soil and in the atmosphere to DDD and then into further less complex molecules. It is also extremely insoluble in water. See the article by Kelvin Klemm in *Environmental Health* (bibliography) for a detailed account.

Methyl Bromide

This is a pesticide so important that the agriculture of the developing world is almost entirely dependent upon it. It is claimed, however, to be responsible for one tenth of the destruction of the ozone layer. Under pressure from the USA, the UN is backing a move to phase out the chemical, but scientists accuse the UN of suppressing data about the serious damage this would do to the developing world (*The Times* 28/8/97).

4.16 Oil spills

Consider just one oil disaster. The *Torrey Canyon* was holed off the Scilly Isles in 1967 and released about 117,000 tonnes of crude oil into the sea. The media were full of pictures of oiled birds (there were over 25,000 of them) but little was said of other species. The limpets on the Cornish coast, for example, were killed not by the oil but by the detergent that was sprayed on the slick to disperse it. The green algae on which they grazed took over. Four years later, however, everything was back to normal. The effect on the birds was disastrous, but it was no greater than an unseasonable storm.

What is the purpose of delving into all this? It is that big numbers make headlines for a short period and then are forgotten. It is not, however, the individual disasters that really matter. It is the attrition over a long period of time. As in this case, the panic reactions of humanity at the time often do more harm than good, but the real effect is the gradual decline of many species over many years as the result of the cumulative results of human activity. Oil slicks out at sea are usually put there quite deliberately. Ancient hedgerows are grubbed up for the sake of efficient farming. Thousands of other human activities cause the decline and, with increasing frequency, the extinction of many species, but unfortunately it does not make a good headline and nobody notices. As with SIFs, the great problem with scares is that they take society's eye of the ball, the real long-term threats are ignored, while we reel from crisis to crisis.

4.17 Asbestos

Asbestos is a term applied to two different mineral species that have extraordinary abilities to withstand high temperatures and are hence invaluable in a number of important applications. Unfortunately, asbestos when inhaled is rather deadly (so is water and a damned sight quicker). As a result the EPA and other agencies demanded its removal from all buildings. The effect was to release large quantities of asbestos into the atmosphere, instead of remaining quite safely where it was. It is not just dose that makes materials poisonous; it is also place.

According to the *Detroit News*, March 1, 1990 Dr Malcolm Ross, of the U.S. Geological Survey, one of the world's leading experts on asbestos, stated "There is no doubt in my mind that the Challenger disaster was caused by asbestos paranoia." Fearing lawsuits and a total ban on asbestos, the Fuller O'Brien Company that had previously supplied NASA with asbestos-containing putty to seal the O-Rings simply stopped making it. NASA was forced to use a substitute putty which failed to protect the shuttle's O-Rings from hot gases passing through the booster joint, and the Challenger explosion of 1986 was a direct result. Despite this, as anticipated by the Fuller O'Brien Company, the EPA's total ban on asbestos was implemented in 1989 — only to be overturned in 1991 by a court decision that the EPA had "insufficient evidence."

4.18 Influenza

If you really cannot manage without something to worry about, may I suggest our familiar friend, the 'flu. It gets the headlines during a particularly severe outbreak, but is largely ignored, even by the most prolific scaremongers. Even in a good year it will kill more of the population than, say, road accidents, which receive a great deal more propaganda. The remarkable and fearful thing about this virus is its built in capacity to mutate. Each year new strains pop up somewhere in the world, an example of evolution in action. We rely on a modest collection of medical teams to isolate each new strain and develop a vaccine in time to give some protection to the most vulnerable members of the race. Every year they look at the odds and make their bet on our behalf, a gigantic gamble for very high stakes. Every now and then a really potent form emerges and spreads devastation around the world. In the Great War of 1914-18, the most mortal in history, the "Spanish" 'flu killed more Europeans than the war itself. Fit young men were dead within three or four days of contracting it. Even as recently as 1996 the death rate in Britain reached 5,000 in one week. Yet where are the SIFs, the high profile professors and the billions of dollars of taxpayers' money they command?

It is likely that 'flu epidemics originate with and are spread by birds, but the amount of human travel since 1914 has increased beyond all bounds. A particularly virulent form could spread around the world in days. My contribution to the scare industry is to predict that the next disastrous world epidemic will be some form of influenza.

4.19 The real thing

Before leaving the subject of scares it is important to emphasise the "crying wolf" aspect. There are things we should be concerned about and develop a strategy for. These real causes for disquiet tend to get buried in the general scare hysteria and hence starved of resources. Perhaps the starkest is the development of antibiotic resistance in bacteria. In 1963 the US Surgeon

General stated that it was time to close the book on infectious disease. This was, to say the least, somewhat optimistic. We are engaged in a constant battle between invention (of antibiotics) and evolution (the development of resistance). There are some disturbing possibilities. For example, MRSA, a highly resistant staphylococcus, has so far been confined to hospital wards, where it can be dealt with by ward closure and isolation. If it escaped into the general population it would be a serious matter indeed. Ultra resistant forms of bacteria can, and do, pop up anywhere in the world. It is a rare event and has so far been dealt with effectively. The possibility of a major and horrifying incident is always there. The debilitated state of scientific medical research and its dependency on giant drug companies is a matter for concern. What is needed is a great deal of **basic research** at the molecular level, and as we shall see that is not what modern bureaucratised research-funding supports.

If there really were a global catastrophe, such as seemed to happen in the sixth century, when a meteorite or volcanic eruption produced a long winter that changed the course of world history, the environmental SIFs will have done their best to leave us ill prepared for it. We would need all the energy we could lay our hands on, including nuclear, and the most efficient forms of farming. On the other hand the fragility of a society so dependent on technological intervention would be exposed, particularly in countries that bask in the security of booming service industries. These would be of little account during a grim fight for survival in the cold and dark.

Chapter 5
Deception and Fraud

Let no man deceive you with vain words
Ephesians

What is the difference between deception and fraud? The dictionary is not particularly helpful, neither is the legal system. It is not simply a question of money; after all, a professional magician deceives us for gain. The essential difference is that the honest professional magician present himself as an illusionist, an entertainer and nothing more. Once he claims to have subverted the immutable laws of physics he becomes a fraud.

I do not intend to go into the parlour tricks that the likes of Uri Geller have dressed up as psychic phenomena; enough distinguished people have wasted enough of their time demolishing them over the years. James Randi, in particular, has done a thorough job. There is however, an aspect that deserves to be aired

At the height of the Uri Geller hysteria there was a naïve coterie of academic scientists and engineers who swallowed the whole thing, hook, line and sinker (over the years the same people swallowed a lot of other things, too). They were vying with each other to collect children with the professed power of spoon bending. Where are those children now?

Frankly, these fringe science merchants in academia are a menace. With every new fad that hits the tabloid press, there they are basking for a few moments in the tawdry reflected glory of one charlatan or another; the same few names over and over again. With the excuse of "keeping an open mind" they pursue one chimera after another. Nothing ever comes of any of it and, as soon as they have wrung the last drop of notoriety out of one fatuity, off they go pursuing the next, trying to hide their desperation and convinced that the next lottery ticket will be the winner; all this to the profound embarrassment of their immediate colleagues. That is all very well, you may ask, but what have the likes of Uri to do with numbers?

Let us make a thought experiment. I go on television, and in a half hour programme I state that by the power of my thought I will stop watches and clocks throughout the country. Lo and behold, dozens of viewers ring in to say that their timepiece stopped as I predicted. Have I performed a miracle?

Take some round numbers. There are, perhaps, 100 million clocks and watches in the country. They might go an average of about ten years without stopping – which is about 5 million minutes. Thus 20 clocks or watches will stop every minute, and in the course of my programme about 600 will stop, whether I make the magic pass or not.

The basis of such deceptions is that we all have great difficulty in comprehending large numbers, such as the population of the country. It has been said that the National Lottery is a tax on people who are poor at maths. I am not saying that people are wrong to dabble in it – they are buying a dream, paying voluntary tax and donating to charity, and as long as they understand that there is no harm. I have occasionally done it myself, knowing how foolish I am being, and when the results were announced I would mentally put away my letter to the Dean of the Faculty. Where it is harmful is when people live with the illusion that they are going to win and conduct their lives accordingly. Part of growing up is the realisation that we are not special. I was cured of it as a child when I first broke a limb, which until then was something that happened to other people. Many people never mature to this extent, and they are natural victims for the predators.

When it comes to dealing with phenomena such as large numbers, scientists learn to live with their incomprehension. Confronted with Uri, Richard Feynman said "I'm smart enough to know that I'm dumb." Which did not mean that he was taken in. He went on to say "Because a good magician can do something shouldn't make you right away jump to the conclusion that it's a real phenomenon." Scientists are the last people to evaluate the work of professional magicians. They are brought up in an ethic where people don't (at least they are not supposed to) set out to deceive each other. I cannot explain half the illusions that I see on television.

We are all more predictable than we would like to think. Given a set of symbols in a certain order many of us will choose the same one. I was caught that way myself by Uri Geller. This is well known to stage illusionists. There is a current trend to make television programs debunking these illusions by showing how they are done. How easily I have been gulled! It is perhaps a shame to put an end to an innocent form of entertainment. It would be a compensation if it increased the amount of scepticism in the general public, but in fact they are being replaced by more sinister developments.

The status of pseudo-science is raised in the popular mind by a plethora of television programmes, fiction and faction. In programmes such as the "X Files" the audience is brainwashed with endless mindless pap. In such productions the bad guys don't wear a black hat as they used to in good old honest westerns; they wear their scepticism. Frequent programmes about unsolved mysteries are designed to leave the groundlings agape and not informed.

One came on the television the day after I wrote the above paragraph. It was called *The Paranormal world of Paul McKenna*. The presenter addressed us – "The easiest thing to be is sceptical and superior. The difficult thing to be is honest and open minded." etc. etc. Sceptics were lampooned throughout the programme. The first item was a faith healer laying on of hands. "Some people believe it allows electromagnetic energy to flow from one body to another. The patent receives a revitalising charge". A dog was cured of arthritis and depression and a rugby player of an ankle injury. Electronic voices were recorded from another dimension – the other side, the spirit world – by a couple of quaint ladies from Minneapolis. The ghostly voices were not heard, but only appeared on the tape.

The *pièce de résistance*, however, was an "experiment" in psychic viewing. "The intelligence community has been using it for years. No one knows how it works it just does." The presenter hid in a wardrobe store, which contained an ironing board, and a selection of ordinary members of the public were asked to draw what came into their minds. The first four participants produced not very much and, as we came to the last one, the audience were hushed. Our hearts were in our mouths. Would this elaborate set and production all be for nothing? Amazingly, the last candidate drew an ironing board. Relief and loud applause all round. How fortunate that the very last participant came up with the goods and saved the programme from ignominious bathos! Imagine the aftermath; intelligence organisations from all over the world would be seeking out this ordinary member of the public. No enemy ironing board would be safe again. We were told

"You can try it for yourself. The distance does not seem to matter". There you have it – no mechanism, no inverse square law. The next item, about a practising Zulu witch doctor, seemed all rather tame.

Why are clearly fraudulent offerings so viable? Once people have made an investment, of time or money, in a product or service, they tend to act in such a way as to justify that investment. Many people, when their investment appears to be threatened, tend to plunge in further and further, the Nick Leeson syndrome. Thus a driver who has paid out good money for a duff device that purports to grant fuel economy will subconsciously drive more economically in order to justify his investment. The academic who has spent time on a failed experiment in parapsychology goes on to the next and the next in the hope of retrieving his investment of time and reputation.

As we have observed, fraudulent promoters latch on to particular word that they have lifted from science. We have already heard about ionisation. What is that these people have with ionisation? Water, unless it is very pure, is already ionised (because of its high dielectric constant this requires relatively little energy): the problem is to de-ionise it. Hydrocarbon molecules, on the other hand, such as those found in fuels, are very hard to ionise. Each molecule requires an energy of the order of 10 electron volts to break its bonds and ionise it. It would require much more than ten megavolts over a distance of one centimetre for an electron to accelerate to this energy in the liquid, but long before this level is reached electric breakdown would occur and there would be a spark. Even if it did occur, the ions would rapidly recombine to form heavier, waxy compounds. In any case, there would be no increase in the available energy, which comes from the exothermic processes of oxidation of the hydrogen and carbon constituents of the fuel, which are not changed by ionisation. Ionisation is just one of those words that pseudo-science has latched onto, possibly as a result of the putative benefits of ionising air, which is relatively easy, but why?

They are similarly hung up on magnetisation. Passing a fluid through a magnetic field has no effect known to science; yet we are offered for sale simple magnets that will improve the efficiency of our engines, prevent lime scale in our water pipes and cure all manners of unpleasant disease. Naturally, all claims are accompanied by impressive and scientifically attested numbers. An American shopping channel sells thousands of "therapeutic" magnets in an hour-long programme. Then there are crystals, but enough is enough.

5.1 I Meet a Quiet Genius

I have nothing to declare, except my genius.
Oscar Wilde at the New York Customs House

Through an introduction from the Department of Industry I had made the acquaintance of a retired military man called Peter Woods, who had set up a Company aimed at putting inventors together with financiers. He wrote to me enclosing a cutting from *Computer Weekly* (March 18, 1982). It was an article by a journalist called Kevin Cahill with a striking headline **A 'Quiet Genius' discovers key to vast data store**. The opening paragraphs failed to inspire me as much as was evidently intended:

> "*The notice on Bart Kahn's door says: Quiet, Genius at work.*
>
> *Inside an intense man talks lucidly about a revolutionary storage device called a charge packet memory.*"

The article carried on effusively about this revolutionary device, and when Bart Kahn played with numbers he did not bother with little ones. He was talking about 9.9 gigabytes of memory. That may not seem a lot by modern standards, but in the early eighties it was colossal. As I read on I grew increasingly uncomfortable:

> "*Initial revelations brought over 1000 enquiries......*
>
> *A Japanese company offered a factory and five year start up financing......*
>
> *But he is determined to keep the memory and its attached computer in the UK....*
>
> *The current CPM, and the computer Kahn built – yes he did that too – is manufactured from standard components........*

Anyway, we went to pay Mr Kahn a visit, Peter Woods, myself and a young colleague from my consultancy practice. I made every effort to suppress any prejudgement I might have been inclined to make about the self styled genius. We arrived at his office, which was in an old detached house. An attractive young lady provided coffee and we sat down for a discussion. He started his obviously well rehearsed spiel, full of technical jargon from a variety of scientific fields. Whenever he go onto a field that I was confident in, I probed with a few questions. For example, he started talking about discrete Fourier Transforms, so I asked what he did about transformation noise. He gave what I came to recognise as his standard answer "We have solved those problems, but I can't say any more about it while there is a patent application pending." After a few minutes of this, he suddenly got up and said "We had better go and visit the lab, as I have other visitors today. We were ushered into his white Rolls Royce and wafted away to the lab, which turned out to be a deserted factory. These were a dime a dozen in those days, as it was the height of the Thatcherite experiments in monetarism. A large computer cabinet stood in the middle of a bare room, humming away, the ways such things are supposed to, and that was about all we saw. His parting words were "I can't let your see any of the crucial papers for patent reasons, but here are a few of our early working papers." When I looked at them later they turned out to be almost identical to my own second year lecture notes on dielectric theory.

Why I was not more forthright in expressing my judgement I don't know. Perhaps I had in mind those famous scientists of the past, who poured scorn on heavier than air flight or the electric light:

> "*... after a few more flashes in the pan, we shall hear very little more of Edison or his electric lamp. Every claim he makes has been tested and proved impracticable.*"
>
> *[New York Times, January 16, 1880]*

I merely stated that if Kahn was right the whole of information theory was wrong. To give an analogy, he was not merely claiming to get a quart into a pint pot, but rather a whole reservoir.

The next I heard of Bart Kahn was on the front page of a tabloid newspaper. He had done a bunk abroad with his wife and family, leaving his girl friend behind holding the baby; the baby in this case being a bankrupt company with huge debts. Apparently he had had money not only from banks but also from a number of leading electronics companies.

For me the most extraordinary event in the whole episode was the quotation from a representative of one of those companies "Now Kahn is out of the way, perhaps we can get on with developing the charge packet memory." All pigs fully fuelled and ready for take-off.

5.2 Save and prosper

Of night and light and the half-light
W B Yeats

The second early experience I had of technical fraud was when I was approached by the representative a small company that made its living by selling equipment that purported to save power and money in the vast arrays of fluorescent lighting found in modern offices. Apparently a rival company had appeared that was selling a device at less than my client could manufacture his. Could I look at the literature and the product and report back on it?

We got hold of one of the devices. The accompanying literature was a gem with all the characteristics of the genre, glossy and bearing a coloured photograph of a large well-lit building. There were graphs (without numbers of course) and tables illustrating the energy savings. It was all based on a unique solid state device within the system. This turned out to be an electronic circuit encapsulated with epoxy resin, which we dissolved away with a suitable solvent. It was nothing more than an eccentrically designed circuit to flash at random a neon light (labelled "saving") and operated on the leakage current of a transistor that drifted up and down with temperature. It was not even connected to the functional part of the system, which was an autotransformer designed to reduce the mains voltage. Anyone could install such a device at a fraction of the cost, if they were prepared to put up with erratic starting, reduced light and shorter tube life.

What has continuously astonished me is that hard-headed businessmen, who would not sign the smallest contract or lease without appropriate legal device, will spend thousands on junk equipment without a thought of taking technical advice. It is quite amazing how putting a randomly flashing light on a piece of equipment will convince people that it is effective. The gadget catalogues are full of them.

5.3 Fuel's Gold

A guaranteed money-spinner is the promise to save motorists' fuel costs. There are some beautiful examples on the Web, full, of course, of impressive numbers and pseudo-scientific jargon. Here is just one of the more delightful ones;

ECOFLOW

A range of fuel saving devices for all reasons. Cut your fuel costs and reduce harmful emissions.

Can be fitted to most Petrol and Diesel Engines in Cars, Bikes, Trucks Boats, Gas and Oil Fired Equipment.

The Ecoflow uses the principle of magnetically induced ionisation.

What is ECOFLOW? It is a range of small but powerful magnetetic (sic) devices manufactured by a cornish (sic) company, ECOFLOW Ltd. They save on fuel costs, reduce emissions and increase power and effiency (sic) of virtually anything that burns a hydrocarbon based fuel. Six Basic products cover everything from a small petrol lawnmower to a large 10 litre diesel engine, plus oil and gas burners ranging from a domestic cooker to a blast furnace. Not (sic) special equipment is needed, no cutting of pipes, just simpley (sic) strap the device around the choosen (sic) pipe and let ECOFLOW do the rest!

Application - PETROL AND DIESEL ENGINES 700 - 1200cc
ECOFLOW FOR HIGH FLOW RATES
Improves MPG (users claim 4% - 20%)!
Increases power!
Reduces particulates!
Reduces maintenance costs!
Reduces clouding and gelling of diesel!

only £63.18 each

5.4 Pseudo-instruments

A miracle, my friend, is an event which creates faith. That is the purpose and nature of miracles......Frauds deceive. An event which creates faith does not deceive: therefore it is not a fraud, but a miracle.
GBS, St Joan

This is the age of technological miracles. People are offered many genuine gadgets that do this that or the other in ways that they do not understand. There is, however, an enormous incentive for the unscrupulous to climb on the bandwagon and sell junk to the unwary. In what follows, look out for the use of impressive jargon that the average punter is unlikely to understand.

The Quadro QRS 250G

This was a plastic box with an antenna which marketed by Quadro Corp of Harleyville, South Carolina, as a detector of just about anything: drugs, weapons, golf balls, even lost coon dogs.

The technical literature was an exemplar of its type:

The frequency chip is oscillated by static electricity produced by the body [of the user] inhaling and exhaling gases into and out of the lung cavity. This static electricity is propagated on the surface of the body to the tracker which utilizes the charge to oscillate the chip. All matter contains exact molecular frequencies. When a magnetic field is created by a contained electrically charged body moving through space at a perpendicular angle moving to its direction, and that field is brought into alignment with another exact field, resonating at the identical frequency modulation, then both objects attract, just as two bodies are attracted toward each other in a gravitational field.

This invention of one Wade Quattlebaum sold for about $1,000 and some schools and government agencies paid out as much as $8,000 for the device. Sandia Labs of Albuquerque, New Mexico, took one apart and discovered that there is nothing inside it, and were threatened with a lawsuit by Quadro. It probably costs about $2 to make. The amazing thing is the sort of people who not only bought this crap, but actually endorsed it as well – schools, drug squads, police, the National Guard etc. See Robert Todd Carroll's *Skeptic's Dictionary* for the fascinating details.

Actually Quadro were one of the rare cases that ended up in court and their activities were put to an end. There is no need, however, to splash out as much as $1,000 for a mere $79.95 you can order:

The Super-Sensor Dowsing Rod from Psi-Tronics Visions.
With which:

> You can dowse the past, present or future. Future events are subject to the laws of probability and free will so it doesn't always work for the lottery. But in other uses you are limited only by your imagination. Locate underground water, pipes, minerals, oil, etc. Locate fish and game animals, or missing persons. I know people who use it to predict the stock market, marketing trends, business opportunities, and to isolate production problems. I know mechanics who dowse to determine mechanical problems in cars, and other machinery and maintenance workers who use dowsing to find underground water lines, leaks, and electrical problems. Professional health workers, chiropractors, dieticians, and people who diagnose illness use dowsing to check their findings. Holistic healers and herbalists use it to prescribe vitamins. In the home, use it to find lost articles and to make decisions. Dowse the telephone book to find a number or the yellow pages to determine who will serve you the best. Check up on your kids to see if they are all right. Check to see if the weather will be good, and what clothes you should wear.

How have you managed without one? Don't you just love the "always" in the second line?

The lie detector

As we have observed the lie detector is a prime example of the Missing Link. It is based on an instrument called the polygraph, which monitors such physiological processes as heartbeat, blood pressure, and respiration. No one has ever produced any evidence that these phenomena are related in any way to the activity of lying. Nevertheless, it has been used, among others, by police departments, the FBI, the CIA, the KGB, the KKK, federal and state governments, and numerous private employers, for that very purpose. I don't know about you, but I would hate to be attached to a polygraph when I go to my bank to discuss my overdraft, even though I always take care to speak the absolute truth (on account of having too poor a memory to be a good liar).

Now consumers can buy a "Truth Machine" which lights up according to the stress levels in someone's voice (*The Sunday Times*, 14 February 1999) and there is even a popular television programme which uses a polygraph in a variation of those dreadful confessional shows.

Apnoea monitors

In 1972, one Dr Alfred Steinschneider published a paper to enormous acclaim that related cot deaths or SIDS (Sudden Infant Death Syndrome) *(q.v.)* to apnoea, or interrupted breathing. As a result a huge industry manufacturing breathing monitors grew up, and each year 30,000 babies were put on breathing monitors at home. The leading company grew by 100 times in five years. Properly conducted research later showed that the theory was spurious, but more of this later.

5.5 Perpetual motion and free energy

The laws of thermodynamics specifically exclude the possibility of perpetual motion or free energy. Proof of their existence would be one of the tests that would bring down the whole scientific edifice. In simplistic terms, there is no such thing as a frictionless bearing. Even the relative motion of the moon is being gradually eroded by tidal friction. Yet for seven centuries people have been coming up with scams based on this idea (see Eric's entertaining account in the Webography). Many of these frauds rely on the abuse of measurement, some of them quite sophisticated exploitation of concepts difficult for the laymen, such as reactive volt-amperes, which are falsely identified as a source of free power.

One Stanley Meyer produced a water-powered car in 1996, but was convicted of fraud by an Ohio judge. Guido Franch was convicted of fraud in 1954 and again a couple of decades later for selling the rights to distribute little green pills that would convert water into motor fuel. For them to work the pills would have to contain all the necessary potential energy, making them the most powerful chemical explosive in history. The list of frauds is almost endless, always growing, and most of them do not end in conviction. Many people still believe that these wonderful inventions were suppressed by the oil industry.

Energy is governed by our Universal Law of Stuff (q.v.). We derived this by a process of pure common sense; so this, as well as science, would fall apart if one exception were found. The tongue in cheek Laws of Thermodynamics for laymen (q.v.) nicely sum up the situation for anyone tempted by these scams. By the way, they do not only work by selling you shares or devices. One web site author has rediscovered the work in this field of Johann Bessler (1712). The punch line comes at the end of the page – How to buy my book.

5.6 Every home should have one

There is a free magazine called *Innovations* with all sorts of high-tech goodies for sale. The October 1998 edition includes such delights as the Sleep Partner bracelet that stimulates the acupuncture points in the wrist to help treat insomnia, the Rumatron magnetic kneepad for muscular weakness, pains and sprains and the NONO breakthrough in treatment for mouth ulcers and cold sores. "*For the scientifically minded, the NONO employs the bio-stimulating effects of low-intensity narrow-band light at a wavelength of precisely 660 nanometres in order to stimulate fibroblast proliferation and mediators of wound repair and inflammatory process healing. In layman's terms the NONO is designed to have beneficial effect on cold sores and mouth ulcers and accelerates healing for scarred tissue.*" If you are impressed by the precision of the number 660, it happens to be the wavelength at which the cheapest light emitting device operates and is probably winking at you from electronic devices all over your house and car.

The most irresistible product, however, appears under the headline **Fight Plaque with the 'ionic' brush:**

> *The remarkable PlusTron Toothbrush has been scientifically developed to help win the war against plaque and tartar. Used just like an ordinary toothbrush, PlusTron emits a safe, imperceptible electronic charge which changes the polarity of your teeth from negative to positive. This has the effect of releasing the grip of plaque from your teeth – the loosened plaque is then drawn towards the negatively charged brush head, leaving your teeth and gums cleaner and healthier than with normal brushing. PlusTron comes with four heads; an extra pack of four brush-heads is also available. Battery supplied.*

For the record, you can put numbers to the fields required to move particles of material about, let alone tear them away from surfaces to which they strongly adhere. The numbers are enormous, and to sustain such fields you would have to maintain very large electric currents in the highly conducting environment of your mouth. In other words you would be electrocuted and burned to death long before such a device could be effective.

5.7 Caveat Emptor

One could go on and on listing devices that are on offer to the public that could not possibly work, but it would not be a fruitful exercise. Most people get catalogues full of such offerings, through the post and in their newspapers and magazines at regular intervals. Sometimes they are mutually contradictory. High/low frequency sounds, for example, will deter moles, rodents and other pests and will/will not also deter cats and dogs and birds. A device for repelling mosquitoes was the only one in my press cutting files that actually produced a prosecution in Britain. A trading standards volunteer tested the device by putting his hand into a container holding 30 of the insects (*The Times*, June 30, 1998). He was bitten 60 times with the machine switched on and fewer times when it was switched off. Innovations (Mail Order), who sold 10,000 of the devices at £7.99 were fined £4,000. Martin Hurst, for the company, said it verified the quality of the of the product by checking that the light went on and it buzzed – anyway it was difficult to get mosquitoes in this country.

Should the State be more active in protecting people from deliberate technical fraud? In saying "Yes" I am in danger of being accused of wanting to have my cake and eat it, since I have in these pages vigorously condemned the Nanny State. There is, however, a significant difference in the two cases. Nannyism involves taking away choice from people that they can quite reasonably exercise themselves (and often doing so on grounds that are, to say the least, scientifically dubious). Technically based fraud and deception do not offer people a reasoned choice. Ordinary people cannot be expected to weave their way through the jargon that is employed by the fraudsters; weasel words like *resonance, ionisation, magnetisation* or *crystals* that sound so impressive to the untutored ear. Advertisers who use scientific language should be required by the law to make their case by scientific tests. It is simply not good enough for the State to shrug its shoulders and say "Let the buyer beware." There is a substantial difference in principle between protecting customers from buying what common sense dictates is junk and what is dressed up in florid pseudo-scientific language. We are, however, on dangerous ground: there is enough junk science around to justify banning almost everything. The acid test is in the claims of the seller. A mobile phone, for example, is sold to provide a communication service, which it does eminently well. If the same device were sold on the basis that its emanations provide a cure for arthritis that would be a different matter.

Unfortunately, there is a little flaw in the above argument. It tends to assume that science and, in particular, scientific medicine are immune to the generation of wrong numbers. We examine this proposition in the next two chapters.

Chapter 6
Wrong numbers in Science

The real purpose of scientific method is to make sure Nature hasn't misled you into thinking something you don't actually know...
One logical slip and an entire scientific edifice comes tumbling down.
One false deduction about the machine and you can get hung up indefinitely.
Robert Pirsig, Zen and the Art of Motorcycle Maintenance.

Science is not infallible. In a sense it is always erroneous. It proceeds by a process of refinement, through a cycle of hypothesis, theory and test. Some people seem to believe that Einstein proved Newton wrong, whereas he simply proved that Newton's theories dealt with the special case of low (and realistic in human experience) relative velocities. Sometimes science has not made sufficient progress to offer help in a particular case; a GP for example faced by a distressed patient with a new or indeterminate disease. It may not know the truth, but it does not lie. Statistical science can only tell the truth in a fuzzy manner, but it does tell the truth. Meanwhile, increasingly the canker of junk science is gnawing away at its bowels, undermining its authority.

It is a sad fact that scientists are among the great generators of wrong numbers and I suspect, having looked closely at only a narrow field as I shall recount later, that what has been revealed is only the tip of a very large iceberg, to coin a phrase. Let us be quite clear that there is no disgrace in a scientist simply being mistaken. As Sir Peter Medawar put it – Science, if it's to be any good, has to take the risk of being wrong. The deplorable thing is the persistence, even the growth, of *bad science, pseudo-science* and *junk science*. Why do we use these three different terms for scientific nonsense? Is there really any distinction between them?

The difference between them can be illustrated by the way they might treat any particular physical event. While I was writing this book, for example, it was announced that the planets of the solar system would become more or less aligned in May 2000. *Pseudo-science* might respond to this event with something like "This is good news for Cancerians on the cusp, who will find wealth and happiness" while *bad science* might say "the combined gravitational pull will cause major earthquakes and tidal waves across the globe". There is a fundamental difference between these two approaches. Pseudo-science not only produces gibberish but also does not bother to say how things will happen – the case of the missing mechanism. Bad science, on the other hand, offers a mechanism but it gets its sums wrong. The combined gravitational pull of all the planets is a tiny fraction of that of the moon, which creates ordinary tides (even the massive Sun has only half the effect because of the inverse square law *(q.v.)* while the nearest planet, Venus, has only 0.00005 of the effect) so any physical effect will be orders of magnitude lower than the prevailing one. *Junk science* will say something in the nature of "A study of 1,746 women in Nebraska shows that when two planets are in alignment there is a 9% increase in toe-nail cancer. We can therefore predict that when all the planets are aligned will be a 35% increase." There is no gibberish and no mechanism, just worthless statistical deduction and extrapolation – wrong numbers.

One can usually recognise junk science by its statistical fiddles. It will usually exhibit one or more of the following:

Confidence levels of less than 95%
Risk ratios of less than 2.0
Claims of proof of cause
Changes of criteria part way through the investigation
Dependence on self-reporting
Avoidance of peer review
On the rare occasions that there are all six you have superjunk.

6.1 Peer review

As we have stated above, one of the telltale signs of junk science is the avoidance of peer review. Does this mean that peer review is A Good Thing? Not entirely. It is very much like democracy – a bad system that has only one thing going for it, that all other possible systems are worse. At its worst, peer review can be grossly abused, not least in maintaining orthodoxies.

The way that peer review works is that editorial offices of scientific publications maintain a register of people who are prepared to put in a lot of work for no pay and are willing to do so promptly. Like democracy this has the demerit that the candidates are largely self-selected. The burden of work is no joke. At one time I was spending one long unpaid day every week solely on refereeing for journals and research councils. After a period of ill health I built up such a backlog that I effectively deselected myself, as people stopped sending me papers to review. I do not wish to denigrate this anonymous band of workers, without whom the whole scientific edifice would come tumbling down, but there are many unfortunate cases where the system is grossly abused. Later in this book I relate my own experiences as a young research student, but here let us consider just one case that has is peculiarly germane to our theme – AIDS.

As we have briefly observed in our discussion of scares, AIDS began as a disease among young homosexual men in Los Angeles in 1981. It spread rapidly among promiscuous homosexual men and drug addicts who shared needles. The HIV virus was identified by 1984 and pronounced by the US Secretary of State to be the sole cause of the disease. The HIV hypothesis rapidly became a dogma and all dissent began to be suppressed. For example, in 1987 Professor Peter Duesberg, a pioneer of retrovirology at the University of California, Berkley, suggested that HIV was not the cause of AIDS. His arguments were never debated and he was effectively demonised.

The case of Gordon Stewart, emeritus professor of public health at the University of Glasgow is even more to the point. He told his own story (THES, May 21, 1999) and a remarkable tale of censorship it is. In the mid-eighties Stewart was consultant to the WHO on social and behavioural aspects of communicable diseases. He was impressed with the fact that full-blown AIDS, where data were reliable, was largely confined to the original groups of homosexual men, drug users and their partners. On the basis of this hypothesis he made accurate predictions of the numbers of cases year by year. The data he offered to WHO were barred from publication.

In 1989, the Royal Society organised a symposium on epidemiology, which endorsed the prediction that there would be tens of thousands of cases in the UK by 1992. Steward pointed out that this was exactly what was **not** happening and was invited to submit a paper to the society's transactions. A four-year correspondence ensued and the paper was rejected. Among the files of correspondence were comments such as **"Why should I read a paper by someone who believes the earth is flat?"**

History has now shown that Stewart's predicted numbers were correct to within 10% of registration of AIDS cases, whereas those of the "experts" were exaggerated by orders of magnitude. Stewart's amazingly accurate predictions have effectively been censored by the politically correct orthodoxy. He has had his papers rejected by *Nature, Science*, the *New England Journal of Medicine* and the *British Medical Journal*.

As we have seen, AIDS provides a prime example of the incredible shrinking forecast. How can it be that wrong numbers triumph so dramatically over right ones? It is that unholy combination of political correctness, political bandwagons, big money (from the taxpayer of course) and media hype. The beauty of it all for the perpetrators of this travesty is that there is no comeback. No one is required to hold up their hands and say "Sorry, wrong number". People like Stewart, who could have saved the massive diversion of resources away from vital medical needs, never receive an apology, or even an acknowledgement. The in-crowd just moves on to develop the next orthodoxy.

There are many other factors at work in the suppression of science. The universities go into decline because of low funding and the comprehensivisation of the higher education system, so the best people leave for better pay and prospects. Big business takes more control of research and imposes secrecy on the researchers. Public funding of research is increasingly bureaucratised and less innovative. And so it goes on.

6.2 The scientific method

The method of science, as stodgy and grumpy as it may seem,
is far more important than the findings of science.
Carl Sagan

We have observed the characteristics of some of the perversions of science, but what are the characteristics of real science? This is, of course, a very large question and the answer cannot be easily encapsulated in a few words. The scientific method comprises a whole body of processes and procedures that have been developed and handed down over the centuries. It is like a language that has many dialects. The French have a tendency to follow the Cartesian method, in which they formally arrange and classify things before entering into experimental mode, while the English have tended to take a more picaresque approach, diving in and rummaging around to find out how things work. The recent bureaucratisation of science has turned them towards a more Gallic mode of progression. There are many great names in the history of the development of science (Grossteste, Copernicus, Keppler, Galilieo, Gilbert, Descartes, Huygens, Newton to name but a significant few) but this is not a history book. To cut a long story short, much of modern scientific method is based on a six-stage process, the last three of which involve endless repetition.

1. Observation
2. Hypothesis
3. Prediction

4. Experimental test
5. Theory
6. Back to 4.

Thus a theory normally only has scientific value if it is capable of making testable predictions. If it does not, it is not science but faith. Science has nothing to say about faith. Any person may believe in anything they wish – fairies, reincarnation, even macro-economics. What they are not entitled to do is call it science.

One of the important requirements of a scientific experiment is that it must be reproducible. We have already seen cases where claims made in one laboratory cannot be reproduced in another, in which case they are deemed to have no scientific value.

Let us look at just two of the major contributors to the development of the scientific method; one from each end of the age of reason.

6.3 Francis Bacon

> *It is useless my son, I have read Aristotle through twice and have found nothing about spots on the Sun. There are no spots on the Sun.*
> *They arise either from imperfections in your telescope or from defects in your eyes.*
> *17th Century Jesuit Professor.*

It is salutary at this stage to go back briefly to the founder of modern scientific method, if only to see how, despite all the changes that technology has brought about, little has changed in the battle for truth. Francis Bacon was born into the Elizabethan era, when English culture was going through its great flowering and set the scene for the Newtonian revolution. In many ways he was a mysterious man, and is still the subject of much rumour, good and ill (from writing the whole of Shakespeare to founding the Freemasons), but it is in his writings that we find the seeds of modern science. At that time Political Correctness took the form of Aristotelianism. The philosophical approach of Aristotle was neatly summed up by Bertrand Russel:

> *Aristotle maintained that women had fewer teeth than men; although he was married twice, it never occurred to him to verify this statement by examining his wives' mouths.*

As a prelude to setting out the basis of the scientific method, Bacon identified a number of fallacies endemic at that time (*Plus ça change!*). He called them the four idols and named them as follows:

> *1. Idols of the tribe*

> These were errors arising directly from human nature. Irrational beliefs that arise within us, because of our experience or fantasies. Modern equivalents would be Christopher Robin escaping being a bear's breakfast by avoiding cracks in the pavement or a Californian achieving immortality by avoiding contact with numerous "toxins".

2. Idols of the cave

These were errors of the individual as modified by his education or environment. Aristotle was the classical example, fabricating a whole philosophy from a few scraps of experience. The modern equivalent has been extensively detailed in this book under such headings as the missing link (*q.v.*).

3. Idols of the market place

These were errors arising from human intercourse and the peculiarities of language. A mathematician and an arts critic in conversation will be at cross-purposes if one of them uses a word such as "parameter". As we have, seen there is scope for gross misunderstanding when areas such as politics and science intersect.

4. Idols of the theatre

These arise from teachings and presentation based on philosophical systems that have minimal foundation in terms of the scientific method. TV documentaries about various scares are an apt modern illustration.

Bacon's chief contribution is his continual emphasis on observation and the experimental method. He was also the first to understand the link between science and technology.

6.4 Karl Popper

Sir Karl Raimund Popper (1902-1994) was one of the great modern philosophers of science. His most important contribution was the elaboration of idea of falsifiability. This is that, for any scientific theory to be of value, it has to make predictions that are falsifiable. If you have a theory that if A happens then B must happen and you devise and conduct an experiment to show instances of B following A you have achieved nothing. If, however, you devise an experiment that would reveal that B does not follow A, you have applied a critical test to the theory. Just one instance of B not following A will nullify the theory. In real science we have to go back to the drawing board and devise new tests to try to nullify our theories.

A related idea is the null hypothesis, which is particularly important for statistical methods. If you have a particular theory then the null hypothesis is that the theory is not true. In the scientific method we try to prove the null hypothesis. Each time we fail we add to the robustness of the theory but we do not prove it. Scientific theories can never be proved, but they can be disproved.

There are obvious difficulties with this purist approach. How, for example, do you set out to disprove Darwin's theory of evolution? It is one of the most successful theories in the whole of science. It makes successful predictions, such as the fact that every few years we need new antibiotics, insecticides and vaccines, but it is impossible to devise a test that would disprove it. One can easily get into deep philosophical arguments in this area, which would not be relevant to our present purpose. Let us be content with saying that science and the scientific method do not mean the same thing. Taxonomy (classification), for example, is an important part of botany and zoology, but it does not employ the scientific method. In general, good scientific theories are those that are falsifiable. It is a necessary but not a sufficient condition for them to be consistent with the facts. Theories that are not falsifiable have to be pretty damned good, like evolution, to be embraced by science.

6.5 Epidemiology

There is less in this than meets the eye
Talulah Bankhead

Epidemiology was once a respectable branch of science and one that saved millions of lives from diseases such as typhus and cholera; but, as the The Book of Common Prayer reminds us, "There was never anything by the wit of man so well devised, or so sure established, which in the continuance of time hath not been corrupted." Sad to say, epidemiology has now become a joke in very poor taste and epidemiologists the pariahs of science – all a bit unfair on the honest ones. How did this descent from respectability into shadiness come about? As with many ills in modern life, it is largely the product of creeping bureaucracy. Once the bureaucrats have cornered the money and power that enable research to be done, they have the patronage to demand the results that suit their purposes. The integrity of science means nothing to them, so if real science cannot give them what they want they commission bad science.

Many of the so-called "results" of epidemiology are used to create scare stories and they fill the columns of newspapers, much to the joy of editors, journalists and proprietors. The common feature is that they all involve marginal statistical evidence – you know, the sort **Headline Man** of Chapter 2 got when he was looking at no effect at all.

Mind you, the news from the epidemiologists is not all bad. According to the *N.Y. Daily News* after a nine year study of 47,000 men, Dr. Edward Giovannucci of Harvard University states that eating tomatoes is an effective way to reduce the risk of prostate cancer. His studies show that 10 servings of tomato rich foods per week reduced the risk by 45% and 4 to 7 servings reduced the risk by 20%. Who are these guys who eat 10 servings of tomato rich foods a week; or, indeed, ten servings of anything per week? I'm a bit of a tomato freak myself and during the season eat them straight off the plant from my greenhouse. Of course, I am at a disadvantage because I don't know how big a serving is – I suppose it's my narrow scientific upbringing. Perhaps I could manage the four servings, which would produce a result not quite up to the standards of **Headline Man**; but I can't help being impressed by the 47,000. That's a lot of men – and a lot of tomatoes. Say you spent 5 minutes a year on each man, interviewing him about his tomato consumption and entering the details into your computer. In an eight hour day you would get through about a hundred, assuming you did not stop for a tomato break – no, hang on a minute, I must have gone wrong somewhere. There aren't enough days in the year. No, say you sent out 47,000 questionnaires every year, you couldn't risk any lower frequency in case some of them started backsliding on their tomato consumption, which would ruin the precision of the study. To deal with each sending out, receiving and recording each questionnaire would take...

Well, in the end I gave up and tried a more modest survey in the village pub, but I couldn't find any men who ate even an average of one serving of tomato rich food every week. What's the matter with them? Don't they care about their prostates? I guess I haven't got what it takes to be an epidemiologist. I just haven't got the evangelical zeal. I was hoping to interest you in asparagus as a sure-fire cure for leukaemia, but you will have to go to Rutgers University for that.

In fact, of course, the tomato scam is just a small part of a large data dredging operation, of which more later.

6.6 A bit of probability

In order to understand just what some of these people are up to we really need to use a little elementary probability theory. Again we need no fancy theorems, just a bit of common sense. Let's start of with the tossing of a coin calling one outcome H, for heads and the other T for tails. If we toss it once we get four events to which we can assign numbers representing their probability:

Neither heads or tails	0
Heads	$\frac{1}{2}$
Tails	$\frac{1}{2}$
Either heads or tails	$\frac{1}{2}$

Thus our events H and T have evens probability, which we call $\frac{1}{2}$. Now suppose we toss the coin twice. We have four combinations that can occur: HH, HT, TH, TT. Now we have no reason to suppose that any of these is less probable than another, so we assign them equal probabilities, totalling 1, and grouping them we get the following:

Two heads	$\frac{1}{4}$
One of each	$\frac{1}{2}$
Two tails	$\frac{1}{4}$

Because "one of each" can happen in two ways we have to give each of them an equal probability and add them; so we have distributed our probabilities in the proportions 1,2,1. If we now toss the coin three times per experiment, we get four possible combinations:

Three heads	$\frac{1}{8}$
Two heads and a tail	$\frac{3}{8}$
Two tails and a head	$\frac{3}{8}$
Three tails	$\frac{1}{8}$

There are three ways of getting each two-plus-one combination: TTH, THT, HTT and HHT, HTH, THH. So we have now distributed our probabilities in the proportions 1,3,3,1 and divided by the total, as the total probability of the events has to be 1. A pattern is emerging and this pattern is known as Pascal's triangle, though it was known to Chinese algebraists in 1303. Try it for four or five and you can prove it yourself:

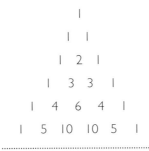

Each number is found by adding the two either side above it. Thus without any complicated calculations we can predict the probability of any outcome for any number of coin tossings.

There is, however, one other little complication we have to take account of and that is that nature does not behave as well as our coin and the probabilities of the two outcomes are not the same. If our coin was biased, the probability of a head might be 0.4 and of a tail 0.6, so wherever we see a T we put 0.4 and wherever we see an H 0.6. If the idea of a biased coins seems difficult, imagine a black bag containing four discs marked H and six discs marked T. You shake it up, make a selection, identify it then replace it. Then for two selections the probabilities are modified to:

Two heads 0.4x0.4   =   0.16
One of each 2x0.4x0.6   =   0.48
Two tails 0.6x0.6   =   0.36

So for any combination all we do is multiply the probabilities together and then multiply by the number of ways we can get that particular combination. We check our calculations by making sure the sum adds up to 1. We can do this for three, four, ten, one thousand or any number of tossings and calculate the exact probabilities. This is the **binomial distribution**; and that is all it is, common sense. Of course it is rather tiring to toss a coin one thousand times, so we get a computer to do it. The modelling in Chapter 2 was done in just this way, common sense applied over and over again. What we got from that modelling was a set of possible outcomes but, now we know the distributions, we can calculate exactly what the probability of each was. Thus when **Headline Man** looked at an event (a particular food) with probability 0.1 among 105 patients he was effectively tossing a coin 105 times that had a probability of heads 0.1 and of tails 0.9. He got the numbers of heads 10,8,13,8,14,8,18,16,8,12 but with the binomial distribution we are now in a position to say exactly how probable each was. We can plot these as a bar chart

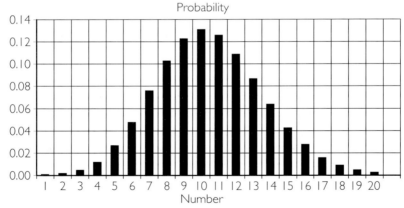

Figure 6.1 Binomial distribution for Headline Man

We could have guessed that the peak would be about 10 from the probability 0.1 multiplied by the number 105, but now we can see one reason why real scientists never accept risk ratios less than 2.0. The number 15, for example, which represents a risk ratio of 1.5 (an increase of 50%!) is one third as probable as the number 10. No wonder Headline Man is such a success and the darling of the tabloids.

Statisticians have evolved a measure of the deviation from the mean that can reasonably be expected. This is the standard deviation, usually represented by σ. It is analogous to what engineers call the radius of gyration and is a sort of average of deviation from the mean. Thus a deviation of σ would be unsurprising and likely to be caused by statistical accident. In contrast a deviation of 3σ would be unlikely (less than 1% probability). It is a common (but not always sound) practice for measurement scientists to reject observations more than 3σ away from the mean. We have already observed that the mean, or expected value, for a binomial distribution is simply obtained by multiplying the number in the sample by the probability for the event (np). Now when p is small, as is the case in the studies we are investigating it can be show that the standard deviation is approximately the square root of this number. This gives us a delightfully simple rule of thumb by which to judge the claims of junk science. If we consider σ likely deviation and 3σ to be an unlikely one, we can build up a table of expected numbers and expected deviations (i.e. statistically significant ones).

Expected number	Likely deviation (insignificant)	Unlikely deviation (significant)	% excess to be significant 10
10	3.2	9.5	95
100	10	30	30
1000	32	95	9.5
10,000	100	300	3

We can see from the histogram above and our earlier modelling that the numbers for an expectation of 10 are reasonable. Thus we only need one number, the quantity expected at random, in order to judge claims of significant percentages of increase due to some putative cause. Surprise, surprise! This is the one number they usually try to keep from us (I trawled through hundreds of junk science press cuttings I had gathered over the year without finding one example) but sometimes they inadvertently give us enough information to be able to work backwards to it. You might well think that ten is rather a small number upon which to base a discovery, but this order of magnitude is in fact extremely common in the annals of junk science.

Be warned, however, the above table can be very misleading, as it does not take into account *confounding factors*. These can be, and often are, greater sources of error than simple statistical variation. It can be roughly reckoned that statistical variation will dominate for small samples, while confounding factors dominate for larger samples. In either case the minimum risk ratio that can be **remotely** acceptable is 2.0. Incidentally, by the same reasoning, if the effect is supposed to be beneficial the maximum risk ratio **remotely** acceptable is 0.5.

A further bit of jargon we have used and need to understand is confidence as expressed in confidence levels and confidence intervals. Most serious scientists work at a confidence level of at least 95%. As we have observed, this is not particularly stringent, as it means there is a one in twenty chance of being wrong by statistical accident. A few of the more shady characters in the business have been known to work at lower confidence levels, e.g. 90%, where there is a one in ten chance of being wrong. Sometimes, as we have seen, the complement of this number, the so-called *P* value, is quoted. Thus the conventional *confidence level* of 95% would correspond to a *P* of 0.05.

Rather more information is given by the confidence interval, which we have also already met. This is a range of values of, say, a risk ratio. An example quoted in *The Risk Handbook* is a study of the putative effects of chlorinated drinking water on certain kinds of cancer. The authors quoted a risk ratio of 1.38, but the confidence interval at 95% was 1.01 to 1.87. Thus not only is the result statistically insignificant in terms of the average risk ratio, there is a one in twenty chance that it was almost as low as 1 on the results. As we have seen, thousands of Peruvians paid for this with their lives. There is a further factor of which to be aware; confidence intervals can be arrived at by rather circuitous routes (e.g. in so-called *meta-analyses*) and there are ample opportunities for less than scrupulous researchers to bend them in a desired direction. What is more, some scaremongers will go so far as only quoting the upper confidence limit (1.87 in the above example, whereas 1.01 is equally likely) and achieve their desired effect without actually telling a lie.

Even when the numbers are superficially reasonable you have to watch out for what is being slipped in under their cover. Here's a headline to conjure with – **Child allergies can be caused by margarine** (*Sunday Times*, April 12th 1998). The article concerned comments by one Dr Csaba Rusznak of the London Chest Hospital on a study carried out by Erika von Mutius of the University Children's hospital in Munich. There is sufficient detail in the article to work back and calculate the numbers involved. 2000 children between 9 and 11 were studied in 1991 in Leipzig under the old regime in 1991 and a similar number in 1996. In the meantime the families had adopted a western style of life, including among other things more pets, central heating, fitted carpets and processed foods. The number of victims of allergy in the first batch is quoted as one in fifty, that is just 40 children. In the second batch this had risen to one in 20, 100 children. Now, by our rule of thumb 60 is clearly a significant increase, a change of 20 would have been more than enough. It is clear that the western lifestyle involves a greater risk of allergy, a not unexpected conclusion, but that is not good enough for our epidemiologists. Flitting past known and notorious allergens such as animal fur and house mites, they home in on margarine, in fact one just component of it, linoleic acid. So we are asked to believe that our sixty excess children, with all their variety of diet and lifestyle, establish that this one dietary component, linoleic acid, is responsible for an increase in hay fever. As they used to say when I was a child – pull the other one it's got bells on.

The smallness of samples used by junk scientists often beggars belief. Following a headline **Mobile phone link to blood pressure rings true** (*The Times* June 19, 1998) we are told "Using a mobile phone causes a potentially dangerous increase in blood pressure." Reading further we find that the claim is based on observation of just ten volunteers at the University of Freiburg in Germany and that the rise observed is at least 5%. Staggering! The experiment that caused the Frankenstein food furore in early 1999 was based on just *five* rats.

By this stage the reader might begin to feel that the author has a bit of a bee in his bonnet. That may well be so, but it is a fact that the abuse of the statistical method is the basis of much of junk science. Its propagators rely on the fact that the lay public, and even some of their fellow scientists, do not understand the elementary statistical theory that they are subverting. It is only by understanding the implications of sample sizes, P values, confidence intervals, risk ratios and confounding factors that we can see what they are up to. However, to give the reader some relief, we turn to other aspects of bad science for the rest of this chapter.

6.7 Lysenko lives

Is there any point to which you wish to draw my attention?
To the curious incident of the dog in the night-time.
The dog did nothing in the night-time.
That was the curious incident, remarked Sherlock Holmes.
Sir Arthur Conan Doyle, Abbey Grange.

Trofim Denisovich Lysenko was a peasant plant-breeder, a protégé of Stalin, and therefore all powerful during the Stalinist period. He was a proponent of Lamarckism. Lamarck was an 18th century French scientist who developed a discredited theory of evolution long before Darwin. In this, evolution occurs because organisms can inherit traits that have been acquired by their ancestors. Thus if giraffes find they can only survive by eating leaves high up on trees, they stretch their necks to reach the leaves and this stretching and the desire to stretch gets passed on (somehow) to later generations. As a result, a species of animal that originally had short necks evolved into a species with long necks.

Thanks to Lysenko many real scientists were sent to the gulags or simply disappeared. Lysenko rose to dominance at a 1948 conference in Russia when he denounced Mendelian thought as "reactionary and decadent" and declared such thinkers to be "enemies of the Soviet people." He also announced that his speech had been approved by the Central Committee of the Communist Party. Scientists wrote public letters confessing the errors of their ways and the righteousness of the wisdom of the Party, or they were dismissed. The result was not only the decline of Soviet biology, but also its agriculture. Lysenko is still admired by creationists and oddly enough his ideas appeal to another intolerant regime, political correctness. Modern versions of his ideas appear frequently in the media.

One of the growth areas in the junk science industry is the generation of theories to account for the development of man's great brain. They appear every month or two. Now, you might wish to take a simplistic Darwinian view that a larger brain would help a tribe defeat a rival tribe, kill the men, rape the women and therefore propagate the genetic characteristics of a large brain. Likewise, an individual would be more likely to rise to the top and have his pick of the females and also be more adept at outwitting his animal prey. The invention of arms would increase the advantage of brain over brawn. It would not be appropriate, however, to accept that the early hominids could be so politically incorrect.

A typical example of the genre was reported by Nigel Hawkes **"Man's debt to spuds"** in *The Times*, April 7th 1999. It was proposed by one Dr Richard Wrangham of Harvard University (where else?). He ascribes the development to the human brain to the introduction of cooked tubers. The good doctor calculates that a diet of 60% cooked tubers and no meat boosts calorie intake by 40% over a diet of nuts, berries and raw tubers, while a 60% meat diet would only offer a 20% calorie boost. An energy rich diet would allow the teeth, jaws and gut to shrink, and the brain to grow. How proud Lysenko would have been, to say nothing of the vegetarian lobby. What would junk science do without the family *solanaceae*?

What has all this to do with measurement? It is the fact that there is none. The dozens of theories of this sort all have one characteristic – they cannot be tested. They make no predictions and therefore cannot be falsified. They all exist happily together in the literature, mutually contradictory but cosy all the same.

6.8 Con? fusion?

It is much easier to make measurements than to know
exactly what you are measuring.
J W N Sullivan.

One of the most famous cases of alleged scientific measurement error happened to involve a former colleague of mine, Martin Fleishman. I will not go into the details as it has been more than adequately covered elsewhere. Dewdney relates the story in a chapter entitled "Genie in a Jar", indeed he takes the title of his book "Yes, we have no neutrons" from the incident. Now there are whole web sites devoted to the aftermath. The argument rumbles on. Briefly, Martin and a former research student, Stanley Pons, had suddenly, and very publicly, announced that they had achieved nuclear fusion at room temperatures. If true, this rendered years of expensive research obsolete and promised the world an infinite supply of cheap, clean energy.

I remember well the breaking of the story in the Spring of 1989. I was sitting in the University Staff Club, of which I happened to be chairman at the time. There was a group of people sitting round a table, most of whom happened to be female administrators. One of them asked me what I thought of the announcement. I replied that my first instinct was that it was a load of old cobblers. "That's just professional jealousy," said another.

I was rather stung by that comment and took to trying to analyse why I had jumped to such a conclusion. In a general sense I suppose I was worried about the something-for-nothing aspect of the proposition, but I also had an uneasy feeling about the initial energy required to bring to atoms close enough together for fusion to occur. That this could be made to happen by squeezing them together in the vast emptiness of a crystal of palladium just did not seem to be reasonable.

I have to admit that my knowledge of both nuclear physics and electrochemistry is rudimentary, to say the least, but measurement is an area in which I claim a little expertise. Thus it was when I looked into the details of the claim that I was even less sanguine. It rested on the production of a small amount of excess heat in an electrolytic cell. My mind went back to my school days.

I was lucky enough, having grown up in a poor part of Tottenham, to go to one of the best schools in the world, before it was destroyed in the great comprehensivisation. I had the pupil's usual disregard for the worth of my teachers, though I now realise that they were giants in comparison with the generation that followed them, all blue jeans and glottal stops. The physics master, Mr Baxenden, was particularly eccentric and he had a number of sayings that he would repeat so often that we all groaned to hear them. How I have changed my mind since! I could write a whole book on the wisdom and application of them. One of his Baxisms (as we called them) was "The trouble with a heat balance is that it doesn't".

Perhaps the repetition of this Baxism will explain why I groaned inwardly on learning that the whole cold fusion edifice was built on the sands of a heat balance. The sheer quantity of bad measurement that occurred in the feeding frenzy following the original announcement has to be seen to be believed. One scientist withdrew his claim of observing neutrons after discovering that his sensor was affected by heat. The first thing I tell my instrumentation students, and repeat at regular intervals, is that all sensors are affected by heat and have to be compensated for it. It's mostly down to a chap called Boltzmann.

It is easy to say in hindsight that an incident is a disaster waiting to happen. Martin is one of those scientists who throw off ideas like a Roman candle; half of them crap and the other half brilliant. Another in the same mould was Denis Gabor, the inventor of holography. Such people are invaluable in the right context, a team in which the wheat can be sorted from the chaff, but get them mixed up in university administrators with large dollar signs flashing in front of their eyes and you have the recipe, as the world discovered, for disaster. See Dewdney and multitudinous web pages for details.

6.9 Misplaced Mysticism

Nothing is so firmly believed as that which we least know.
Michel de Montaigne

Frequently the principles of science are twisted to justify conclusions that are unscientific. I once heard a preacher using the principle of least time as an example of an unexplained mystery of the universe. This is the principle that a ray of light going between one point and another through varying media always takes the route that takes the least time. How does it know where it is going to end up?

Here's how my old physics master, Mr Baxenden, explained refraction. Imagine a row of soldiers marching across hard ground, when they meet a ploughed field at an oblique angle. The first soldier to meet the ploughed section slows down and then the second and so on. Because the soldiers on hard ground are moving faster the whole row turns through an angle determined by the difference in marching speeds.

The principle of least time then emerges with no mystery. Each soldier keeps marching and tries to keep parallel with his companions on either side. He arrives at any point on his route by the least time and his whole path is determined by his starting point and direction of motion. In particular, he does not know where he is going to end up.

6.10 Beyond the Fringe

People only see what they are prepared to see.
Ralph Waldo Emerson

Arthur Koestler, the author and well-known nut case, left money to endow a chair in parapsychology. Real scientists in universities around the UK fought a strong rearguard action to prevent it coming to their own institution. Those at Edinburgh University drew the short straw and found themselves saddled with the Koestler Professor of Parapsychology, one Robert Morris. Surprise, surprise! He found marginal (i.e. statistically insignificant) evidence that "something strange was going on" and Edinburgh found fame by seeing press photographs of victims sitting in its laboratories with half table tennis balls taped over their eyes purportedly receiving information from "senders". Possible mechanisms suggested involved "energy fields" and "unidentified particles" and there is possibly a genetic component to ESP. Hands up those who thought he was going to say "I have been wasting my time for the last twelve years." There is one thing you have to admire about ESP researchers, their persistence. Never, in the field of human con tricks, has so little been achieved by so many for so much effort. If you do enough trials (and twelve years is a long time) you are virtually certain to get some "startling" results.

The James Randi Foundation offers a substantial prize for the first real demonstration of the paranormal. Secured in a special account at Goldman, Sachs & Co sits one million dollars in negotiable bonds waiting to be awarded to any individual or individuals who provide evidence under proper observing conditions of any psychic, supernatural, or occult power or event.

While the million dollars sits there it is pointless to waste further ink and paper on comment.

6.11 The fragility of DNA

One of the great scientific discoveries of the twentieth century has been the existence, nature and structure of deoxyribonucleic acid. The science of genetics began in 1866 with the work of the Austrian monk Gregor Mendel, but his massive contribution was virtually ignored until 1900, when several plant breeders independently rediscovered his findings. As the century went on chromosomes and their building blocks, genes, were identified as the key to inheritance. In 1944 the Canadian bacteriologist Oswald Theodore Avery proved that deoxyribonucleic acid (DNA) performed the rôle of code bearer. He extracted DNA from one strain of bacteria and introduced it into another. The second strain not only acquired characteristics of the first but passed them on to subsequent generations. This led to furious activity and competition to break the code. By 1953, geneticists James Dewey Watson of the United States and Francis Harry Compton Crick of Great Britain had broken the code and worked out the structure of DNA. The result was a massive growth of the new science and, as is the way of the world, a massive growth of wrong numbers, mainly through the linear extrapolation fallacy and its variants (q.v.).

It turns out that DNA is extremely fragile and DNA lesions occur in cells at an astonishingly high rate (see Jaworowski in *What Risk?*). All organisms, including human beings have developed efficient methods of repairing the damage, otherwise there would be no life left on Earth. Despite this well-known fact, major scares have been generated by the fallacious extrapolation from high doses to low ones. In reality it can often be demonstrated that low doses of toxic substances and radiations can have beneficial effects (*hormesis*). Jaworowski gives examples in the case of ionising radiation where authors have ignored clear hormetic effects in their own results. The fact is that small doses of radiation are good for you. The evidence is overwhelming (over 1000 scientific publications). Even back in the Manhattan Project in 1943 it was found that animals exposed to radiation lived longer and had more offspring than uncontaminated controls. Yet all this has been ignored by the regulatory authorities. The EPA, for example, continues to pursue the chimera of radon in the home.

Another potent example is the great free radical scare. These entities are charged combinations of atoms that normally exist only for a short time. They are essential to a number of chemical processes, including those in living cells. We are told that free radicals damage DNA, presumably as a result of high dosage experiments. The result of extrapolating these results down to very small concentrations has led to a whole chain of missing links that end up with the antioxidant "breakthrough". The reasoning is that, if free radicals are bad, then anything that neutralises them must be good. The most remarkable turn round was with red wine. After years of attack by the alcohol SIFs, it was suddenly the flavour of the month, because it contains *flavinoids*, which are anti-oxidants. University groups were actually paid large sums of money by grocery firms to establish which varieties of wine were best for your health. By large sums I mean, for example, the £5 million paid by Safeways to Glasgow University to test 65 different wines. As a result Chilean Cabernet Sauvignons were held up as the best wines to stave off heart disease and cancer.

Eventually someone did some more science and found that all alcohol was beneficial (in moderate doses). Another group claimed that tea was more effective. They were generously financed by a well known tea merchant.

Our old friend the tomato, we are told, is rich in *lycopene*, which gives it the distinctive red color. Lycopene is a powerful antioxidant, more potent than *beta-carotene*. Therefore the lycopene molecule "may" act to block the initiation of the cancerous process.

6.12 Life on Mars

In August 1966 researchers from NASA and Stanford University shook the world with the announcement of possible signs of ancient microbial life in a rock from Mars that was found in the Antarctic. Since the announcement, fragments of the rock have been sliced, probed and measured by dozens of scientists in many fields, encouraged by more than $2 million in new funding from the good old American taxpayer, in an intense effort to test the extraordinary claim. Today, most scientists who have studied the samples, or studied the studies, have concluded that the various lines of evidence in the rock are either disproved, shaky or inconclusive

The rock, we are told, was blasted off the planet's surface some 16 million years ago in an asteroid impact. Well, that's a definite number. How do they know this? Damned if I know. The evidence that created all the stir was deposits of carbonate minerals within the rock's interior cracks, possibly deposited by Martian groundwater billions of years before. The evidence included wormlike shapes that resemble fossil bacteria swimming in formation, incompatible minerals mixed in a way that is sometimes associated with organic activity, carbon compounds that sometimes suggest decayed organic matter and small crystals of an iron oxide known as magnetite that, on Earth, is a by-product of bacterial activiity. Of course, only a cynic would suggest that this all had something to do with NASA's need for more funding.

6.13 Medical Science

In this chapter we have seen just a tiny, almost random, sample of the more blatant cases of abuse in science. You will find hundreds more in the Bibliography and Webography. If you look in detail at virtually any narrow field, as I recount later of my experiences as a young research student, you will find many more. Again our old friend "tip of the iceberg" comes to mind. There is nothing new in bad science. At the beginning of our century the notorious Blondlot was describing rays that did not exist, as entertainingly described by Dewdney. Nevertheless, something startling has happened to science in the second half of the twentieth century. You could not find a more cogent illustration of this than in medical science, a topic close to all our hearts and lives, which is the subject of our next chapter.

blatant cases of abuse in science. You will find hundreds more in the Bibliography and Webography. If you look in detail at virtually any narrow field, as I recount later of my experiences as a young research student, you will find many more. Again our old friend "tip of the iceberg" comes to mind. There is nothing new in bad science. At the beginning of our century the notorious Blondlot was describing rays that did not exist, as entertainingly described by Dewdney. Nevertheless, something startling has happened to science in the second half of the twentieth century. You could not find a more cogent illustration of this than in medical science, a topic close to all our hearts and lives, which is the subject of our next chapter.

Chapter 7

Trust me, I'm a doctor.

Formerly, when religion was strong and science weak, men mistook magic for medicine; now, when science is strong and religion weak, men mistake medicine for magic.
Thomas Szasz, Science and Scientism

7.1 The doctor's dilemma

I would not like it to be inferred from what follows that I am unsympathetic to the medical profession. They are in the front line, confronted by people in distress, weighed down with bureaucracy and grossly overworked. The exploitation of young house surgeons in hospitals has been one of the scandals of the age. GPs continually have to weigh probabilities on the basis of sparse and often incorrect information following a woefully inadequate training to do so. In the surgery they cannot duck the issue. When I was a child and taken to the doctor, more often than not I was given the usual pink medicine, in retrospect obviously a placebo. Modern patients are more sophisticated. They pressure doctors to give them, for example, antibiotics, the over-use of which is a time bomb that is ticking away under the foundations of world health. I do not absolve myself from the guilt. They now turn up at the surgery armed with sheets of print out from web-sites that they have part understood.

We have an odd relationship with the medical profession. We call them *doctors*, for instance, when very few of them hold a higher degree from a university. This derives from the old practice, mainly among the ignorant, of calling any learned person doctor, a word literally meaning *teacher*. Fitzgerald's Omar Khayyam, himself when young did eagerly frequent doctor and saint and heard great argument, but this did not mean that he was a valetudinarian. Our attitude to doctors has changed from the over reverential to the patronising. This can be largely attributed to the political shift in about 1982, when Shaw's dictum that "all professions are conspiracies against the laity" became a tenet of the governing philosophy. Their imperious pronouncements of former ages have been reduced to nagging, which leads tortuously to their meriting a chapter in a book on the abuse of measurement. Much of modern medicine is still little more than old wives' tales.

Some of the things doctors tell us are plain stupid. For example, in their campaigns against obesity they say it is linked to various diseases, such as arthritis, which have mentioned. I can tell them from personal experience that is obesity is a *symptom* of arthritis. Most of my life I was embarrassingly thin, but in middle age I developed arthritis in the hips, largely as the price of my earlier addiction to football and other sports. I had to give up all sport and became embarrassingly fat; it seemed almost overnight. Things improved a bit when I had a total hip replacement at a relatively early age and I became a bit more mobile, but despite a great reduction of my intake of food and drink I have to live with a certain amount of excess flesh. I do not like this, but mainly for reasons of aesthetics and comfort. One of the things I have learned from my researches for this book is that a certain amount of obesity, particularly in older people is not a health danger, despite all the propaganda.

This is one of the *confounding factors* that the epidemiologists routinely ignore. It is unlikely that everyone who adopts a sedentary life, and therefore gets fat, does so voluntarily. There may be many medical reasons, an undeclared heart problem for example, that might lead to premature death, but in the surveys the symptom becomes the cause.

Much of medical "fact" is little more than hearsay and folklore. Someone will put forward an unsubstantiated hypothesis (say that cholesterol in food clogs up the arteries) and in no time at all it is accepted dogma.

7.2 Medical Research

> *First get your facts; then you can distort them at your leisure.*
> *Mark Twain.*

There is something particularly emotive about ethical problems in medical research. We are all concerned about our own health and, of course, the number grinders add to our anxiety. In addition, vast amounts of money are floating about, provided initially by the taxpayer and the customer, but doled out in large quantities by government agencies and drug companies. At the bottom of the heap are hoards of humble academic researchers on low pay and with poor or non-existent career structures. It is all a recipe for disaster: yet, harking back to Larkin's lines that "Sexual intercourse began / In nineteen sixty three" Stephen Lock points out that misconduct in scientific research began in 1974. Stephen Lock and Frank Wells are the editors of the definitive text in this area "Fraud and Misconduct in Medical Research" to which I am much indebted and will refer to in the remainder of this chapter as F&M.

There have, of course, been many cases of dubiety in the past, such as that of Sir Cyril Burt (whose famous studies of the importance of heredity in the determination of intelligence, based on the testing of many sets of twins, were said to contain fraudulent data slanted to emphasise the rôle of heredity), but they tend to be ill-documented. The accolade for the defining event therefore is awarded to William Summerlin, who in 1974 used a felt-tip pen to fake a successful skin transplant from a black mouse to a white one. The sheer fatuity of this attempt has led to a tendency to ascribe this and many subsequent aberrations as the products of mental illness (Summerlin was given a year's sick leave on full pay). It has many of the common aspects of such cases – the initial reluctance of the scientific community to admit that a blatant fraud had occurred, leading tortuously to a denouement in which a distinguished laboratory director carried the can and had his career destroyed.

Summerlin's case did not, of course, involve wrong numbers and the abuse of measurement, but the majority do. Lock cites sixty-nine cases (in the USA, UK, Australia and Canada) in which data were fabricated or falsified: all this is in addition to a number of cases of plagiarism and forged qualifications. These were the instances that were officially reported and dealt with. Are they, to coin a phrase, the tip of an iceberg?

The most common practitioners of deceit are GPs taking part in drug trials. The motivation appears to be a mixture of two of our identified causes - indolence and avarice. GPs can make a tidy sum of extra income by taking part in trials, but the work is demanding and time-consuming. By a tidy sum I mean, for example, £700 per patient that was paid to Dr Siddiqui, a Durham Psychiatrist, back in 1988 for trials of an anti-depressant. Since he fabricated the results it was, in the time-honoured phrase, money for old rope.

7.3 Where have all the nurses gone?

'Tell me — like you done before.'
'Tell you what?'
'About the rabbits.'
Steinbeck — Of Mice and Men

Let us look a little more closely at three of the more notorious villains from Australia, which has the dubious honour of being second only to the USA in this field. For more detail read the entertaining chapter entitled "Baron Münchausen at the lab bench" by Norman Swan in F&M.

Professor Michael Briggs was the archetypal big-time scientific fraudster. Witty, larger than life, darling of the media, he was able to garner funds in great quantity from the drug companies. His publication list was long, but with hindsight meretricious rather than meritorious. When he descended upon the sleepy southern Victoria town of Geelong in 1977, the new Deakin University felt that they had acquired an international star who would put them on the map. Right from his first appearance before the appointments committee, however there were doubters as well as enthusiasts. By the early 1980s there was increasing disquiet, particularly for Dr Jim Rossiter, a local paediatrician and member of Council, and Mark Walqvist, Professor of Human Nutrition.

The evidence began to pile up. There was a letter written by Briggs to medics in the USA from a non-existent Deakin laboratory advising them to use an oral contraceptive from his largest donor. Findings presented at a Spanish conference appeared to be fabricated. Reports of disturbing conversations trickled back from overseas. Briggs was quoting remarkable numbers in his trials with unprecedented compliance: and so it went on. Some of Briggs' subjects were purported to be nurses from the Geelong Hospital, but Rossiter, who was a consultant there, could find no trace of them. Finally Rossiter was moved to check on Brigg's qualifications and found that his putative PhD from Cornell University was nothing more than a master's degree.

At this stage the story moves into a familiar authority-reaction mode. Authority split into hawks and doves. The hawkish Vice Chancellor, Professor Fred Jevons, pressed for a formal enquiry but found himself stymied by the dove-like Chancellor, Justice Austin Asche. Briggs managed to thwart the enquiry with the help of the University staff association.

Rossiter and Walqvist began to suffer in their professional and personal lives, the inevitable fate of whistle blowers, and received threatening phone calls in the middle of the night. The University was split in two. Briggs suddenly ended the process by resigning and fleeing to Marbella in Spain, but the case exploded when the London *Sunday Times* tracked him down and extracted a grudging and partial confession.

Briggs suddenly and helpfully died of "liver failure". The affair died more gradually. There was an internal report that produced a calming official account. The sufferers were the innocent, as usual. Junior colleagues of Briggs had their careers permanently damaged. Dr Jim Rossiter suffered most from maintaining his honourable stand and Professor Jevons had his name sullied by evasive manoeuvrings of the Chancellor in Council. Swan's final and trenchant judgement is that the Australian research institutions learned nothing from the whole episode.

Dr William McBride was another playboy of the southern world. Society gynaecologist, media guru, friend of prime ministers, creator of his own research institution into birth defects, he made his claim to fame as the discoverer of the dangers of thalidomide.

The first ripples on the waters of this tranquil pool were stirred by a junior scientist in McBride's institute. Phil Vardy innocently opened a letter, addressed to both of them while McBride was away, to discover that he was cited as co-author of a paper he had never heard of. It appeared to refer to a small, uncontrolled study he had carried out some months before. It related to hyoscine, a common travel sickness medication related to components of Debendox, (Benedictin in the USA). Vardy had administered this to a small group of rabbits with no significant results. In the paper, however, there were extra rabbits, controls and accounts of the section of foetuses (which were, in fact, still intact in jars). Unknown to Vardy, the paper, which claimed evidence of birth abnormalities, had already appeared as evidence in a US court case in which McBride appeared as an expert witness for litigants against the manufacturers of Benedictin.

Vardy found himself in the unenviable rôle of whistle blower. His approach to the Dean of Medicine of the University of New South Wales, having received no satisfaction from McBride, was rewarded with advice to keep his head down, since he was in a no win situation (accurate, if unethical). Seven other junior scientists backed him and insisted on an enquiry. By the time it happened Vardy had already resigned. The committee viewed the evidence and insisted that the paper be retracted. This was never done, though a small paper was published that admitted to errors in doses.

The juniors who had supported Vardy were all effectively sacked by McBride. Vardy left Sidney an embittered man with no PhD and a broken marriage. McBride continued to appear in Benedictin trials in the USA. Back home, he lied and cheated his way through various investigations, with considerable support from his friends in the media. He resigned from the foundation, only to be re-instated after a boardroom coup. Norman Swan obtained some of the original lab books from Vardy and in a radio broadcast blew the gaff.

Finally, McBride was hauled before the Medical Tribunal of New South Wales under the Medical Practitioners Act, the longest and most expensive trail of a doctor in history. He eventually admitted to publishing false and misleading data, claiming that he had done it "in the interests of humanity". He was struck off and subsequently lost an appeal. In 1994 he published his autobiography, *Killing the Messenger*, in which he put himself in the rôle of victim of the international pharmaceutical industry, which had Vardy in its pay, managing entirely to avoid the issue of deliberate fraud.

Dr Ashoka Prasad, a psychiatrist at the Health Research Institute in Melbourne, claimed to have found a remarkable correlation between schizophrenia and seasonality. An anonymous biostatistician found these data suspicious and asked the Santa Claus question "How could he have had the time to look through 16,000 records?"

There was an enquiry, but Prasad managed to stall it with the aid of an expensive firm of lawyers. It transpired that his PhD was fictitious and his DSc was from a non-existent university. His legal contortions were only thwarted by resort to the privilege of Parliament. Amazingly, "Professor" Prasad turned up after all this in Canada, where he supplied to the *British Medical Journal* a letter proving his innocence, which turned out to be from a scientist six months dead. His career ended with his being struck off in Canada, but not before he had chaired a session of the World Psychiatric Conference ad received press coverage in British Columbia as a putative nominee for the Nobel Peace Prize. There is a clear difference between this case and the other two. Prasad was a fantast and not a very bright one, who was bound to be exposed sooner rather than later. Briggs and McBride were quite different. They were powerful personalities, who had cultivated the media and the establishment and had made themselves wealthy in the process. They had cleverly and cold-bloodedly perverted science for their own gain. The one thing all three have in common is that they by-passed the peer review system, which, despite all its inadequacies, filters out much that is dross.

Is medical research more prone to fraud than other branches of science? Despite its greater financial temptations, the answer is probably no, but the consequences are such that people are more likely to look for it.

What I find most extraordinary in all this is the apparent bland indifference of the institutions to the fact that all these farceurs had laid false claims to the possession of university degrees. Keynes, quoting Lenin, remarked that "There is no subtler or surer means of overturning the existing basis of society than to debauch the currency". The currency of universities is their academic standards, as reflected in the degrees they award, which, incidentally, delineates the tragedy of what has happened to the British university system. This act alone should have meant their instant condemnation and banishment. Yet, to the end, those in authority, such as the egregious Justice Asche, prevaricated to the detriment of the righteous few.

7.4 The Mouse's Tail

Wee, sleekit, cow'rin, tim'rous beastie,
O what panic in thy breastie

I'm truly sorry man's dominion
Has broken nature's social union,
An' justifies th'ill opinion
Which makes thee startle
At me, thy poor, earth-born companion
An' fellow mortal
Robert Burns – To a mouse

One of the richest sources of wrong numbers in cancer research is tests on rodents. The strains are specially bred to be prone to cancer (Sprague-Dawley rats, Fischer rats or B6C3F1 mice). These poor creatures, genetically programmed to get cancer just by living, are subjected to enormous doses of whatever chemical the researcher pins his claim to fame on. Such research reached the height of absurdity with the attempt to generate a scare base on saccharin. Dr. Samuel Cohen, a pathologist at the University of Nebraska, later showed that the massive doses of saccharin combine with rat urine to create crystals in the bladders of the animals. Those crystals, in turn, lead to cellular changes that cause cancer. According to Cohen, human urine is vastly different from rat urine, does not react with saccharin the same way and we now have enough understanding to know that this is a rat-specific phenomenon. Yet, despite this evidence, a board of independent "experts" recommended that it remain on the US Government's list of suspected carcinogens. As *The Wall Street Journal* (June 9, 1997) put it:

The poor rodents. Alar, nitrates, aminotriazole, cyclamates, saccharin ... Short of modeling
smallsize sleepwear laced with the flame retardant tris (number 9), there is no

substance, no indignity rodents haven't endured. They can probably sprout tumors at the sight of an approaching lab coat. Maybe it's time for the animal rights lobby to take up the cause of mice and their rat cousins.

These studies are a fine example of the multiple missing link *(q.v.)* in that they rely on a hidden chain of unjustified assumptions:

1. Normal rats would react to the chemicals in the same way as the special rats.

2. Humans would react in the same way as normal rats.

3. (and worst of all) the effect of small doses can be extrapolated from massive doses.

Let us be quite clear about what we mean by massive doses. To give an example: there was a successful attempt to create a scare about the use of Alar, a growth regulator, on apple crops. To receive the equivalent dose to which the hapless rodents were subjected, you would have to drink 38,000 pints of apple juice a day. As a result of the scare, apple growers had lost an estimated $250 million and processors another $125 million, while the good old US taxpayer received a bill of $15 million for the Department of Agriculture's emergency purchase of leftover apples.

As if this were all not farcical enough, it has been shown that genetic drift has increased the tendency spontaneously to develop cancer in some of these rodents from 32% to 50%, which means that to get a statistically significant doubling they would **all** have to die. It would take a whole chapter to give an account of the flaws in this type of research. See the Junkman for copious examples. The net result is that thousands of harmless substances are branded as carcinogenic. Everything from dioxins to diesel exhaust has been shown to cause cancer in these poor creatures, and are therefore branded by the EPA as potential human carcinogens. The costs to industry, and hence the ordinary consumer, are vast. The only people who benefit are the junk scientists and their patrons, the bureaucrats.

The great irony in all this is that the scaremongers, in developing and using these rodents, have undermined their own thesis. The existence of these pathetic creatures proves that the body does not need the presence of carcinogens to develop tumours. The phenomenon is a largely genetically determined accident.

7.5 The cot-death catastrophe

One of the most tragic events in human life is the unexpected death of a baby, but this makes it fertile ground for junk science. The case of the apnoea theory for Sudden Infant Death Syndrome or SIDS is a remarkable illustration of Langmuir's Laws *(q.v.)*. The story was powerfully presented in a television documentary (BBC *Horizon* **Sudden Death**, 25th February 1999).

One Dr Alfred Steinschneider established himself as a foremost authority in this field. He developed a theory that children at risk from SIDS could be identified by bouts of apnoea, or temporary cessation of breathing. His most famous case was the poor farming family of Tim and Waneta Hoyt who lived in a remote corner of New York State. They had already lost three babies when they met the good doctor, and lost two more afterwards. Steinschneider had hypothesised as a result of their experience that the disease was hereditary. The fourth and fifth babies were taken in for lengthy monitoring by Steinschneider at his hospital. When they were returned home they soon died. Steinschneider's paper on the subject of his theory was published in the prestigious medical journal *Pediatrics*. It was a sensation and eventually received over 400 citations in the medical press. As a result a whole new industry grew up to provide breathing monitors for anxious parents. The National Institute of Child Health and Human Development gave him their biggest ever research grant: over $4.5 million dollars. He was then able to mount a massive research programme to prove his theory. Unfortunately the results were not what he expected and he began to modify his theory (as Langmuir predicted) to explain the discrepancies.

In 1982 a major cot death conference was held in the States. Professor David Southall (Paediatrician, North Staffordshire Hospital) reported on his properly conducted study. Few were prepared for his results. He had looked at the breathing patterns of over 9,000 British babies and put the results away so that they could be used later in the search for a link between apnoea and cot death. When they were taken out and compared with what actually happened to the children, there was no evidence of any link at all. The theory was unmitigated nonsense.

Texas forensic pathologist Linda Norton had worked on cases which she was convinced were multiple child murders, but found Dr Steinschneider's paper being used by the defence to claim these cases were serial cot death. She first read the paper in 1976. She said "Many of my colleagues and I have a saying that one death in the family – SIDS, two – big question mark, three – you're dealing with murder. The entire concept of multiple SIDS in the same family raised a huge red flag for me." She drew the paper to the attention of Bill Fitzpatrick (Onondaga County District Attorney, Syracuse, New York) whose reaction was "I was frankly dumbfounded that there could be a record of what appeared to be 5 murders that had been read probably by thousands and thousands of doctors throughout the world and yet no-one had ever brought it to the authorities' attention. What made me sure that these cases were murder were the circumstances of each baby's death. They were always at a particular time early in the day, they were always at a time shortly after the father had left to go to work. Every baby died while they were in the exclusive custody and control of the mother, while the last two babies spent the vast majority of their short time on earth in the presence of doctors at a hospital where nothing ever happened to them; yet both babies died the day they were released to their mother."

Twenty-two years after Dr Steinschneider had first written about her family tragedy, Waneta Hoyt was arrested for murder. On 23rd March 1994 she confessed to the killing of her five children. Once she had lawyers, she retracted her confession, so the case had to be proven. Dr Alfred Steinschneider testified that the last two children had suffered from apnoea and that it was so severe that they had needed to be resuscitated. The nurses refused to corroborate his claim and, indeed, said they had expressed fears that the children were going home to be murdered, while there was nothing in the hospital records to support him either.

Not only were the last two Hoyt babies sacrificed to this specious theory, but it was used to secure the release of many parents accused of infanticide. It is difficult for a normal person to believe in a bizarre condition called Munchausen's by Proxy, in which parents enjoy the attention they get from doctors and nurses when their children are ill, so they fake or induce symptoms in their otherwise healthy babies, but mothers have been secretly filmed doing it. Deaths from SIDS were subsequently reduced by half simply by the advice to put babies to sleep on their backs. I would never have thought of doing anything else.

7.6 The tamoxifen fiasco

Tamoxifen is a drug that was thought to be effective in the prevention of breast cancer. Trials were started in the USA by the National Cancer Institute. A British-led study, involving 4,500 women in Britain, Australia, New Zealand, Spain, Finland, Switzerland and Belgium was hoped to reach a total of 7,000 women, with the results not expected for several years. Suddenly the Americans stopped their trial and announced that tamoxifen reduced breast cancer by 45%. The scientists from the rest of the world were outraged. Not only had the Americans ruined the trial by "unblinding" it, but they demonstrated that they had been cheating all along – the whole point of a blind trial is that you do not know how the results are progressing, so that you cannot exercise any influence over them.

Officials at the Institute defended their decision to end the 6-year-old tamoxifen drug trial. According to Associated Press (April 7, 1998) Dr Leslie Ford said that the agency was following the standards set for the tamoxifen trial when it started. She said the trial was designed to ask whether tamoxifen could prevent breast cancer. "We all felt the question had been answered". She said a statistical evaluation showed that there was a clear difference in the incidence of breast cancer among women taking the drug compared to women who were not. Since half of the 13,388 women in the trial were getting placebo, the study was stopped so that all of them could benefit from the drug.

"The Americans have unblinded the trial, which means it will be unbalanced and they will not be able to answer many questions," said Dr. Trevor Powles of the Royal Marsden Hospital, London. Powles, who in 1986 headed the first pilot study on the tamoxifen's supposed anti-carcinogenic effects, added "It looks as though the benefits of the drug are likely to substantially outweigh the risks, but it was too early to be sure. Dangers include an increased risk of getting endometrial cancer – cancer of the lining of the uterus – and blood clots in the lung."

"You start to wonder what the hidden agenda is," said Michael Baum of University College Hospital, London, the other co-chairman of the British-led study. "Is the National Cancer Institute of America trying to defend its budget or something like that? And I don't think this is just sour grapes or British conservatism."

The fact is that we may now never know the benefits and dangers of this drug. Indeed, the British and Italian trials failed to confirm that there was any benefit at all. Shares in the British-based Zeneca Group, which produces the drug, rose immediately on the American announcement. It is yet another example of scientific publication by press conference. The people involved ought to be drummed out of whatever learned society they belong to.

7.7 The state of the art

Medicine, in many ways, serves as a microcosm of modern society. It has risen, through the benefits of scientific method, from a set of primitive superstitions to a modern art, in which science is combined with human instinct; only to begin a further descent into a new form of primitivism. Much of this is recorded in a book by James Le Fanu *The rise & fall of modern medicine*, in my view one of the most important books of our time. The current obsession is with the belief that the way to health is by changing lifestyle. It arises from the combination of junk science with the political correctness movement. It reaches the extremes of fatuity when the dietetic Gestapo impose their fetishes on eighty and ninety year olds in nursing homes. A ninety seven year old man was refused his usual second egg because it might raise his blood cholesterol (Letter, *The Times*, June 17th, 1999). Although he is only a statistic of one, you might think he has made his point better than the dietician has by reaching such an age.

7.8 The rise

Le Fanu's book came out just as I was putting the finishing touches to this one. As a result I immediately scrapped much of what I had to say on the subject. He said much more than I, and with much greater authority. It is sobering for me to realise just how much I have undervalued the progress of medical science in the first half of this century. Without it I would now be dead or, at best, a cripple. Le Fanu lists the twelve definitive moments of Modern Medicine (though I make it thirteen).

1949	Cortisone
1941	Penicillin
1950	Smoking as the cause of lung cancer
	Turberculosis cured with streptomycin and PAS
1952	The Copenhagen polio epidemic and the birth of intensive care
	Chlorpromazine in the treatment of schizophrenia
1955	Open heart surgery
1961	Charnley's hip replacement
1963	Kidney transplant
1964	Prevention of strokes
1971	Cure of childhood cancer
1978	First test-tube baby
1984	Heliobacter as the cause of peptic ulcer

Few could argue with this list (though I would be inclined to quibble at the use of the word "cause"). The transformation of human life and expectancy brought about by these developments would be difficult to overstate. Modern medicine had proved to be the most powerful agent for the improvement of the lot of mankind since the dawn of human history. How could such a success story ever go sour?

7.9 The watershed

Le Fanu pinpoints the exact moment when medical science reached a turning point. In this text I have made much of the sea change that occurred for science in general at the beginning of the decade of the eighties. This was the time when irrational, unscientific thought had grown to such an extent that it began to outweigh rational scientific thought. In medicine, the storm clouds had been gathering for some years. The seemingly endless supply of new drugs was beginning to fade. There were many reasons for this, not least the new regulatory regime that followed the thalidomide disaster. Technology was triumphant, including my own subject of instrumentation, which encouraged the indiscriminate use of tests. The new and highly effective procedures were now so expensive that they were an important drain on the economy. Bright young people were deserting clinical research in droves for the lucrative uplands of procedural specialities. At this critical juncture, up popped one Thomas McKeown with a specious theory that was to change the world.

McKeown was Professor of Social Medicine at Birmingham University. He published in 1979 a book called *The Role of Medicine* that launched an attack based on the view that the enormous improvement in health in the preceding century had not come about because of the progress of medical science, but by social changes. His argument was summed up in one graph – the number of deaths per million from tuberculosis against time, which showed a continuous, almost linear, fall from 4,000 per million of the population in 1838 to 350 per million in 1960. The discovery of the tubercle bacillus in 1885 and the discovery of Streptomycin in 1945 were merely points on the line that represented no discontinuity.

Before we go any further let me explain why I have used the contentious word "specious" to describe this theory. First and foremost, McKeown forgot (or, more likely, deliberately ignored) the clear evidence that it was medical intervention that had caused this decline in mortality. The tubercle bacillus propagated itself by initiating coughs and sneezes that allowed it to spread in millions of droplets. It had been well known for the whole of the period in question that the medical practice of confining consumptives to isolated sanitoria restricted the spread of the disease. The proportion of patients so segregated corresponded closely with the progressive decline of deaths. Read Le Fanu for other counter-arguments.

Despite this convincing refutation, the damage was done and McKeown had launched *The Social Theory*, that was to come to dominate health policy for the remainder of the century. In this theory there are basically two sorts of disease, *Diseases of Poverty*, which were infectious diseases like tuberculosis, and *Diseases of Affluence*, which were the new enemies of cancer, strokes and heart disease. The discovery by Sir Richard Doll and Sir Bradford Hill that cigarette smoking was a major risk factor in lung cancer was an important prop to the theory. The obvious cure was for everybody to adopt a more ascetic lifestyle.

The theory could not have been launched at a more propitious time. It was seized upon by politicians, who had become alarmed at the mounting costs of medical care and research. The environmental lobby, which had begun to burgeon from the publication of *Silent Spring* in 1962, was cock-a-hoop. An army of epidemiologists, vegetarians, dieticians, gurus, journalists, bureaucrats and many other groups came together to force the new way upon a bewildered public. As the revolutionary army grew, it split into factions, as they tend to. In particular, there were the dietary proponents, such as Sir Richard Doll, and the environmentalists, such as Professor Samuel Epstein, who shrilly traded insults (and fallacies) with each other in the science journals and the popular press. People did not know whether to put their ill health down to bacon and eggs or electricity pylons. Medical science went into rapid decline. Even the doctors were deserting in favour of the new nostrums.

Failure of the Social Theory

The Social Theory failed from the outset. Although it was based on fallacious premises, there is nothing scientifically wrong in this failure. As we have observed, science progresses by the disproving of theories. The damage was done, however, by the refusal of its priesthood to accept the fact. Epidemiology retreated into a fantasy world that owed more to Lewis Carroll than the patron of rigorous epidemiological techniques, Sir Bradford Hill. It is summed up by Feinstein's remark rendered by Le Fanu as "*The most striking feature is the insouciance with which epidemiologists announce their findings, as if they do not expect anyone to take them seriously. It would, after all, be a serious matter if drinking alcohol really **did** cause cancer.*" The epidemiologists quite happily continued to publish conflicting results in their journals. Coffee/alcohol/ pets did/did not cause bladder cancer/heart disease/multiple sclerosis and on and on. Nothing was free from suspicion and everything was fair game – hair dryers, sewing machines, radio masts, tampons, pylons – almost anything in modern life. In any serious scientific discipline just one such disagreement would cause the immediate convening of an international conference to resolve the matter one way or the other. By the early eighties, however, the Social Theory had developed a momentum of its own. Its advocates had spent enormous sums of charity and state money. To admit that they were wrong would be to destroy their own reputations and, worse, their livelihoods. There was also a strong political momentum. Organisations such as the EPA were cornering huge sums of taxpayers' money on the back of the Social Theory and were prepared to disburse it to anyone who conformed to the creed. The theory was also in tune with the *zeitgeist*. It was, indeed, very popular. Market fundamentalism, self-reliance, physical fitness abstinence from tobacco and alcohol and general asceticism were all manifestations of the faith. Business lunches were replaced by mineral water and jogging. Gurus like Sir Geoffrey Rose of the London School of Hygiene would appear on television accompanied by portentous images decreeing that "the modern British diet is killing people in their thousands from heart attacks." Freed from the complexities of scientific method anything was possible. Immortality was just around the corner. The public turned from butter to margarine, from sugar to saccharin only to find that they were (or were not) at risk from a new set of diseases. Inevitably scepticism began to set in and the faithful had to turn to new and bigger issues – the hole in the ozone layer, global warming and all the other phantasmagoria that we have covered.

7.10 The Fall

As Le Fanu aptly demonstrates, the casualty in all this was scientific medicine. Society was walking away from the real battle against disease. The momentum was lost and the incredible rate of achievement of the first half of the century almost ground to a halt. One aspect of this diversion was the new genetics, a potent cause but one not entirely relevant to our present concerns. The social theory is another matter.

It would be inappropriate to sift through all of Le Fanu's evidence, but one egregious example will suffice. Coronary heart disease was the characteristic killer of the first half of the century. From the beginning of the century it increased linearly, until it had doubled by 1950, becoming the most common cause of death in middle aged men. Then it began to decline, so that by 1980 it was almost back where it started. This is the classic pattern of an epidemic, but no agent had been identified. This left the field open to the social theorists. As was to be experienced with AIDS later, the panic that this engendered ensured that virtually any project offering a solution was guaranteed copious funding.

In the USA 360,000 men were interviewed to find the 12,000 at highest risk. Most were smokers with high blood pressure and elevated blood cholesterol level. They were then randomly assigned to an "intervention" or a "control" group. The first were harassed into conforming to the healthy living regime, while the second were left to carry on with their normal lifestyle. The first setback was that the researchers came up against the body's capacity to regulate itself. Even though the saturated fat in the diets of the intervention group were reduced by a quarter, their cholesterol level fell by only 5%. A similar WHO programme was initiated in Europe. To cut a long story short, in both studies it transpired that the intervention group were no less likely to suffer a heart attack than those who had been left to live their lives in peace. Out of every 1000 intervention subjects 41 died, while the number for the left-alone group was 40. Meanwhile the incidence of heart disease in the general population all over the western world had gone into a steep decline, while the fat intake had remained steady. By this time there were parties interested in keeping the pot boiling. Not only did the social theories have their reputations on the line, but drug companies had made a substantial wager on drugs to lower blood cholesterol. In the face of mounting conflicting evidence the social theorists just stood their ground. They simply ignored the science and made *ex cathedra* pronouncements that bacon and eggs caused heart attacks. Journalists picked it up and it became accepted that Western food caused Western disease. Opponents were dismissed as being in the pay of the food and farming industries, who were intent on peddling lethal foodstuffs to the public.

That was when the "number" became important. Everyone had to know their number (their cholesterol level). The president of the American Heart Association launched its Campaign Against Cholesterol (financed by Merck). By the mid-nineties thousands of healthy people were taking cholesterol-lowering drugs, paying out £3 billion a year to drug companies. The cholesterol bandwagon was theoretically blown apart by two observations. One was that clot-busting drugs were a much more effective treatment for victims of heart attack than cholesterol reducers. The other was that a bacterium, *chlamydia,* was found to be present in two thirds of patients who had heart attacks. Suddenly the behaviour of the phenomenon as a classical epidemic was not so strange.

It is quite clear that dietary fat has little relationship to blood cholesterol or the risk of heart disease. Indeed the whole "healthy" lifestyle, stopping smoking or starting exercise, has no effect at all. This, of course, was no impediment to the new social theorists. Diet, passive smoking and undesirable behaviour of all sorts were "proved" to cause cancer, heart disease etc. This was done by abandoning the constraints of scientific method. Sir Richard Doll, freed of the intellectual rigour imposed by his mentor, Sir Bradford Hill, published *The Causes of Cancer* claiming that he had proved that food caused a third of all cancers. As Le Fanu observes, medical advice had become indistinguishable from quackery. So it remains today. The Chief Medical Officer recommends that those wishing to avoid cancer should restrict their meat input to the equivalent of three lamb chops per day.

This has been a grossly oversimplified version of the account so eloquently presented by Le Fanu with copious references. The main import in the present context is that medical science is representative of what has happened to science in general. Insubstantial, fantastical theories are accepted by the populace, and more importantly their rulers, in the face of concerted scientific contradiction. In a couple of decades we have retreated from the peak of successful, rational science to the condition of the Roman emperors, who determined their actions from the state of the entrails of freshly slaughtered chickens.

Chapter 8

The demon drink and
the noxious weed

A preachment, dear friends, you are about to receive
On John Barleycorn, nicotine and the temptations of Eve.
"Cigareets, whuskey and wild, wild wimmin" Red Ingle

This started out being a small sub-chapter, but as I discovered more and more chicanery it grew and grew, until I had to give to give the subject a chapter of its own. The political climate is such that these matters are difficult to write about and get a fair hearing. Even some of the respectable authors and publishers I have cited in this book have shied away from these matters. This is the high ground for SIFs and bureaucrats and I fully expect to be crucified for trying to honest about it. It is also, however, the area that illustrates more than any other what this book is all about.

8.1 Health warning

Before I get into some less popular remarks let me make certain things clear.

> *Drunken driving maims, kills and should be punished savagely.*
> *Gross abuse of alcohol destroys health, wealth and happiness.*
> *Smoking cigarettes significantly increases the probability of contracting serious and fatal diseases (and also reduces the probability of some other rather nasty ones).*
> *Tobacco and alcohol are addictive to those who are susceptible.*

8.2 The things they tell us

Here are some of the many quoted statistics you might have come across:

> *300 smokers die every day.*
> *A heavy smoker is 24 times more likely to die of lung cancer.*
> *One in six fatal road accidents involves alcohol.*
> *The maximum safe intake of alcohol is 21 units per week for men and 14 units per week for women.*

Here are some of my own:

> *1000 non-smokers die every day.*
> *A heavy smoker has a more than a 99% chance of dying from something other than lung cancer.*
> *One in three fatal road accidents involves tea.*
> *The optimum intake of alcohol for maximum longevity is 21 units per week for men and 14 units per week for women.*
> *90% of statistics are made up (including this one).*

Where do they get these numbers? Alcohol Concern simply tell us that "General guidelines state...", but most of them come from official bodies, as we shall see. Various numbers pop up in the newspapers, e.g. the Wall Street Journal "One in eight smokers gets lung cancer." Journalists, of course, never reveal their sources, or 'come to that' whether they have any. The odd thing about the 300 smokers dying every day is that it is a gross underestimate. About 1800 Britons die every day and about 30% of them are smokers, so the figure should be over 500, since everybody dies.

8.3 Alcohol

I don't drink liquor. I don't like it. It makes me feel good.
Oscar Levant

Ethyl alcohol has been a companion to man since the dawn of civilisation, probably following the accidental fermentation of fruit sugars by ever-present yeasts. Like many things in life it has been simultaneously a blessing and a curse. Depending on the dose it can be a stimulant, a depressant or a deadly poison. At its worst it induces alcoholism, a physical and chemical dependence that leads to brain damage and early death. At its best it is promoter of health, a social lubricant, a great stress reliever and a source of ineffable pleasure in the form of fine wines and ales. Above a certain concentration in the blood, which varies with individuals, alcohol increases reaction time and impairs judgement, making the operators of vehicles and machinery a danger to themselves and others.

Alcohol has always been integrated into the life patterns of the Latin races, but the Anglo-Saxons were particularly prone to a degree of drunkenness (the Norman conquerors even had a term for it, *à tirelarigot*) which seems to persist to this day. At various times in history alcohol has posed serious problems. For example, gin (or mother's ruin) became a great social evil in the UK during the 18th century, when it was so cheap that one could get "drunk for a penny, dead drunk for twopence."

How can the rational being make a judgement on the use, if at all, of such a substance? Where is the information upon which to make that judgement? What are the numbers involved, and who is using them to lie to us and frighten us?

There are two critical numbers the individual needs to know about. At what level will his own health be damaged and at what level will he be a danger to others if he drives or operates machinery? The simple answer to both questions, which is immediately offered by the zealots, is zero. This is clearly wrong, as it is unquestionably proven that moderate ingestion of alcohol increases health and life expectancy. Let's face it alcohol is dangerous stuff; but so are motor cars, exotic holidays and carving knives. Used moderately, it can enhance and prolong your life. Used immoderately, it can ruin and shorten your life. From time to time, society has made efforts to come to terms with the problems generated by alcohol, the most notorious being prohibition.

On December 22, 1917, with majorities well in excess of the two-thirds requirement, Congress submitted to the states the 18th Amendment to the Constitution, which prohibited "the manufacture, sale, or transport of intoxicating liquors". This inspired an era of moral decay and social disorder, mainly because of the intolerable searches, seizures, and shootings by police who, with their token enforcement, seemed to threaten intrusion into the private lives of law-abiding people. The worst result of all was that the Mafia gained its first foothold in the United States through its bootlegging profits.

Prohibition failed as a policy. You cannot uninvent alcohol any more than you can uninvent the atom bomb or the computer virus, but unlike those products of technology it is not wholly bad.

8.4 Drinking and driving

This is an emotive subject. I can almost hear the SIFs sharpening their knives as I write. It is again one of those questions about drawing the line. The rational, scientific approach is to determine as accurately as possible where the threshold is for increased danger to others and draw the line there, but this is not good enough for the SIFs and bureaucrats.

For the sake of honesty, I have to relate my own experience in this area before I make comment. Some friends of mine own a country pub, miles from anywhere and virtually devoid of public transport. It was often my habit to take a short diversion on the way home from work for a pint and a chat. One day after leaving the pub in my car I saw two policemen running to their vehicle. They caught me up and after following for a mile or two flashed me to stop. I asked why they had stopped me and they said that my car had been seen parked outside the pub. They took down my particulars, breathalised me and when I passed asked me to wait ten minutes before they repeated the process. Again I was clear. Then they allowed me to proceed on my way but followed me all the way home. We passed through my own village, a solemn procession of two vehicles.

It is probably a sign of the times that the average reader sees no wrong in all this, but until recently, from the time of Magna Carta, it was an Englishmen's right to proceed on the Queen's highway without let or hindrance if he had committed no offence. There was a brief period when the so-called "Sus Laws" were in operation that this was not so, but those laws, which were largely aimed at young urban blacks, were withdrawn as a result of protests about individual liberty. Stop and search has since been revived. The SIFs have created such a hysterical atmosphere that it is now considered normal for parking outside a pub to be seen as antisocial behaviour.

It reminds me of a story Bernard Miles used to tell about the village busybody who chided him because his barrow was seen left outside the village pub every night. "The next night I left it outside her house – that 'ad 'er!"

It so happens that, being an academic, I had done a considerable amount of research into the threshold for increasing probability of accidents occurred. It happens to be exactly where the limit was set in the UK, 0.08%.

Let us consider one of the more thorough investigations, which was carried out by Kruger et al of the University of Wuerzberg and was a refined version of an earlier study in Grand Rapids. In view of my confessed "criminality" in this area, I will not go into my worries about the statistical methods employed, but take them at face value. At least they considered drivers who had caused an accident and tried to provide a comparison with the general driving population, which are both rare in such studies. Going straight to the conclusions drawn from this investigation, with respect to the likelihood of accidents and BAC (Blood Alcohol Content):

> If no one with a BAC greater than 0.08% drove, a reduction of 96% would result. Thus, if the legal limit for DUI (Driving Under the Influence) in Germany (0.08%) was an effective deterrent against driving with a higher BAC, this would mean that nearly everything that could be done to prevent alcohol-related accidents would have been accomplished. Thus, countermeasures directed at those persons driving at BACs higher

than 0.08% can be expected to be most effective in reducing the number of accidents attributable to the effects of alcohol. In contrast, measures directed at drivers with BACs less than 0.08% cannot be very effective. At most, 4% of all accidents attributable to the effects of alcohol may be prevented.

Note that these percentages are of the total estimated to be due to alcohol, i.e. 10.8% of all accidents. Thus if all driving at above 0.08% were prevented it is deduced that about 10% of accidents would not occur. Acting below this threshold would prevent less than 0.4%, which is well below any reasonable level of significance.

The conclusion must be that the right threshold was chosen for the original legislation and any limit set below this threshold would be purely punitive. It saves no lives and satisfies only the SIFs. The person who has a pint while driving home from work poses no extra risk to anyone. In fact the two studies mentioned above suggest that **there may be even less risk at this level than in the general population.** To be consistent the SIFs, who are addicted to marginal statistics, should insist that all drivers should have one drink before they start. Furthermore, there was a very strong relationship with age, and younger drivers were much more likely to have an accident due to alcohol than older ones. In general, the driver at the legal limit is no more likely to have an accident than one with no blood alcohol, but above this the risk begins to increase rapidly. The research can never be done again because legislation is in place in most countries that prevents comparisons being made.

Those pushing for harsher legislation should think through the consequences. Of particular concern are rural communities. These days we have, more than ever, urban governments for urban people. Country dwellers have had their railways and buses taken away by the politicians and then find themselves under attack for driving the cars upon which have become so dependent. It is all very well telling them take a taxi or share a car, but those options are pie in the sky for many country dwellers. With the decline in the church, the country pub is often the last cohesive institution in remote areas and it is heartbreaking to see some of these businesses being destroyed by policemen lurking around them in the hope of improving their computer ratings for arrests, without getting into the difficult business of catching burglars. 29% of English parishes now have no pub and the proportion is rising. A rural pub closes down almost every day. A frequent comment heard when policemen are seen skulking around country pubs is "When you get burgled they don't want to know." I am ashamed to say that I am one of the many people who no longer call in on my friends' pub – not because I would be intending to commit an offence, but because I have a horror of the harassment and intimidation that goes with it. Once the local police spy has your number in her book that is what you are in for.

I would not wish to leave this subject without a further reference to the members of pressure groups. Mothers Against Drunk Driving (MADD) began in 1980, after a 13-year-old girl was killed by a drunken driver who had several prior offences. This was an appalling crime that deserved to be punished by imprisonment with the key thrown away.

8.5 Active smoking

"It is quite a three pipe problem."
Sherlock Holmes in The red headed league by Arthur Conan Doyle

Tobacco or *nicotiana*: named after Jean Nicot who introduced it into Europe around 1560, a member of the plant family *Solanaceae* which also includes tomato and potato plants, was discovered by the early native Americans, who enjoyed the aromatic golden tobacco leaves that were indigenous to their land. It is named after Tobago, which Columbus discovered it in 1498, and according to legend, derives from the shape of a Carib pipe smoked on the island.

George Washington, as Commander of the Revolutionary Army, issued a public appeal to supply his troops. Said the future President: "If you can't send money, send tobacco." Washington was himself a tobacco farmer, as was his colleague Thomas Jefferson, the third President. In modern times the family fortune of Al Gore also came from tobacco. By 1994, tobacco was the seventh largest cash crop overall in the US, representing just under 3% of the total value for all cash crops and farm commodities. Indeed, at over $4,000 per acre, tobacco is clearly the most valuable crop – exceeding the combined dollar value per acre for such leading cash crops as wheat, hay, soybeans, corn, cotton, peanuts, and tree-nuts. Tobacco is valued by its adherents as a source of pleasure, a reliever of stress and a substantial aid to cerebration and concentration. Like most things in life it brings a mixture of risks and rewards.

I do not propose to use a lot of space on the direct effects of smoking. For the sake of argument I will take it largely as read. There have been many studies, unfortunately often obscure and contradictory, but on the whole the findings of the earliest ones, that cigarette smoking increases the probability of lung cancer by up to 24 times, appear to be largely confirmed, though results vary wildly. One contribution to the variation is probably the lack of control on data about inhaling. Cigars and pipes appear to offer a lower risk, but figures tend to be unreliable, as the data are smaller in number. Also I do not propose to say much about the giant tobacco corporations. Although their reaction to the revelation that smoking was a major risk factor in lung cancer was to launch a contemptible programme of lobbying, prevarication and obfuscation, these are not activities that are encompassed by our main theme.

It should be mentioned that cardio-vascular disease, emphysema and other cancers are also implicated, but sorting out the evidence from the dogma is far from straightforward. There are unexplained curiosities; such as the fact that the world's heaviest smoking nation, Japan, has about one sixth of the rate of coronary deaths of the UK. There is a lot of junk out there and tobacco has become a devilish icon for the political correctness movement. Not only is it a symbol of the old order, but its elimination is a manifestation of the power of the movement. The fact remains that, even if the propaganda is totally over the top, cigarette smoking is a health hazard.

So, please do not read any of this as an invitation to take up cigarette smoking. Cancer is not the only issue. You only have to look at what is claimed to be the cross-section of a heavy smoker's lung compared with a healthy one, or listen to a life-long inhaler heaving to cough up the phlegm, to appreciate the depredations that inhaled smoke inflicts on a delicate organ. This chapter is about your right to accurate information on which to base your life choices. If, given all the information, you choose a route of self-mutilation that, in this author's view, is your affair, but do not expect the SIFs and bureaucrats of the nanny state to take a similar view. I have an abhorrence of boxing and body-piercing — seeing some forms makes me feel physically ill, and they are a health hazard — but I do not arrogate to myself the right to ban them. What people do with their own bodies is their own affair, as long as they have been made aware of the consequences.

8.6 Passive smoking

I heard a female SIF say on television "We all know the effects of passive smoking". Well, I have looked at the evidence and I'm damned if I know. Let's see what the experts tell us:

Here's what the American Lung Association has to say about second hand smoke:

- *Secondhand smoke contains over 4,000 chemicals; 200 are poisons, 43 cause cancer. Secondhand smoke has been classified by the Environmental Protection Agency (EPA) as a known cause of cancer in humans (Group A carcinogen).*

- *Secondhand smoke causes lung cancer and other health problems. The EPA estimates that secondhand smoke causes approximately 3,000 lung cancer deaths in nonsmokers each year.*

- *Secondhand smoke is especially harmful in young children. EPA estimates that secondhand smoke is responsible for between 150,000 and 300,000 lower respiratory tract infections in infants and children under 18 months of age annually, resulting in between 7,500 and 15,000 hospitalizations each year.*

- *Secondhand smoke is harmful to children with asthma. The EPA estimates that between 200,000 and 1,000,000 asthmatic children have their conditions worsened by exposure to secondhand smoke.*

- *Secondhand smoke can make healthy young children (less than 18 months of age) sick; it can worsen asthma, cause pneumonia, ear infections, bronchitis, coughing, wheezing and mucus. According to the EPA, the buildup of fluid in the middle ear, which may be contributed to by secondhand smoke, is the most common cause of hospitalization of children for an operation.*

- *Individuals can take several steps to reduce their exposure to secondhand smoke, including:*

- *If you smoke, quit!*

- *Keep smoke away from you and your family by asking people not to smoke in your home.*

- *Make sure your child's day care and schools are smoke-free.*

- *Use "No Smoking" signs, buttons and stickers at home, at work, and in your car.*

- *Eat in smoke-free environments.*

- *Seek a smoke-free worksite.*

- *Support clean air laws that protect you from secondhand smoke.*

Pretty scary stuff, eh? You can find the same numbers from the same source in hundreds, possibly thousands, of different posters, books, leaflets, Web sites and Presidential Decrees. After all, the Environmental Protection Agency is a major Government agency in the largest democracy on earth. So they must know what they are talking about. On their own estimates they are responsible for regulations that cost more than $140 billion a year, roughly $100 billion spent by industry and $40 billion by the Government (i.e. the good old American taxpayer). So, how do their claims stand up under examination?

Let's make a start with the first of these numbers. 4000 chemicals: Wow! Well, in fact all plants (including *nicotiana*, the Tobacco Plant) and animals (including you) contain thousands of chemicals, many of them poisonous and carcinogenic. Consider just one of them. Many newspaper articles proclaimed the discovery of the carcinogen Benzopyrene in cigarettes, and implied that this is the cause of all lung cancer. One Dr. Huber and his colleagues inconsiderately pointed out that a room full of non smokers would have an approximate reading of 0.1 to 1.0 nanograms. A room full of smokers would have a reading of 0.3 to 1.5. Incidentally, just a reminder that a nanogram is one billionth of a gram. Human beings absorb between 1000 and 5000 nanograms of Benzopyrene every day. It is in our water, it is released whenever any organic product is burned and a grilled hamburger or steak will add another 2500 nanograms to your daily intake. Unfortunately for the health freaks vegetables like spinach and lettuce are also carriers.

By the way, talking of nasty substances, nicotine is found in many common vegetables (potatoes, tomatoes, aubergines etc.) as well as tea. It is estimated (Med Sci Res. 1993, 21, 571-572) that eating a normal portion of potatoes equals three-and-a-half hours in a smoky room.

As for substances being poisonous – as we have seen, everything is poisonous. You can kill yourself with distilled water or pure oxygen if you have enough of them. Some essential vitamins are poisonous in quite modest doses. If you read through the effusions of the health lobby you will find that they never talk about just nicotine, it is always "nicotine, a poison," As Steven Lewis puts it "One of the pillars of modern toxicology is the notion that what makes a poison is the dose." He was somewhat forestalled by the Renaissance physician Paracelsus half a millennium ago, "Nothing in itself is poison or cure, everything depends on the dosage".

Your stomach contains, along with a cocktail of enzymes, dilute hydrochloric acid, which is essential for digestion and hence life. If you were to drink concentrated hydrochloric acid you would die a horrible painful death, the lining of your mouth, oesophagus and stomach being burnt away alive by the potent chemical. As we have seen, substances are "proved" to be carcinogenic by painting them undiluted onto the shaven skins of unfortunate rodents who are bred to be susceptible to cancer (animal rights SIFs please note).

Days after I had written the above, Alistair Cooke, in his famous *Letter from America* on BBC Radio 4, remarked on one of the constituents found in bottled drinking water "Arsenic in small doses is a temporary preservative. In large doses it is a permanent one." Arsenic! There's a name to conjure with – shades of Victorian melodrama and horrible death. In fact, prior to the discovery of penicillin, it was used for the treatment of syphilis. Arsenic is only poisonous in doses over about 50 mg. In parts of Austria it is used as a tonic.

The EPA applied to environmental tobacco smoke (ETS) in 1992 a statistical technique called meta-analysis is in which the data from multiple small studies are combined to make one large study. Most respectable scientists would agree that meta-analysis might just be appropriate for combining carefully controlled animal experiments or well-regulated clinical studies, but not for epidemiology! However, our heroes did not stop there, because it still did not produce the right result.

Let us be quite clear about it, by all the conventions of science and applied statistics the EPA study established that there is no significant risk of lung cancer due to passive smoking. What did they do about it? They moved the goalposts. They actually reduced the confidence limit from the normally accepted lower limit of 95% to 90%, equivalent to doubling the chances of being wrong to one in ten. It was even worse than this, but I don't want to get too deep into details of statistical methods. There are many other serious defects in the EPA report; such as ignoring about twenty confounding factors and choosing to ignore a study that produced a statistically significant decrease in risk. So after all this knavery, what result did they come up with? They calculated a risk ratio of 1.19. In case you have forgotten our guidelines from Chapter 2, risk ratios of greater than 3 are normally considered significant. One might even stretch a point and go down to 2, but never lower. If it were not so unprincipled and shameful it would be laughable and pathetic. As a basis of comparison a report in *The Times* (Aug 6, 1997) quotes a study in Uruguay that produces a risk ratio of 4 for the development of lung cancer in heavy consumers of dairy products. That is an increase of 300%, compared with the EPA's 19%, which presumably means that some 50,000 Americans will die each year of eating rice pudding. As a correspondent in the next day's *Times* asks "What are my chances if I am regularly in the same room as rice pudding eaters?"

The most extraordinary thing about the EPA-ETS fiasco is that, after four major statistical fiddles, they could only come up with a pathetic risk ratio of 1.19. Even four out of ten of our imaginary scientists in Chapter 2 did better than that on a non-existent effect and the margarine farceur did twice as well in percentage terms.

The American Lung Association – as other groups favouring the harder new air standards – have received millions of dollars in EPA grants in recent years. Several of the scientists pushing draconian regulations have also received major EPA grants. Mind you, the ALA were pretty ungrateful recipients, since they sued their benefactors, forcing them to apply even more rigorous standards and, entirely co-incidentally, increasing their own powers significantly.

Here's a nice little quiz from the Junkman:

Below are two quotes and two epidemiological studies. Match'em and win!

> *Quote #1:*
>
> *The evidence [concerning carcinogenicity] remains statistically significant and conclusive... the summary estimate of relative risk is 1.19 (90% confidence interval 1.04-1.35)...*
>
> *Quote #2:*
>
> *Another question is whether one should consider [relative risks] on the order of 1.19 (95% confidence interval 1.05-1.35) of substantial importance. We agree that the association is rather weak, and it may be argued that a [relative risk] of 1.2 is at the limits of reliability for an epidemiologic study. Therefore, the association... is essentially a negative result.*

Study #1:

U.S. Environmental Protection Agency. 1992. Respiratory Health Effects of Passive Smoking: Lung Cancer and Other Disorders (EPA/600/6-90/006F).

Study #2:

Bleiker E.M.A. et al. 1996. Personality Factors and Breast CancerDevelopment: A Prospective Longitudinal Study. J. Natl Cancer Inst. 88:1478-82.

Occasionally, one of these so-called scientists inadvertently lets the cat out of the bag. Fortunately nothing gets past the Junkman. Here's an abbreviated version of his comments on one such paper:

> *For those who follow weak association epidemiology, Elizabeth Fontham and crew are infamous for reporting a link between environmental tobacco smoke (ETS) and lung cancer, playing a key role in EPA's ETS "risk assessment" (at least that's what EPA calls it) and OSHA's proposal to ban workplace smoking.*
>
> *They have now published a study reporting that nonsmokers with a family history of lung cancer have a 30 percent increase in lung cancer risk. Although the reported study outcome is not statistically significant (95% C.I. 0.9-1.9), the study is notable in that when Fontham and crew adjusted their data for ETS exposure, the reported risk of lung cancer did not change. Fontham's spin on this is that her reported association is strengthened by the fact that ETS-adjustment did not change the reported result.*
>
> *Could it be that Fontham and crew may have overlooked the more interesting implication of the ETS adjustment? Do the reported results show that ETS was not a risk factor for lung cancer?*
>
> *Heavens to Betsy! How could this be? In her study on ETS (JAMA 1994;271:1752-9), Fontham was sure that ETS was associated with lung cancer risk! Did Fontham really mean to report results to the contrary? Did these results slip by the authors, peer reviewers, and editors?*
>
> *Given that this new study has more cases than her ETS study, should Fontham revisit, reconsider and maybe even (gulp!) update her ETS study? Or, are Fontham and crew so brazen that they think they don't have to reconcile new results with old results?*
>
> *Will EPA and OSHA staffs have meltdowns? Did EPA adequately assess the risk of relying on Fontham's ETS study? Will OSHA propose to ban Fontham from further study of lung cancer? What about the tobacco plaintiff lawyers? What will they say? Will they sue Fontham and crew for violating their civil (suit) rights?*

Let it not be supposed that the EPA are the only group at it. Before I turn to the subject of smoking on aeroplanes, let me declare an interest. I have been twice quite seriously ill with lung infections after long distance flights, ending up attending hospital and having a cocktail of antibiotics and steroids. My GP practice told me that this had become a common phenomenon. The destination was immaterial. Only the overnight flight was significant. I consulted friends in the airline industry and learned that since the introduction of non-smoking flights the airlines had cut back on the filtering and refreshing of air, thus saving substantial amounts of money. A senior flight engineer told me that with my susceptibility I should avoid non-smoking flights. Fat chance! Unless I want to go to Japan.

Anyway, I tried to find out how the smoking ban came about. The first ban was apparently enacted by the US Congress in 1987. As an afterthought they commissioned a research report from the Department Of Transport (DOT). Now, it seems that this report has mysteriously disappeared off the face of the earth, so I reluctantly have to rely on a summary from Canada FORCES, which is a pro-smoking lobby group entirely funded by private subscription. To cut a long story short, what the DOT figures show is that there is a negligible difference in exposure between smoking and non-smoking flights. FORCES have a nice way of summing them up:

> For flight attendants working on a plane that allowed smokers, the exposure-rate, yearly, would be slightly less than one-fifth of one cigarette. And the highest possible estimate for flight attendants working full time and exclusively in the smoking rows of a plane and only and exclusively on the longest-distance flights soars all the way over to an annual exposure-rate of anywhere from 4 1/2 to 6 cigarettes. Not even the EPA in its wildest hysteria has cited the equivalent of one cigarette every 5 1/2 years (or even 5 1/2 in one) as a lung-destroying, death-dealing hazard to human health.

I wonder why the report disappeared. While we are at it, here are some more awkward numbers:

> A study by Dr. Anna Kalandik and associates at the Medical School of the University of Athens discovered that the Greek population has the highest per capita consumption of tobacco in the world and the lowest rate of lung cancer among modern nations.

> The average American life expectancy is 75 years, which surely must be a tribute to its largely smoke-free environment. Unfortunately Japan, a country notorious for its heavy addiction to the weed has the world's highest average life expectancy, at 79.1 years.

What I find particularly disturbing is the involvement of much of the American scientific establishment in all this duplicity. One of the most chilling quotes I have ever heard was attributed to an American epidemiologist "Yes, it's rotten science, but it's in a worthy cause. It will help us to get rid of cigarettes and to become a smoke-free society." It is one small step on a long and dangerous road when you start excusing bad science on "moral" grounds. Such roads can start comparatively innocuously but end in sending 6 million innocents to the gas chamber. Science cannot be moral – it is either good science or bad science. My moral might be your immoral. Neither of us has the right to subvert science in the propagation of our own morality.

On August 19, 1997, the Board of Health for Amherst, Massachusetts voted unanimously to impose a total smoking ban in the town. Its expert witness, one Dr. Michael Siegel, a professor of public health from Boston University, claimed his research shows bartenders who do not smoke inhale the equivalent of one-and-one-half or more packs of cigarettes a day and that "220 bartenders working in the state today, if they continue to work for 40 years, are going to die from their exposure." Even the EPA itself had concluded that extrapolation from atmospheric measures to cigarette-equivalents units of disease [is] a complex and potentially meaningless process. Only the Junkman refused to take this lying down and found that Seigel had but one publication in this area and that made no reference to any such calculations. In any other area of "science" Seigel would have faced disciplinary proceedings for the fraudulent fabrication of data, why not this one?

Amherst has gained a unique position in history by this act. It is the first authority since the Nazis in 1930s Germany to institute a complete ban. The Fuhrer even attributed the success of Nazism to his giving up smoking, a position he shared with Mussolini and Franco, while the effete leaders of the allies (Churchill, Stalin and Roosevelt) were all aficionados of the weed.

Lest it be thought that I am implying that this quackery is restricted to the USA, here is a headline about my own University from the *Southern Daily Echo* while I was writing this section:

CLAMPDOWN ON SMOKERS

Warden appointed to enforce hospital ban

Southampton Health Chiefs are believed to be the first in the country to appoint a smoking detective to stop people lighting up in the hospital grounds.
....
A spokesman defended the scheme and said it was something worth spending our money on.
He said: "Smokers gather at the main entrance and pollute the air for patients who are walking into the hospital. We are spending our money on tackling what is a health hazard for patients."

By the way, for "our money" read "your money". Note that the area concerned is outside the hospital in the open air, mostly notable for its heavy vehicle exhaust pollution. The same hospital was obliged to pay £40,000 compensation to a widow whose husband had been denied a heart by-pass operation on the grounds that he smoked five cigarettes a day. Was this the first execution for political incorrectness?

In March 1998, the tobacco industry were vilified for releasing a report that the WHO had commissioned and were trying to suppress (*Guardian* headline – **Foul play by tobacco firms**) to the effect that passive smoking does not cause lung cancer. You have to hand it to the SIFs; they never miss a trick. I wrote the above sentence two days after the headline came out and took a short lunch break, turning on the radio. Almost the whole of the radio news was taken up by a report from an "independent" panel of scientists revisiting the whole passive smoking fiasco. It was all there – incredibly accurate body counts for cot deaths, lung cancer and heart disease, a repetition of the mantra of indisputable scientific evidence, a professor from Bart's (of all places) to lend gravitas, a disinterested Chairman of the Parliamentary Select Committee complaining that he had to endure passive smoking outside the BBC building where the smoking refugees gather. It happened to be National No Smoking day and a white paper was in preparation from the Department of Health on the next phase of repression. It is symptomatic that putting one side of an argument at a critical time is "foul play" but not the other. By the time of the television evening news the hysteria had reached a peak. Now *one in two* smokers would die of their habit. The man from Bart's (one Professor Nicholas Ward) had more of his fifteen minutes of fame, proclaiming among other *scientific facts* that 80 cot deaths a year (one in five) were caused by passive smoking, which also increased childhood asthma by half. Terry Kavenagh, a non-smoker, was wheeled on to say that he *believed* his lung cancer was caused by other people's smoke. The risk ratio had risen to a *staggering* 1.26. What a junk-fest the press held on the following day!

The ultimate ploy occurred during these broadcasts, when a Labour MP claimed "It would be illogical for the Government to ban beef-on-the-bone and not ban smoking." There you have it, not only do two illogicalities make one logicality, but each ban, however senseless, justifies the next one. The way I see it is that the Government can pose any ban it wishes on its hapless victims. The voters have only themselves to blame. It is not, however, entitled to abuse the name of science as a justification.

In a typical scare story American viewers were subjected to an advertisement by an outfit called CDC (Center for Disease Control and Prevention). It was based on the ONLY study (Fontham *et al.*, 1991, yes her again) that showed an increased risk, and that was 34%. It ignored ELEVEN similar studies that showed no statistically significant increased risk. The advert went:

> *Did you know that if you're exposed to secondhand smoke where you work you've got a 34% greater chance of developing lung cancer? That's an awful big risk if you're not even the one doing the smoking. Tell your employer you want to work in a smoke-free environment. Then call 1-800-CDC-1311 for more information on secondhand smoke. Because we're all at risk. This message brought to you by the CDC and this station.*

The 34% chance is another way of saying the risk ratio is 1.34, i.e. insignificant in honest science. Moreover, the 34% increase, even if it were an honest figure, is on an absolute risk of the order of 0.01%, which still gives a risk of the order of 0.01%.

8.7 Benefits of smoking?

Are there any benefits of smoking? Here's Woodrow Wyatt on the subject:

> *In February, the Australian Bureau of Statistics published a national health survey taken in 1989-90. To much surprise, it revealed that, generally, the health of smokers is better than that of many former or non-smokers. Unsurprisingly, the worst sufferers from hypertension caused by stress were the ex-smokers (16.1 per cent) and the "never smoked" (13.4 per cent); the steady smokers registered 7.4 per cent.*
>
> *It is well known that smoking, particularly at work, relieves stress, and to outlaw it increases demands on hospital beds. Even the US Surgeon General, in 1964, recognised that Parkinson's disease (a degenerative disorder of the nervous system) occurred at around half the rate among smokers. In the International Journal of Epidemiology, in 1991, a review of 11 studies showed that non-smokers suffered 50 per cent more Alzheimer's disease than smokers. And researchers at Erasmus University Medical School, Rotterdam, found that more non-smokers had early-onset dementia than smokers.*
>
> *In Daily Telegraph, Dr. James Le Fanu wrote: "Smokers have a 50 per cent reduced risk of developing Alzheimer's and the more smoked, the greater the protection." The New England Journal of Medicine. in 1985, reported that endometrial cancer of the womb occurs at around 50 per cent the rate among smokers as non-smokers. Colon cancer and ulcerative colitis also seem to be about 30 and 50 per cent respectively less frequent among smokers according to articles in the Journal of the American Medical Association and in the New England Journal of Medicine, in 1981 and 1983. The American government's first Health and Nutrition Examination Survey has found that osteo-arthritis is five times less likely to occur among heavy smokers than non-smokers.*
>
> *I do not claim that smoking by those with unhealthy diets cannot activate illness (that passive smoking may be dangerous is a preposterous joke). But we urgently need a serious, objective, unbiased study of the causes of ill health, including the advantages and disadvantages of smoking, the impact of faulty diet and of inherited genes. It requires open minds, not the blinkered political correctness of the Department of*

Health. Telling the truth would unmask the futility of the many millions of pounds of public money wasted on ill thought-out and unscientifically based attacks on smoking. The campaign against smoking has certainly caused more crippling illness and premature death than if it had never begun.

Incidentally, the 50% reduction figures are just about on the borders of significance. The 30% is not, though it is almost twice as good as the EPA's risk ratio. Wyatt's point that smoking is one of a number of factors, including diet, that act together to affect the probability of cancer is unassailable. This is the only explanation for the politically embarrassing figures from Japan and Greece.

What of the 3,000 per year who were condemned to death for passive smoking? The good news is that, as far as real science is concerned, they are alive and well and living in the USA. As to the Class A Carcinogen it is Class A Hogwash.

Incidentally, there is an even more tortuous campaign to link passive smoking with heart disease. Once more real scientists are struck by the case of the missing mechanism. The question they ask is "How can passive smoking have an effect on the heart, when the exposure to this internal organ to the relevant chemicals is substantially less then the concentrations found in the daily diet?" The answer is still awaited.

I do not wish to take up any more space with the statistical nonsense that is spewed out by the anti-smoking lobby. It has already taken up far more of this book than I ever intended, and I have discarded far, far more examples than I have included. See, for example, the FOREST home page or the Junkman to learn more than you wished to know on the subject.

In case the reader has forgotten I end this chapter as I started it

Health warning
Drunken driving maims, kills and should be punished savagely.
Gross abuse of alcohol destroys health, wealth and happiness.
Smoking cigarettes significantly increases the probability of contracting serious and fatal diseases (it also reduces the probability of some other rather nasty ones).
Tobacco and alcohol are addictive to those who are susceptible.

Chapter 9

Measurement and the Law

Lawyer: one skilled in the circumvention of the law.
Ambrose Bierce

One of the most fertile grounds in which bad science can thrive is in the law courts. Things are bad enough in Britain but the state of the legal system in the USA is really quite pathological. The consequences do not only affect the citizens of that benighted nation, but have implications all over the world. American lawyers are completely out of control. They openly trawl for customers in damage suits for injuries that are imaginary or invented. Everything from passive smoking to the Presidential Penis is fair game in their search for mega-fees. It sometimes appears that Britain looks at America, determines what is worst in that society and then adopts it. The British legal system is rapidly adapting to the American model.

Here's a typical advert from a Milwaukee law firm:

FEN-PHEN/REDUX DIET DRUG USERS
Millions of dieters have been prescribed fen-phen and Redux diet drugs in the last few years. Many of those dieters are now suffering from medical problems caused by those drugs. Injuries caused by those drugs include serious heart valve damage, heart lesions and primary pulmonary hypertension (increased blood pressure in the blood vessels of the lungs). In a recent study one-third of fen-Phen/Reducx users were found to have significant heart lesions.
If you or a family member suffered from one of those injuries you may know of the link between the injury and the fen-Phen/Redox drugs. It is not too late to file a claim. This law firm is presently helping many victims, and is interested in helping many more, no matter where they live.
Call us or your family lawyer and arrange a confidential consultation to see if you can be helped. Our firm has been involved in many national product liaility litigations, including Dalkon Shield, L-Tryptophan, and breast implants
For further information, please telephone our toll free number and ask to speak to one of our registered nurses.
There is no charge for initial consultation.
Attorney's fees are only charged if you win your case.

For the record, the so-called study was based on 24 women and disease was confirmed by surgery in only five of them. The total number of prescriptions for this drug combination was about 18 million in 1996. Junk science claims that obesity causes 300,000 deaths in the USA per year. Talk about having your cake and eating it! Since the users of the drugs are by definition obese, and obesity is said to be a cause of heart disease, a correlation would be hardly astonishing. See the Junkman for a detailed account. What I find startling is the lack of professional control on these people. For example they use the clause "it is not too late". The so-called controversy was then less than a month old, for heaven's sake. If I used such tactics as a chartered engineer I would be drummed out of the profession (at least I would like to think so).

The notorious Prasad case (q.v.), in which the psychiatrist faked data on schizophrenia and seasonality, almost failed at the outset. Prasad hired a fancy law firm to represent him and they wrote individually to every member of the relevant committee threatening defamation proceedings in the Supreme Court. None withdrew and Prasad was eventually found to have faked not only his data, but also his PhD and DSc degrees, together with the claimed award of a prestigious prize. Because of the fear of defamation, the report of the investigating committee had to be released in Parliament under privilege.

Debendox, an innocent drug as far as can be determined, was taken off the market for no other reason than that it would be too costly to defend. The only evidence against it was the fabricated data from the notorious McBride (q.v.), but lawyers need little more on which to base their fee-generating schemes. Even after his exposure McBride was being paraded before the courts by unscrupulous lawyers.

The lawyers in the case of the State of Florida versus the tobacco companies made in excess of $1 billion. I loathe the use of the cliché "obscene" in relation to sums of money but I am hard put to find a better word in cases such as this. The case is a logical absurdity from the outset. If all these people died prematurely from tobacco consumption, they would not need treatment for hip replacements and all the other gerontological conditions that clog up the health industry, so would be considerably cheaper. It amounts to little less than official extortion. The tobacco companies, unloved and unlovely, are an easy target and they have made enough money from addiction to be worth plundering, but it is not they who pay – it is the smokers, who deserve to be punished for their political incorrectness.

Do not underestimate the temptation that the legal system puts before a humble scientist. I make ten times the hourly fee for quasi-legal advice that I do as an external examiner in a highly specialised subject at a leading university, and that is only a fraction of what the lawyers get.

9.1 Expert Witnesses

In a trial, barristers are playing a game in which they are making up the rules as they go. Any witness, however knowledgeable, can be trapped into appearing to talk self-contradictory nonsense. Some top barristers are very clever at mastering a brief – I have often been amazed at the rapidity with which they pick up the jargon of my own trade. They have no need to resort to the crudity of the "Have you stopped beating your wife?" variety; but the webs they weave by carefully pre-planned lines of questioning can be equally insidious. All this is done before an audience of twelve innocents, who are unused to the way the game is played and lost in any technical jargon. The expert witness who ventures into this minefield is bold indeed, but the mental equipment that some of them take along can be quite startling in its inadequacy.

I was called in as an expert witness at a late stage in a case involving industrial instrumentation. The other side had moved that their expert witness should be the only one to give evidence. I looked at his statement. It began "I studied electronics at Southampton University", and I felt there was something strange about the wording. My secretary had the job of looking after the departmental archives, so I asked her to look this chap up. It transpired that he had failed his second year examinations and had been asked to leave. This tells us something about the arrogance of lawyers. They would not allow an unqualified person to practise at the bar, so why to they take expert evidence on measurement from someone who is not a chartered engineer or physicist?

When a scientist does find himself in the position of an expert witness he could do better than to heed the advice to forensic scientists of D. H. Garrison, Jr, of whom more later

> ...one needs to stand one's ground. And this means more than just Do Not Testify To Methods Beyond Your Expertise or Do Not Selectively Ignore Evidence To The Contrary or Do Not Overstate Your Qualifications. Standing your ground means you have to get in the face of anyone who even hints at being a Bad Scientist. You'll need to gently redirect the novice Bad Scientist at times, showing him the light and letting him know where you stand. With the more seasoned advocates (prosecution OR defense), you may need a chainsaw to carve out your turf in the Bad Scientist's office, be it a medical examiner's office, a lawyer's office, or a supervisor's office. Draw the line. Let them know that Enough Is Enough. After all, you're the bastard child of both Science and Forensics. They'll expect you to be incorrigible. J. Robert Oppenheimer said it best when he wrote: "The scientist is free, and must be free to ask any question, to doubt any assertion, to seek any evidence, to correct any errors."

Perhaps the best way to illustrate the abuse of measurement that can occur in a court of law is to examine just one infamous example of cross-examination.

The Rouse Case

Norman Birkett was appearing for the prosecution in this case in 1931, in which Rouse was charged with the murder of an unknown man, whose charred remains were found in Rouse's burnt-out car in circumstances calculated to suggest that the victim was Rouse himself. Part of the evidence for the Crown was the slight but significant looseness of the joint at the tank end of the pipe leading to the petrol tank of the car.

The expert witness for the Defence was one Arthur Isaacs, a "practical engineer" claiming experience of relevant conditions, but making no claim whatever to qualification as a "theoretical engineer". He went into the witness box to say that in his experience he had found that extreme heat could cause a loosening of a nut, owing to the distortion of the metals in cooling off. The cross-examination went as follows:

> "What is the coefficient of expansion of brass?"
> "I am afraid I cannot answer that question offhand."
> "If you do not know, say so. What do I mean by the term?"
> "You want to know what is the expansion of the metal under heat?"
> "I asked you what is the coefficient of expansion of brass. Do you know what it means?"
> "Put that way, I probably do not."
> "You are an engineer."
> "I daresay I am. I am not a doctor, nor a crime investigator, nor an amateur detective. I am an engineer."
> "What is the co-efficient of expansion of brass? (pause) You do not know?"

and so on.

A number of comments can be made in respect of the abuse of measurement in court:

1. Birkett's tactics were disgraceful. A man was on trial for his life and he set out to discredit the witness in the eyes of the jury.

2. The witness was a fool to put himself in this position. He was clearly unqualified and asking to be taken apart, but the Defence was equally incompetent in selecting him. Any engineering undergraduate should have been able to deal competently with the question.

3. The question, in fact, has no answer. There is, indeed, no such thing as brass. The term applies to a whole family of alloys of copper and zinc, which can also contain aluminium, iron, manganese, nickel, tin or lead. As an undergraduate I spent many an hour peering through a microscope drawing the metallurgical structure of two-phase and three-phase brasses. They all have different coefficients of expansion. Even for one of them, if you measure the coefficient of linear thermal expansion before and after heat treatment you will get a different answer.

4. Even if there had been an answer, it is not the sort of number that even an expert would keep in his head, but he would know where to look it up.

9.2 Loads a money!

> *Dr Johnson observed that did not care to speak ill of any man behind his back, but he believed the gentleman was an* **attorney.**

Here's a news item that speaks for itself

> *February 6, 1998*

> *Web posted at: 7:55 p.m. EST (0055 GMT)*
> *MIAMI (CNN) -- A $349 million settlement of a landmark secondhand smoke lawsuit will stand, despite controversy over paying $46 million to attorneys and nothing to the flight attendant plaintiffs, a judge said in an order released Friday.*
> *The class action lawsuit, in which some 60,000 nonsmoking flight attendants sued the tobacco industry for secondhand smoke injuries, was settled last October.*
> *The lawsuit alleged the cigarette makers knew the dangers to nonsmokers of cigarette smoke, and hid the health risks from flight attendants and other Americans.*
> *It was the first class-action lawsuit against the tobacco industry -- and the first suit addressing secondhand smoke -- to go to trial.*
> *In the settlement, the tobacco industry agreed to pay $300 million to create a foundation to study the effects of cigarette smoke on flight attendants, and to pay the legal fees and expenses of the flight attendants' attorneys.*
> *While the settlement was in the flight attendants' favor, a small but growing number now feel the agreement was harmful because it left all 60,000 flight attendants out in the cold.*
> *Their frustrations center on Stanley and Susan Rosenblatt, husband and wife attorneys who represented the flight attendants and negotiated the settlement.*

Now that's real US enterprise for you! Making $46 million out of an injury whose existence is not even recognised by real science.

9.3 The litigation explosion

> *'No! someone's got to be summonsed' –*
> *So that was decided upon.*
> *Marriot Edgar – The Lion and Albert*

When I began writing this book I drafted a paragraph expressing the hope that things in Britain would never reach the pass that they have in the USA. Before I had finished it, the contingency fee system had been borrowed from America and there were advertisements on television soliciting potential compensation claimants. If you doubt the severity of this crisis read Frank Furedi's account in his essay for the Centre for Policy Studies entitled *Courting Mistrust*.

Expenditure on compensation and legal fees in Britain has reached a staggering total of the order of £5 billion. In the National Health Service alone it is £500 million. Much of this activity is invisible, as only about 2% of cases ever reach court. During the past twenty years the number of practising lawyers in Britain has more than doubled and legal fees represent about 1.3% of the Gross Domestic Product of England and Wales. The cost is borne by every citizen, but it is not just financial. There is now a culture of litigation-avoidance that diminishes the quality of life of all of us. For example, playgrounds are closed and the outdoor activities of young people are even further restricted.

In all this, of course, junk science and measurement abuse are deeply involved. The fact is that, however flimsy the case against it, a company will simply cave in rather than run the risk of adverse publicity in a court case. Here is Furedi on the subject:

> *Personal injury lawyers know that companies do not want bad publicity. Lawyers identify such concerns as weaknesses they can exploit and use to pressurise companies to settle in order to avoid litigation. This approach is promoted in a well-known handbook, Pollution & Personal Injury: Toxic Torts which offers advice to would-be litigates in the field of environmental law. The authors argue that since companies have to worry about their 'own public image' and their 'relations with the media' they may not opt pursue an avenue 'potentially fruitful in litigation' but which might harm their 'wider interest'. The authors have rightly concluded that the threat of negative publicity places pressure on organisations to come to secret out of court settlements.*

There you have it – legalised extortion. Companies come to regard it as business expense, like paying off the Mafia. They are insured and they can set it off against tax. Thus the ordinary citizen pays for all this in three different ways – in higher prices for goods, higher insurance premiums and higher taxes. The situation can only get worse. With big Governments, such as the EU, pouring out legislation on bills of rights and environmental acts, often based on pure junk, the scope for this sort of blackmail will continue to increase. Local authorities encounter ever-increasing bills and they face a £100,000 excess on their insurance policies. The tenuity of some of the claims beggars belief, like the man who won £45,000 in an out of court settlement from the Trafford Health Authority on the grounds that one of the causes of his killing his mother was the Health Authority's negligent discharge of him. Among others, sportsmen, referees, holiday tour operators and many others now have to carry insurance against potential litigation that would not have been possible a decade ago.

Solicitor Anthony Barton (*The Times* June 1, 1999) states that "In more than 80% of alleged negligence cases the only beneficiaries were lawyers and so-called experts. Scarce resources for patient care are diverted to lawyers' fees with scant regard to the merits of the claims. Most allegations of clinical negligence are not sustainable." He explains that low-value cases are settled regardless of merits to avoid irrecoverable defence costs.

9.4 Science and the law

Increasingly the law impacts on the work of scientists and rarely in a beneficial way. The influence of lawyers in the cases quoted in this book has been almost wholly malign. They have contributed nothing to the search for truth but have subtracted everything in the way of large fees. Even the attempts by scientists to regulate themselves are frequently sabotaged by lawyers. As we have seen (§7.3), in one case action had to be taken under parliamentary privilege to by-pass the manoeuvrings of the lawyers. As in any profession there will always be rogue scientists. By the nature of things honest scientists are going to be poor and the crooked ones rich, which puts the legal system on the side of the crooks. At a minimum, members of scientific disciplinary bodies should be protected by law.

It is, however, in the making of law that science is at its greatest disadvantage, even more so at the end of the millennium with a word wide trend to leftish governments. It is in the nature of left wing governments that they are more likely to yield to the influence of SIFs. By constant pressure SIFs change the intellectual climate, so that legislation once too draconian to contemplate gradually becomes acceptable. Consider the achievements of the anti-semitic SIFs in 1930s Germany. We ourselves are now experiencing a sinister new trend, enforcement by denunciation. The release of wartime records show that 28 Gestapo were able to rule a million people by the use of denunciations. Every German was at risk; even if their only offence was that they did not fit in. It is one thing to report a crime, but now people are invited to report inappropriate behaviour, like parking outside a pub. So what if it saves lives? You could save even more lives by forcing everyone to have a blood test very week.

The secretive, corrupt and undemocratic EU is one of the most potent sources of bad law based on bad science. Every year it pours out over a thousand decrees that have to be obeyed by all citizens of the benighted continent. The situation is worse for Britons, whose over-zealous officials act to impose the most onerous and detailed interpretations, whereas those in other nations are more laid back. Health and safety regulations alone have cause such a burden of bureaucracy and control that science labs are shackled, particularly in the field of education. Science, like medicine, now has to be practised defensively, for fear of litigation. In pursuit of the Holy Grail of a risk-free society, politicians, lawyers and bureaucrats are increasingly interfering in every aspect of our lives. They will not be satisfied until we are all living in cocoons from which we never emerge. Science simply cannot thrive under these conditions. It seems likely that it will have to follow manufacturing and move out of the over-regulated world into the more picaresque one.

9.5 Think of a number

The law has always been opaque and wordy, but a new trend has emerged in our number-obsessed society. Numbers put into an act of Parliament become enshrined as icons. The numbers are arrived at by a bargaining process to which the ordinary citizen is not a party. You can bet that any interested SIFs will have plenty to say and have plenty of junk science to back up their arguments. However crude and inappropriate the measurement, whether the number produced is slightly under or over the prescribed limit can have dramatic effects on individuals and corporations. Often the ordinary citizen is left floundering; being compelled to make a judgement on an arbitrary number. The legal age limit for selling politically incorrect goods to individuals is an example. The poor retailer has to make a judgement as to whether the customer is of age or not, and in an age range in which people are maturing at vastly different rates. The result is, in the very least, embarrassing all round. A customer at my local pub took great offence when she was challenged about whether she was eighteen, pointing out the she had been married for five years.

As soon as a number is put into the law, the bureaucratic machine is set in motion. There is no room for nuances. Produce a measure marginally one side of the legal limit one thing happens, marginally the other side something else happens. It all makes the bureaucrat's life so simple. As a result, the legalised number generates a great deal of activity around the limit defined by that number. People who are just above or just below or might be in the region of the number face legal harassment. Only a small fraction of activity involves the gross violators, who would formerly have been the sole target of the legal process. Once you have a number sanctified by the law and available for the use by over-zealous officials you have the recipe for all sorts of Alice in Wonderland scenarios.

Lobster quadrille

Fisherman Keith Hall from Eyemouth on the Borders was hauled up before the courts facing a potential £5,000 fine for catching undersized lobsters. Of his catch of 64 officials claimed that five were under-size – three by one millimetre and two by two millimetres. The official EU limit was that the distance from a point behind the eye to the base of the shell should be at least 85 mm. Now what kind of genius can determine the location of such points to within 1mm? Hall took his lobsters into the court and the case was thrown out.

This case is doubly illustrative, because the bureaucrats had a hidden agenda. They thought that Hall was fishing out of his proper territory and were using the law to harass him into conforming to their view of appropriate behaviour. This is a sinister and frequent motivation for measurement abuse.

9.6 Instrumentation and the law

My own subject of instrumentation has been a key provider for numbers in the law. Obvious examples are the Doppler radar and the so-called breathalyser, a crude and unselective instrument that as a measure of drunkenness is somewhat inferior to the old-fashioned chalk line. However, it produces a number, which immediately comes under pressure from SIFs who want to change it to conform to their own prejudices. The policemen are lurking outside pubs because they have been given an instrument that enables them to enhance their computer rating and league table position without too much effort. Deprived of that instrument they would have to go out and catch burglars, which is what most people would prefer them to do. Instrumentation has also had a marked effect in civil law.

Shot in the foot

One of the features of modern medical practice is that doctors come to believe that there is a technical solution to every problem. They are not unique in this. Instrumentation has become so all pervasive that everybody expects that they can pick up an appropriate probe, point it at the problem, Star Trek like, and get a number that provides the solution. The case of obstetricians is a salutary one for every professional person to read, learn and inwardly digest. Le Fanu, in his book The rise & fall of modern medicine has a section entitled Foetal Monitoring: Technology and a Shot in the Foot.

The shift from home to hospital deliveries produced a decline in maternal and infant mortality rates, but babies were still dying in labour (about 3,000 a year in the USA) while three times that number were born with severe forms of brain damage, such as cerebral palsy. Two obstetricians at the University of Southern California hypothesised, as a result of tests on monkey foetuses, that the cause was deprivation of oxygen. This led to a strong movement to introduce foetal monitoring into all obstetrics wards. Instruments were developed to produce numbers from the foetal heart rate and blood acidity that would act as an indicator of foetal distress. It was an expensive business (about $100 million in the USA) but the originators claimed that it would save about $2 billion in long term care of brain damaged children. The technology was introduced on a wide scale, despite a backlash from the natural childbirth movement. The results as time went by were less than convincing; the techniques tended to miss babies that were oxygen deprived and initiate Caesarean sections when they were vigorous. The real pay-off, as ever, was for the lawyers. Any reading in the hands of a hostile witness can be made to seem abnormal. The result was a massive drain on the resources of the medical industry.

Furedi reports that litigation bill for obstetrics alone in the UK was £264 million in the years 1995 to 1998. The costs of employing the 250 consultants necessary for the efficient running of the obstetrics service was only £15 million a year. The cost, of course, is borne by the ordinary citizen, and not just in money. The total annual cost of litigation to the British National Health Service represents about 100,000 major operations, such as hip replacements. Yet the subject is barely discussed in public and queues for operations are put down to miserly Government funding.

As we noted in the discussion of medical science, this sector is a microcosm of what is happening in science in general and, indeed, in the whole of society. Doctors, faced with a puzzling case, routinely call for a batch of tests. Laboratories full of the latest computerised instruments endlessly churn out numbers, most of which are quite irrelevant. Yet they are creating a hostage to fortune. Once the numbers are written down, they can be subpoenaed by a clever lawyer and used for fee generation. Lawyers in Britain now take about £1 billion in gross fees on personal injury cases alone.

Digital instrumentation in spreading throughout society. It is creating and memorising numbers, always with the best intentions. Your car records such things as when it last had a service and it is quite capable of recording a lot more about your driving habits. That might be useful to you, but if the numbers are subpoenaed by a ruthless lawyer to bamboozle a jury into making you fork out for large sums to those claiming some sort of injury you might not be so grateful. Every time you make a telephone call or use a computer online the entire activity can be recorded. Fine if it used for catching criminals, but that is not what most of the law is about.

On the whole I have been fortunate in largely avoiding brushes with the law. I did have one experience that is relevant to the argument. My car broke down and it was towed to the nearest garage dealing with that brand. I paid what seemed a large sum for a repair and drove away. A few days later the car broke down again and the process was repeated. After the third occasion on which this happened, I took it to my regular garage, who quickly diagnosed a faulty cold-start timer costing £20. Having already paid out several hundred pounds I refused to pay the third bill on the grounds that I had not received reasonable service. The garaged sued me in the small claims court and I had to appear in judge's chambers. The representatives of the garage failed to turn up and the claim was thrown out. A few months later I was informed that the garage had managed to get the claim reinstated. By this time I had (foolishly I know) discarded or lost some of the documentation. My opponents turned up this time, armed with computer print-outs of all the transactions. The judge agreed that I had been ill served, but on the grounds that there were *lacunae* in my evidence split the difference on the claim. Not only did I have to pay out, but I found that a county court judgement against me was recorded, which would affect my credit rating for the next six years.

This trivial case epitomises the position of the ordinary citizen in the face of computerised businesses. We know we should keep all documentation of transactions, but our houses would soon fill up with paper if we did. Lawyers thrive on documentation. Big cases in America produce roomfuls of it. Every piece of paper represents fee income. We are all forced to adopt the paper chasing habits of the lawyers.

When big businesses fight each other in court the legal bargaining and paperwork become endless. Such cases are almost invariably settled out of court. When I have been involved in such cases as an expert I have never known the nature of the final settlement and have been forbidden ever to discuss the case, or even if there was one. Naturally, because of the nature of my specialism, these cases have involved instruments, but I cannot use them to illustrate my theme except in the most general terms.

It is clear that an important and growing issue for all of us is the sheer quantity of information that we are required, often by law, to be cognisant with, and that is the theme of our next chapter.

9.7 Forensic Science

One way in which science has become an increasing presence in legal activity is in Forensic Science and Forensic Medicine in particular. Some Forensic Scientists have made such a name for themselves that their pronouncements are treated as though they were handed down in tablets of stone. Their infallibility is, to say the least, questionable, but that is another story. There is, however, no doubt that science has made a great contribution to the realisation of justice. Among the important disciplines that have made this contribution are firearm and ballistic tests, serological and toxicological tests, examination of hairs and fibres, mineralogical and metallurgical tests, DNA matching and document examination. In all this there is, of course, endless opportunity for bad science and junk science. See, for example, the entertaining essay on Bad Science by D. H. Garrison, Jr, of the Forensic Services Unit, Grand Rapids Police Department, Michigan, which has appeared in a number of Forensic newsletters and has been posted on the web. Here are just three of Garrison's more pertinent examples that happen to involve wrong numbers:

> An accident reconstruction expert with a computer is hired by a plaintiff's attorney to determine the speed of the defendant's vehicle in a two-car collision. The expert enters into his computer program the road surface drag factor, skid and yaw mark lengths, and the location and severity values of the vehicle damage. The first run of his computer program produces an unrealistically high speed for the defendant's striking vehicle. The expert changes his drag factor estimate and tries again. The figures are still outrageous. Three program runs and several crash data changes later, the speed determination begins to look more believable. The defendant's attorney begins his attack with a subpoena for all five of the expert's computer printouts.

A .223 Remington bullet is found lodged in a house several hundred feet to the rear of a rifle practice range at which .223 weapons are frequently fired. The investigators want to know if it is possible for a .223 bullet to fly the several hundred feet necessary to reach the house, so they ask a firearms examiner. The examiner, who had recently invested in a ballistics program for his home computer, took down the range, wind speed, bullet shape, temperature, barometric pressure, and several other pieces of data. His computer charted the results. Finally, his answer to the investigators was, "Yes, it's possible." As a qualified firearms examiner, he had already known that the house was well within the range of the .223 cartridge and could have given the same answer when first asked the question . . . without computation.

A city truck driver runs a stop sign and causes an accident with serious injuries. Instead of relying on the skidmarks, crush damage, and scene evidence, the city authorities order a traffic investigator to conduct acceleration tests to determine the maximum possible speed the truck could have achieved in the one-block distance leading up to the crash. Because the truck involved was disabled in the accident, the traffic investigator uses a motorcycle to run the one-block acceleration test and reports back a peak speed of 35 miles-per-hour for the city truck.

Forensic Scientists occupy a strange middle ground between the lawyers and the scientists. It is important for social good that they remember all the time that they are scientists first, with the regard for truth that this implies. Lawyers, with their disregard for the truth, find more natural allies with the bad scientists who largely inhabit this book.

9.8 Phantom Precedent

A new technique that has been refined by SIF organisations is the threat of massive potential liabilities based on legal precedent, which very effectively terrorises most organisations. I remember when the anti-smoking SIFs in my own university began their ultimately successful campaign to ban smoking on the premises, they frequently referred to the case of Veronica Bland as a legal precedent for potentially huge financial liabilities. I took the trouble to find out what this case was all about and discovered that it had never been tested in court. This woman sued her employers, Stockport Metropolitan Borough Council, in 1993 on the grounds that environmental tobacco smoke had caused her asthma. The case was settled out of court by the council's insurance company. It was not even debated in the council chamber.

Local councils are particularly prone to these settlements out of court, which are then falsely held up as examples of legal precedent. The latest wave is for stress-related injury, in which "precedent" was established by one John Walker in 1994, who received £174,000 in an out of court settlement with Northumberland County Council. In the case of Beverly Lancaster in 1999, Birmingham City Council admitted liability and paid up £67,000, so it really was a judgement rather than an out of court settlement, even though the issue was not properly tried. Unison, the public health services union, was dealing with 7,000 stress related cases by this time.

Now, I am not claiming that stress is unimportant (indeed, in the next two chapters I shall try to establish that it is has been disease of the nineties) but these councils, by insouciantly handing over their taxpayers' money, have exposed all employers to massive potential liabilities that will eventually come from the pockets of ordinary people in taxes, prices and insurance premiums. We are not talking peanuts here; on the basis of the Lancaster settlement and the Unison backlog there is a potential half billion pounds liability. It has never been debated or budgeted.

The situation is quite perverse. It is possible for a local council with a particular political agenda to collude with an employee, create a legal precedent and, in effect, decide future national policy. This is all done at the taxpayers' expense and with no regard to future expenditure commitments or general effect on the electorate. Legal precedent is like loss of virginity – after the first time it is plain sailing. It is also, of course, a nice little earner for the lawyers, but then what isn't?

9.9 Envoi

Now we all know decent, hard-working lawyers who are a boon to their clients in times of distress. Nevertheless, I would not wish to leave this topic with the case understated. The legal profession as a whole now poses the major threat to western civilisation. Imagine a situation in which a patient has a tumour that is 1% of bodyweight and rising. That is how the costs of compensation and litigation relate to GDP in Britain today. It is not just a benign tumour, i.e. non-productive, but malignant and counter-productive. Litigation avoidance has become a major preoccupation in both public and private bodies. Just as doctors are increasingly practising defensive medicine and adopting procedures they know to be unnecessary, so are Government bodies and large corporations. Just one example is the increasing employment of stress counsellors to avoid stress-related litigation. Valuable time of the best people in all these organisations is wasted in covering their backs. If the employee does something stupid, the employer is liable. They were even told that this might be the case if an employee blinded himself watching the 1999 eclipse in work time and had not been advised of the dangers by his employer. An American museum paid out because it failed to post a "mind the step" sign.

Lawyers have a stranglehold on the elected legislative chambers in Britain and the USA by sheer weight of numbers. For example, they make up 40% of the membership of Congress (217, compared with 9 engineers and no scientists). It is no coincidence that not only are the leaders of these countries lawyers, but so are their wives. Nobody is going to upset the legal apple cart. The Mafia and the Freemasons have nothing on them when it comes to protecting their own and their right to corner increasingly large proportions of the national wealth. It would be a serious matter if **any** occupational group took over Congress in this way. A congress dominated by plumbers would build a land fit for plumbers.

Again, you might think that I am straying from the point. Much of this book has been about the junk scientists and bureaucrats who produce all the wrong numbers that plague us. They, however, only make the bullets. It is the lawyers in their rôles as legislators and litigants who fire them. It is also they who nurture junk scientists and the bureaucratic institutions that sustain them. The torrent of legislation they pour out ensures that the ordinary citizen cannot make a move without some lawyer getting a rake-off. Lawyers are the latter day bounty hunters, gambling for billions of dollars and achieving wealth beyond the dreams of avarice.

Chapter 10

Information Overload:
The abuse of computers

Was there a place for him in this modern world, where systems mattered more than people?
P D James — A Certain Justice.

Fifty years before I sat down to write to begin this book I was in my first term at grammar school. I had saved my pocket money and bought my first thermionic valve (or vacuum tube) for four shillings and sixpence. Also haunting the ex War Department shops at that time were a Manchester University academic engineer, Fred Williams, and his research assistant, Tom Kilburn. They were working on a rather different scale than I, building a machine that weighed over a ton. There had been large computing machines before — first Colossus and then ENIAC — but at 11 am on Monday, June 21st, 1948, the first ever stored-program was run and, for good or ill, the world had changed forever. The predictions of Alan Turing in the 1930s were at last coming to fruition. Effete Britain, exhausted by war and run by innumerate toffs, was not the place for its many inventions of that time to be developed and it was largely left to America to exploit this extraordinary breakthrough. IBM bought the rights to Williams and Kilburn's storage tube and a period of computing hegemony began. By the time I graduated in 1959 I was working on the commercial offspring of the Manchester computer, Pegasus. In what seems no time at all, Intel had developed the first microprocessor and IBM, almost by accident, used it to create the Personal Computer. The PC took on a life of its own and society began to change with a rapidity never before experienced. Data gathering became cheap and powerful with awesome consequences.

A few years ago there was an article in the press about a village policeman who had been reprimanded because the computer showed that he had not made enough arrests. Anyone who lives in a village knows that the last thing village policing is about is making arrests. Once people start gathering data, however, they have to use it. If you make arrests the criterion for success, you automatically get arrests, but you don't get good policing. The police are out harassing motorists while burglars, who are difficult to catch, are given free reign. The police become less and less popular and crime flourishes. This is another illustration of the fact that you cannot measure anything without changing it, and the measure you use controls the nature of the change. Patrick Moore, for example, after the fourth burglary at his home, criticised police for spending too much time on bullying motorists rather than trying to catch criminals (*The Times*, Nov 26, 98).

In 1996 I received a letter from the Automobile Association pointing out that my wife and I had called them out five times in one year. They enclosed a leaflet called "Fair Play" which spoke of a few irresponsible individuals who did not maintain their vehicles and had more than their fair share of the service, so in future would be asked to pay more. I wrote back telling them that I considered it a disgraceful letter to send to people who had been paying subscriptions for thirty years and had hardly used their services at all. They wrote back saying that they would reconsider "my case" in the light of future calls. This incident is typical of the sort of activity that is generated by computer records and the computer's ability to sort them. If they had kept full records they would have known that the calls were nothing to do with poor maintenance. We had each managed to run a battery down by leaving the lights on (I did not know that it was possible in my Saab) and the other three occasions were due to an intermittent fault that an incompetent garage had difficulty in diagnosing. Their heavy-handedness and their computer lost two long-standing customers. They have since sent me about thirty letters explaining the benefits of membership.

10.1   Information received

Imagine a school with children that can read or write, but with teachers who cannot, and you have a metaphor of the Information Age in which we live.
Peter Cochrane

One of the most perceptive commentaries on the information eruption was written by Richard Chartres, Bishop of London ("Beware of repetitive soul strain – too much data can be dangerous" *The Times* 30th December, 97). He tellingly quotes the existentialist Kierkegaard – "The evil in the daily press consists in its being calculated to make, if possible, the passing moment a thousand or ten thousand times more important than it really is. But all moral elevation consists first and foremost in being weaned from the momentary." Chartres adds that the hyping of the momentary has the paradoxical and anaesthetising effect of reducing everything to a dull average. How perceptive that is! Wading through the mountain of press cuttings that I gathered for the purposes of producing this book proved to be a profoundly joyless and brain-numbing experience.

What has all this to do with measurement? Well, information is one of the things that engineers try to measure, and very important it is too. They can determine how much information can pass through a communication channel (in bits/sec) or what average amount of information there is in each symbol (the Source Entropy, about 3 bits/symbol in what you are reading at the moment). What they cannot do is determine the value of such information in human terms (e.g. scientific, artistic or entertainment). Engineering and science cannot make a value judgement on a particular sentence; so, for example, the following are all equally valid in information theory terms:

To be, or not to be: that is the question;
The Gostak distims the Doshes.
Thousands to die from eating margarine (used in cakes).
We hold these truths to be self-evident, that all men are created equal,........

It is clear to the impartial observer that information overload is a massive cause of sickness in our society. There are, of course, some modern occupations for which it is even worse than it is for the rest of us. People who are trapped behind screens in dealing rooms of banks are burnt out at an age when most of us are just beginning to develop our careers. While I was writing this in late August 1997, there were three near misses at Heathrow in one week. The pressure on air traffic controllers is intolerable. Their whole working day is haunted by the thousands of human lives in their hands and they are bombarded by numbers from a system that is in permanent overload. The proposal to turn such activity over to a profit making business is, and I cannot avoid the cliché, an obscenity.

Much of the information that bombards us is plain silly. This is partly due to the activities of scumbag lawyers in the US, where doing something stupid can be lucrative for both client and attorney. But it does not wholly explain the prevalence and sheer imbecility of everyday announcements. The *New Scientist* collected a few gems:

> On an insect spray – Kills all insects. Warning, harmful to bees.
> On a pre-packed dessert – Do not turn upside down (on the box bottom).
> On a sleeping draught – May cause drowsiness.
> On an electric iron – Do not iron clothes on body.
> On a child's cough syrup – Do not drive car or operate machinery. Avoid alcohol.
> On a packet of peanuts – Contains nuts.
> On an airline pack of peanuts – Open packet. Eat contents.
> On a chain saw – Do not try to stop chain with hands.

It is not just the receipt of information that induces stress. The demand for it is equally onerous. I have seen it in my University colleagues under the impact of four different kinds of audit that did not even exist five years before.

10.2 Computer modelling

> *The purpose of computing is insight, not numbers.*
> R W Hamming.

I have been modelling with computers all my professional life. I began with a simple analogue computer and over the years proceeded through the whole range of digital computers to the point where I have more computing power under my desk than the whole world had when I started. Computer modelling is an immensely powerful tool. It can also be an immensely misleading one. A computer model is only as good as the assumptions on which it is based. More and more, as I wade through the chronicles of junk science, I am horrified at what I see. When you are faced with a system as complex as, say, the global climate, even the most powerful computers are woefully inadequate to model them, but this is not the greatest limitation. The ultimate barrier is our own understanding of the systems themselves. Many of today's modellers are like the man in the parable who built his house upon sand.

Another way in which computer modelling can be misleading is when it is carried out in isolation from all other relevant spheres. A cogent example of this occurs in transport modelling. It is easy to show that road traffic can be reduced simply by allowing traffic jams to occur, a fact lauded by anti-car SIFs, but if you ignore the impact of the loss of millions of man-hours on the real economy you are bound to arrive at a destructive conclusion. Of course, it is crazy to be so dependent on one mode of transport; but after the 1963 report by Lord Beeching there was a drastic reduction of branch lines, irreversibly removing about three-quarters of the rail mileage; demonstrating once again the old adage that if you ask a silly question you get a silly answer. This is another area in which politicians fail to look at the real economy (except, of course, when they are in opposition). They rejoice in a strong currency sustained by licensed usury through high interest rates, neglecting the decline in the manufacturing and farming industries. One of the Thatcherite myths that still persists is the delusion that a modern nation can thrive on service industries alone – taking in each other's washing. The trouble is that the bills for such policies do not come in for decades, when the politicians that adopt them are long gone.

Computer modelling is one of the most powerful tools now available to science. Unfortunately, it also one of the most abused. I have been obliged to use some computer modelling to illustrate some of the essential points in this book, but I have been careful to make clear from first principles the basis on which it was done. When I pick up an article on computer modelling today I find that I am given no idea of the basic premises on which it operates. Yet such methods, as we have seen, have been used to generate some of the major scares in our scare-ridden age.

10.3 Computer packages

One of the characteristic features of the computerisation of science is the reliance on computer packages. As I found out the hard way using Microsoft Office to compile this book, software does not do all that it claims. About a quarter of the time taken to write this book was absorbed by Mr Gates' bugs. Many researchers plug numbers into such packages, particularly statistical ones, in complete ignorance of what the internal churning involves, and publish the results. One of the epidemiological studies on alcohol that I quote later uses a computer package to verify the significance of its conclusions. Among the items the results are adjusted for are age, smoking, cholesterol, body mass index, social class, father's social class, education, car use, deprivation, angina, ischaema on cardiogram, forced expiratory volume, bronchitis and diastolic blood pressure. It is a major, and in my view totally unjustified, assumption that the effects of each of these items is known; but it is worse than that. Deprivation, for example, was ascertained from the postcode. I know multimillionaires and relative paupers who share the same postcode; what is their level of deprivation? It might not matter if we were dealing here with a large sample, but as we shall see, when you look into the studies, the crucial categories on whom the conclusions (and the consequent media scare) rely contain such small numbers of people (single figures) that they cannot possibly bear the weight of all that data manipulation.

10.4 The rise of Spreadsheet Man

> *Out of the air a voice without face*
> *Proved by statistics that some cause was just*
> *In tones as dry and level as the place.*
> *W H Auden Shield of Achilles*

The spreadsheet is the apotheosis of management by computer. It is a wonderful array of numbers set out in rows and columns. It is infinitely malleable. It obfuscates while pretending to clarify.

In olden times the governing classes ruled by the sword. Now they have beaten their swords into spreadsheets. Spreadsheets are a magnificent thing –you can make them prove anything you like. I have done it often enough myself, usually to extract money from the system. The beauty of the spreadsheet is that you decide what you want the bottom line to be and you juggle about with all the other figures until you get it. All the entries in the rows and columns are related to each other by a means that you predetermine, so if you change one, many of the others change automatically. In no time at all you have created something very obscure and very impressive.

When we see the results, such as great institutions diminished beyond recognition, it is not at all obvious that it was all done by numbers. How did these Gurus of the Spreadsheet achieve their dominance? As with most great societal changes it took the form of a political movement. These things tend to show up in exaggerated form in Britain, where the peculiarities of the electoral system tend to produce governments with large majorities on very small swings of votes. One of the few accurate chroniclers of what was going on was Anatole Kaletsky in his *Sunday Telegraph* column. Here is a shortened extract from his swan song article in May 1994:

Major's Maoists are the enemies of conservatism

Britain is now ruled by a band of fanatical believers in Mao Tse-tung's permanent revolution. By calling themselves Conservatives or management consultants, by wearing grey suits or old fashioned hairdos, by spouting verbiage about "basic values" or implementing full-cost accounting, these zealots have managed to disguise their true intention, which is nothing less than the overthrow of the British state through the destruction of all traditional institutions, and their replacement by a market-place of 55 million buyers and sellers, who devote themselves exclusively to trading not only in goods, services or assets, but also in education, culture, loyalties and even human lives.

The ascendancy of the blue-rinse Maoists can be traced back to the end of the Thatcher Government, a turning point that can be dated precisely to the middle of 1988. That extraordinary year of hubris saw an outburst of revolution unparalleled in Britain since 1945. To name but a few examples there was Nigel Lawson's last "great reforming budget", there was legislation to introduce the poll tax, there was the White Paper to turn the National Health Service over to the accountants, there was the decision to privatise water. Finally there was the White Paper on Broadcasting, which proudly laid out the plan to wreck commercial television and to encourage John Birt's ritual disembowelment of the BBC".

Keletsky goes on to mention various fiascos that resulted from this dogma: the ITV franchise auction, the Channel Tunnel, the National Lottery and so on. Finally he gives a chilling account of a discussion with a Government Minister, which confirms that all this was not an accident of inertia but the result of a commitment to permanent revolution:

"This man calls himself a Conservative. Yet there seems to be nothing he wants to conserve...

This then was the background that left the field wide open to The Managers – that huge anonymous presence that devote their lives to playing with numbers. To them numbers are all: nothing else matters, people, institutions or traditions. Under a Government calling itself Conservative we had fallen into a trap made of the fundamental myth of Socialism – that everything can be planned. Real Conservatives know that tradition is society's way of arriving at solutions to problems that cannot be planned out of existence.

10.5 A last straw

And why does England thus persecute the votaries of her science?
Why does she depress them to the level of her hewers of wood and
drawers of water? It is because science flatters no courtiers, mingles in
no political strife.
Sir David Brewster, 1830.

Allow me to indulge myself by devoting a paragraph to the event that was a defining moment for me personally. It was the point at which I finally ceased, in my mind, to be a member of the Conservative Party. As a local Party Chairman I had spent much of the eighties acting the reverse Canute, trying to stem ebbing the tide of membership. I was often surprised at the variety of events quoted by departing members as the last straw, and I suppose that many people would be surprise at mine. It was, in fact, hearing of the proposed closure of Bart's Hospital, the bald realisation that seven hundred years of tradition meant nothing to our leaders; all that mattered was the numbers. I had clung on through all the indignities and offences of the eighties, even to the point of going through the motions of defending the poll tax, but this one incident brought home that the sheer obnoxious philistinism of the party was now too blatant to be bearable. It was not simply that I had once had the privilege of working closely with the Bart's researchers and had gloried in being part of the tradition. I think I had more in mind the words of historical writers (such as the inspiring Canadian, Thomas B Costain) that the foundation of the great hospitals (St Thomas's, St Bartholomew's, Bethlehem, Bridewell and Christ's) together with the great universities marked the end of the Dark Ages. It seemed to me that we were entering a new Dark Age, but the invader sweeping aside the culture was from the inside, Spreadsheet Man.

Bart's had meant something special to me. It represented the endurance of institutions through history, the integrity and disinterest of science, sheer quality and honesty of intellect and devotion to truth and the well-being of mankind. How my illusions were to be shattered when it later took up junk science!

10.6 Downsizing

An expert is a person who avoids small error as he sweeps
on to the grand fallacy.
Benjamin Stolberg

The world-wide wave of downsizing was the great triumph of Spreadsheet Man. The gurus stalked the world preaching the benefits of humanectomy. Numbers were used to prove that people could be disposed of. Throughout industry, and even in academia, fewer and fewer people were doing more and more work. Stress levels were rising. Then the bills started to come in. Boeing, for example, found itself paying out over a billion dollars to try to bring its workforce back into operational condition. In my capacity as an industrial consultant I visited many smaller instrumentation companies who had forgotten how their own products work. Many of them had mortgaged their future, and even their very existence, sold their birthright for a message of pottiness. There is a class of businessmen who are known in the trade as "three-year men". They come into a company as chief executive and for the first year they blame everything on the previous regime. In the second year they institute a programme of redundancies and cutbacks on investment, such as research and development. In the third year they produce marvellous figures for profitability. They then leave for another similar post elsewhere. Their CVs show that they have turned round company after company and the numbers prove it. In reality they have left behind a trail of burned out hulks.

10.7 The dumbing down of BBC Radio 4

Today, thanks to technological progress, the radio and television, to which we devote so many of our leisure hours once spent listening to parlour chatter and parlour music, have succeeded in lifting the manufacture of banality out of the sphere of handicraft and placed it in that of a major industry.
Nathalie Sarraute, Times Literary Supplement, June 1960.

There is an Americanism that summarises the changes in our culture in the late twentieth century – dumbing down. This ugly locution for an ugly phenomenon aptly describes what is happening right across the cultural spectrum – media, education, politics etc. Whether it is an inevitable consequence of the universal franchise is a moot point, but numbers come into it. Obviously part of the pressure comes from individuals out to make a quick buck, media moguls and the like, but it is more widespread than that. The mere fact that numbers are gathered at all, and computer technology makes that all too easy, creates a climate in which the so-called lowest common denominator dominates. Audience research figures are a case in point. Because one person actually listening to a concert or discussion is valued less than two who are using a radio station as aural wallpaper, there is more and more emphasis on the undemanding in broadcasting schedules. That this should be happening in public service broadcasting is evidence that this is more than just a commercial phenomenon. It is part of a general pattern of change, that can be described by other ugly words – bureaucratisation, centralisation and so on. For all the anxiety that is expressed about the loss of bio-diversity, there seems to be little concern about the diminution of human diversity.

A tragedy for British culture as great as the assault on the universities was the decline of the BBC in general and its radio service in particular, which was once the envy of the world. Again it is intriguing that numbers play such a large part, especially in their use to justify the depredations of the dominant management caste. In this case the numbers come from computers operated by RAJAR, the radio industry's audience research agency.

The writing was on the wall when the delightful homely names (Home Service, Light Programme and Third Programme) were replaced by clinical numbers (Radios One, Two, Three and Four). Suddenly we had generic radio. Gone were the days when the likes of Peter Ustinov would pop up on the Third Programme and entrance us with some of the best comedy around. The great delight of BBC radio was serendipity, now it was replaced by a mind-numbing predictability. Symbolically, radio programmes were exiled to a ghetto at the back of the BBC's journal, *The Radio Times.*

The pronouncements of the various controllers who came and went at the BBC reminded me of a lesson in human nature that I received as an apprentice. I had just joined a new shop and my first job was to help turn all the benches through 90°, so that they were parallel with the short wall rather than the long one. I asked why we were doing this.

"Because there is a new foreman"

"What has that got to do with it?"

"Well, whenever we have a new foreman the first thing they do is to order the benches turned. They have to make an impact. It's the way the Suits operate. We have turned the benches six times since I came here."

In the case of Radio 4, Spreadsheet Man had an identity, which is unusual, one James Boyle. However, he went about his task in the usual bureaucratic way. Stage one – discover a crisis. The technique used in this case was the isolated statistic (q.v.). It was the fact that over 600,000 listeners deserted the channel when the morning topical show *Today* had finished. Now, being a naïf adherent of the channel, I fail to be surprised at this. After all, it is then 9 am when most of us have to bend to our daily tasks. But to Spreadsheet Man it is a disaster that can only be averted by hacking away up to twenty favourite programmes.

Brenda Maddox (remember her from our Good Guy list?) was one of the few journalists to question this reasoning. She pointed out (**Spin doctors take the knife to a healthy Radio 4**, *The Times*, July 30, 1997) that the figures actually tell a completely different story. Radio 4 had steadily raised its share of the national audience to an astonishing figure of 10.2% at a time when the number of rivals was increasing beyond all reason. She also inconveniently reminded us that a similar exercise in 1993 to "improve" Radio 1 had caused a massive and permanent loss of audience. Hutber strikes again.

Consider just one programme that was wantonly destroyed in this exercise, *Week Ending*. This was a late night show (remember the excuse for its execution was an audience drop at 9 am) that was a breeding ground for the best in comedy on radio and television. Milly Jenkins, in an obituary notice (*The Times* August 20, 1997) listed some of the talented writers and comedians who had served their apprenticeship with this programme (Tracey Ullman, David Jason, Griff Rhys Jones, and many, many others). The number of comedy TV programmes that can trace their descent from this programme form a roll call of all that is best in British TV, but none of that will deflect the bureaucrats of the Birtish Broadcasting Corporation in their quest for change and blandness.

Scarcely a month had gone by before Spreadsheet Man was at it again – this time furnished with a completely different excuse, the cost of digital TV (and what a cock-up that was, but that is another story). Sir Christopher Bland (Oh, what a Dickensian aptness to that name!) set about the extinction of the rich and various news programming and its replacement by a uniform service across the whole empire. On this occasion, oddly enough, the funeral bakemeats did not coldly furnish the tables for the next celebration, since he suffered a defeat (temporary, of course) at the hands of the entrenched interests within the organisation. Nevertheless, the march of the Brutish Broadcasting Corporation towards uniform inanity proceeded with only minor hiccups.

It was all very typical that politicians who, with a few honourable exceptions, had blithely ignored this dismemberment of one of the jewels in the crown of British culture, only reacted when they suddenly discovered that it involved the banishment of *Today in Parliament* to the scheduling ghetto of Radio 4 long wave and the elimination of other parliamentary coverage. On March 12th, 1998 they held a short debate on the subject. Members from all parts of the House expressed their outrage. The view was summed up by David Winnick MP "……..if they show contempt for Parliament itself, inevitably we will show contempt for those who at present control the BBC."

If you think that I am straying from the subject, remember that all this stemmed from numbers produced by the computers of RAJAR. I would also remind you of remarks in the introduction about the mode of progression of bureaucrats. I realise as I write this that, after a lifetime of addiction to it, I have barely listened to Radio Four for several months. I did not stop for any deliberate reason, but simply drifted away. The controllers, however, have made it clear that they do not want me in their audience. If you are old, intelligent or have an attention span longer than ten minutes, you are deemed not to deserve a radio network of your own.

The pay-off for this act of desecration was not long in coming. Within four months a total of nearly 800,000 people had deserted the Radio 4 audience, about 15% of the total (*The Sunday Times*, August 23, 1998). By any measure that is a startling achievement. The *World at One* news slot, which had been slashed in order to fit in a new series of quiz shows of mind-boggling banality, suffered a 20% loss of audience. James Boyle was not available for comment, but a BBC spokesman said "We are playing a long game." Oh yeah? Of course, many of the deserters would later drift back. They had no where else to go.

The scale of the disaster was elaborated in an article in the *Sunday Times* (November 1st, 1998) **Boyle set to go in Radio 4 disaster**. Even *The Archers*, the world's longest running soap opera had lost more than a third of its audience. The quality quiz shows (*Mastermind, Round Britain Quiz, Brain of Britain*) had lost thirty percent. It was all summed up by Radio 4's brilliant veteran writer and broadcaster, Barry Took, "Radio 4's problems are just a symptom of the crisis at the BBC on which the old programme-making culture has been destroyed." Change a few words and he could be talking about the universities.

I thought that I had completed this section, scaled the depths to which a once noble institution could be brought by Spreadsheet Man. Far from it! It was subsequently revealed (*The Sunday Times*, December 13, 1998) that the BBC had drawn up a hit list of some 60 programmes. What was the basis of this? Believe it or not, it was the cost per listener in pence of each programme. Long standing items under threat such as Alistair Cooke's *Letter from America*, perhaps one of the finest contributions in the history of broadcasting and an invaluable piece of living history, were estimated to cost 5.7p per listener as against the network average of 1.37p. A BBC spokesman said it was essential to analyse efficiency. "We have a duty to licence payers to ensure that we are extracting the maximum value from our programmes". This is the ultimate and typical triumph of Spreadsheet Man; having driven away a substantial part of the audience for quality programming he can then demonstrate on his computer that their cost per programme makes it nonviable. Lord Reith must be spinning in his grave. I had foolishly thought that the whole point of having public service broadcasting was to free it from this grubby sort of commercial calculation, so that quality could prevail. In a BBC policy document James Boyle was urged to concentrate on a more affluent audience from "active thirty somethings" to "older solos". Now why, I wonder, would a public service broadcaster be concerned with the affluence of its audience? A cynic might take the view that it is being softened up for privatisation. Privatisation, of course, makes multi-millionaires of bureaucrats.

I am reminded of the remark of a British Council official in a Far Eastern city, who like many of us was lamenting the rise of bureaucracy and audit — "We will end up with one scholarship world-wide, but it will be perfectly administered." Perhaps BBC Radio will end up with one programme (a cheap actor reading end-to-end pornography?). Under Director General Sir John Birt, the BBC had become the epitome of the Thatcherite internal market. Bureaucrats, focus groups and external consultants burgeoned, while journalists and programme makers felt increasingly under siege and demoralised. Despite all this, the BBC is still the best broadcasting organisation in the world, which says a lot for the rest of them.

Now, it might seem a little perverse to choose, as the culmination of a chapter on the abuse of computers, the doings of what many people will consider an obscure branch of the media industry. It is, however, illustrative of the social consequences of insisting on extracting numbers to characterise a complex social phenomenon. People become so wrapped up in the measurements that they forget the tenuous basis on which they were made. The numbers have become more important than the things they are supposed to represent. Measurement has been elevated to a cult and extended to areas of human activity in which it has no rightful place, which thought leads us to the next chapter

Chapter 11
Measuring the unmeasurable

Where is the wisdom we have lost in knowledge?
Where is the knowledge we have lost in information?
T S Eliot, Choruses from 'The Rock'

Measurement, for so long the Cinderella of science, has suddenly become so powerful that a dangerous sophistry has taken hold – that everything can be measured. That this is clearly untrue is self-evident. Examples are trite but true. How do you measure the beauty of a rose, the impact of a poem, the worth of a friend or the intensity of mental pain? For a measurement scientist it is almost equally absurd to ask – how do you measure the relative worth of schools, hospitals or universities? Fear not! The politicians and bureaucrats will find a way.

11.1 Feeding the Machine

Many schoolteachers, university professors, general practitioners, policemen and others have been queuing up in increasing numbers to retire early. Is it because they don't like the job? No – it is the paperwork. The great Moloch that is our Government and Bureaucracy demands greater and greater sacrifices of time and stress. Everything has to be measured, formulated, put in a league table. Never mind that the results are at best unreliable and totally without meaning or relevance, while at worst they exacerbate the situation. All that matters is the numbers. The wastage of national human resources in the relentless gathering of numbers has reached staggering proportions.

11.2 The Audit Explosion

It does not follow that because something can be counted it therefore should be counted.

Harold L Enarson

Michael Power is Professor of Accounting at the London School of Economics. His book *The Audit Society – Rituals of Verification* is a trenchant analysis of the all-pervading presence that auditing has established throughout our community in a relatively short time. There is a particular resonance in the title of his opening chapter – **The Audit Explosion**. This is no hyperbole: in terms of the length of human history, the decade it has taken for this form of activity to grow from a background one to a dominant one is effectively instantaneous. Why has it happened now? An obvious answer is that the technology has become available. The computer, with its ability to store, retrieve and sort vast amounts of data, has made it possible and, as the existence of computer viruses illustrates, if it can be done it will be done. Equally important, however is the political climate. The overwhelming creed of the individual and the elevation of personal greed in the early eighties has brought with it a lack of trust of all people and institutions. Once honoured concepts of service, dedication and self-sacrifice have been consigned to the dustbin of the past. Everyone is guilty unless proven innocent. Trust has been replaced by monitoring. The growth rate of state auditing bodies since the cataclysmic early 1980s has been phenomenal. There is not just the National Audit Office and the Audit Commission; almost every branch of public activity has its own equivalent – medicine, schools, universities, charities etc.

The overall result of all this is a massive drain on resources, not just financial ones but even more importantly skilled manpower; for, naturally, no additional resources have been allocated for the purpose. As Power puts it "methods of checking and verification are diverse, sometimes perverse, sometimes burdensome and always costly".

Where has this all got us? It is difficult to find an area in which the audit explosion has made things better in any reasonable sense (I exclude a certain amount of financial auditing, which is largely inescapable) and the general effect is a magnificent demonstration of Hutber's law. Another telling heading of Power's is **The Essential Obscurity of Auditing**. At the end of most of these lengthy and costly exercises people involved seem little the wiser. One thing that can be said is that they substantially change the behaviour of the auditees. The audit becomes the goal. All activity is geared to optimising the outcome of the audit, regardless of the objectives of the institution (as now trendily laid out in the "Mission Statement"). The very criteria of success in life have changed dramatically in a couple of decades. From the police to the professoriate the key to success is plodding, uninspired conformity.

11.3 Examination fever

Yes, I could have been a judge but I never had the Latin,
never had the Latin for the judging, I just never had sufficient
of it to get through the rigorous judging exams.
They're noted for their rigour. People come staggering out saying
"My God, what a rigorous exam" – and so I became a miner instead.
Peter Cooke, Beyond the Fringe

One of the most emotive ways society has of generating numbers is examinations. The main thing that examinations test is the ability to pass examinations. As a young lecturer I had the experience of supervising the undergraduate project of a student who turned out to be a superb researcher. His undergraduate project produced two scientific publications and a patent. He was, however, one of those people who fold up under exam conditions and only got a third class degree. The rules of the system did not allow me to recruit him as a research student and a remarkable talent was lost to academe. Equally I have known many students who obtained brilliant firsts and would never make engineers if they tried all their lives. How can I say all this and still support the examination system? Well again it is like democracy, a lousy system that produces appalling leaders, but all other known systems are worse. Exams are essential, but not the be all and end all; it is only the inflexibility of the bureaucratic system that makes them so. Talking of appalling leaders, education is a great playground for politicians and bureaucrats.

The pass rate in the UK school Advanced Level examinations remained remarkably steady for decades at about 70%. Then in about 1982 (note the year – a lot began to happen then) it began to rise steeply and continuously at about 1% per year and at the time I was finishing this book it was still doing so. The results were hailed as a success for the education system and evidence of improving standards. Critics and doubters were pilloried as "sceptics and cynics" (where have I heard that before?) and were largely ignored. Meanwhile Industry was increasingly complaining of the decline in literacy and numeracy among its new recruits, and universities were removing more and more material from their first year syllabuses, especially mathematics, as the students could not cope with it. How do I know all this? Well, over the period I visited several hundred companies and was told first hand in no uncertain terms. I was also external examiner in several of the leading university engineering departments.

How were these "improvements" achieved? By reducing syllabuses, simplifying questions and, above all, modularity. Students love modular courses. They rapidly develop the capacity to bone up on a subject, take the test and then forget it all overnight. By the time they reach industry or university they have all the grades and none of the knowledge.

Politicians need to generate favourable numbers. They can use the education system to do this relatively cheaply. Not only school passes but also higher education participation rates go up, while unemployment goes down. Universities are forced to lower standards. Nonsense! You might say. How can they be forced to lower standards? In fact it is quite easy. While reducing the funding per student you also make it follow the student, so that each failure represents a loss of income. As a result we get a system in which nobody fails. Any academic who protests is told "Very well, which of your colleagues are you going to make redundant?" So universities had been obliged to whittle away at the content of first year courses and devise more and more fantastical schemes to prevent or condone failure.

If you don't believe me take it from David Anderson, an A level candidate writing to *The Times* (Aug 18th 1997):

> *"Having studiously read exam papers, syllabuses and textbooks from previous years, I have no doubt that over the past decade there has been a phenomenal slide in the difficulty and rigour of the A-level examinations............More difficult material has been constantly "falling off" the top end and replaced by new material derived from GCSE."*

Hutber strikes again!

Of course, the political manipulation of numbers is not restricted to examinations. The UK had one of the lowest levels of university participation in the advanced world. Then suddenly, overnight, it had one of the highest. How was this done? Simply by calling all the polytechnics universities, and it did not cost a penny. On a visit to Singapore at the time, I was asked by a university dean "Why does Britain want all these Mickey Mouse universities?" My reply "Pass" was rather weak, but I knew really. In time to come it will be realised that the real tragedy in all this is the loss of the polytechnics. Meanwhile Singapore, a country the size of the Isle of Wight, was doubling its number of polytechnics from two to four and magnificent they are too. Purely by coincidence there was also a substantial difference in the economic performance of the UK and Singapore (even with the Asian financial crisis).

Suffer the little children

One of the worst aspects of examination fever is the way it is affecting the very young. Even three year olds are now under pressure to prepare for their future progress tests. At a time when they should be learning the skills of life through play, they are subjected to the stress and anxiety that plague the lives of the rest of us. Some people are simply not made for examinations, but the everybody-passes principle has been extended to the everybody-gets-examined fetish; all so that the system can satisfy its appetite for numbers. The effect on some young people is appalling, leading to serious ill health and even suicide, but the machine must be fed.

The way these little children have been dragged into its maw must be the most distressing and distasteful result of audit madness. With the threat of teachers being paid by results, it can only get worse. Children as young as three are audited, assessed and dragooned into conformity. Lengthen the school day! Cut the holidays! More homework! More terms! Their job is to be good little worker ants, fulfil their norms and contribute to the Audit Society. Arrogant, ignorant bureaucrats dictate just how many hours and minutes they must spend on each subject, regardless of their individual needs. At the other end of childhood, coroners' reports on suicide victims are now a familiar feature of the examination season. The used to say that schooldays are the happiest days of your life. Some joke!

11.4 League Tables

Education is what survives when what has been learned has been forgotten.
B.F. Skinner

The spreading lunacy

League tables were once confined to the sports pages of newspapers, but within a couple of decades our world is awash with them. Why has it happened now? One of the main reasons is the ease of producing them for the compilers. It is not, of course, easy for the thousands who have to endure all the extra toil and stress that the data gathering imposes; but Spreadsheet Man simply has to enter those data into his computer and with the press of a couple of keys they are all added up and ordered in what ever way he wishes. The politicians then lap them up as concrete evidence on which to impose policies on their suffering subjects.

As it happens the league table craze was not started by politicians, though they rapidly took them up with great enthusiasm. The first such event that had an impact on my own life and work was when newspapers began to publish league tables of university examination failure rates. This wholly mischievous exercise started the long decline in academic standards that is still going on. The worst performers in these tables were the country's leading engineering schools, which traditionally had a failure rate of about 25%. It is a fact of life that this proportion of the entrants is simply not suited to the profession. It was always so and ever will be. The word soon went around in heavily coded academic language that this had to stop, and the "everybody passes" era began. To cut a long story short the end result has been that the bachelor's degree is now no longer regarded as an appropriate qualification for a chartered engineer, and to achieve this status you now need a master's degree. Worse, a quarter of the students in the final year of bachelors' courses should not be there, either by ability or motivation, and their presence spoils the educational experience for everybody else, staff and students.

The league table mentality seems to suffuse everything in the media. It is often implicit and used to reinforce some propaganda point. A newscaster, for example, commenting on the third worst drought of the century – "What is happening to our weather?" One possible reply is that it is better than when we had the first and second worst droughts. Our society seems to have a need to rank things. It does no harm until someone uses the ranking to form and implement policy. It is only during the nineties, however, that explicit league tables have taken their place as a major plank of Government policy.

Consider just one set of league tables that landed on my doormat as a special supplement to *The Times* on 23rd February 1999:

11.5 Primary Schools

Obviously we cannot deal with this in detail. *The Times* summary took up 20 pages. The following represents just the top and bottom sixteen in a table of performance of local authorities. It also gives only the total scores and does not divide them into English, Maths and Science:

Isles of Scilly	278.6
London, City of	270.4
Richmond upon Thames	234.5
Wokingham	220.9
Surrey	220.9
Kingston upon Thames	217.2
Windsor and Maidenhead	217.0
Solihull	216.9
....	
....	
....	
Greenwich	157.2
Walsall	156.8
Bradford	155.8
Hackney	153.1
Sandwell	152.2
Tower Hamlets	150.5
Newham	149.5
Nottingham, City of	138.4

Now what can we learn from such a table? Harking back to our observation that policemen can damage your health (§2.4) we could suggest that a number of things could be predicted about each area without much fear of contradiction. We could, for example, rank them similarly with some accuracy according to:

> Average family income
> Number of trees per acre
> Average number of cars per family
> Number of policemen per thousand
> Life expectancy
> Ethnic mix
> Number of books per household
> and on and on

The fact is that we can learn nothing from the table. Any reasonably well-informed person could have a pretty good stab at the ranking without performing any tests at all. It might be helpful for a particular school to know whether its average score is going up or down, but its position in the table is of no possible use to anybody. A technical definition of information is "that which removes uncertainty", in which case these tables contain no virtually information at all. Yet millions of children, teachers, bureaucrats and journalists have wasted much time and stress in gathering and manipulating the data. Why? It is done simply because it can be done. This is not to say that tests themselves are entirely wrong — they can be stimulating and a helpful part of the educational process. These tables are there merely to satisfy the machine and justify the existence of spreadsheet man in his various guises. Moloch was the god of the Ammonites to whom children were made to pass through fire. As long as he is fed the elders are satisfied.

The same criticism applies to the tables for schools in particular areas. With a few notable exceptions they simply encapsulate a description of the social conditions around each school.

11.6 Secondary Schools

We could go through exactly the same exercise with the league tables for secondary schools, but it would be rather repetitive. Let us look at another aspect of the effect of such an exercise. It was decided that the ranking of schools would depend on the number of children reaching grade C in five of the GCSE examination subjects. As soon as the first tables were published the whole school system swung its effort behind children who might get just five with a bit of pushing. Children who were not going to get them and those who were going to get them easily were relatively neglected. Lo and behold, the scores began to go up. What you measure is what you get. Politicians congratulated themselves on a great improvement. Hutber (q.v.) might have a comment on that.

11.7 The universities – Hutber rampant

As I have spent most of my professional life in universities I should air my prejudices before I go on to talk about the measurement aspects. First, I have no axe to grind or sour grapes regarding my own department. It was awarded maximum points in both major audit exercises. I take no credit for this, particularly the teaching assessment, to which my attitude was like that of Woody Allen's about death — I was not worried about it, but I did not want to be there when it happened; so, I took my only ever sabbatical leave. One of my main reasons for joining the university system (apart from my love of teaching and research) was to get away from the nonsenses of the industrial management system. Little did I know that by the end of my career universities would be run in exactly the same way — remote overpaid central managers making bad decisions on false information about dejected staff. I had no desire to manage or be managed. I appreciated good leadership and did my best to provide it when my turn came. I was proud to be part of a system that was as good as any in the world. The deterioration began, like so many adverse trends, around 1982. It was not so much the savage cuts in funding, though they were pretty devastating, as much as the short-termism of the Thatcher Government. One year they even allocated the funding after all the students had been offered places. The traditional university committee system (about which I complained as much as any, but oh to have it back!) was unable to cope with these rapid twists and turns. Once centralised management was in place, it was easy for the Government to impose the whole gamut of Management Techniques.

The rationale for all this was a typical piece of Thatcherite double-think. Britain was too successful at innovation and not successful enough at exploitation. Japanese research had determined that a large proportion of the world's great innovations in science and technology had arisen in Britain, but had been exploited elsewhere. Britain had too many Nobel prizes and not enough industrial muscle. The solution was to put the industrialists (who had failed) in charge of the universities (who had succeeded). It is like saying the left leg is diseased, so we will amputate the right one.

The universities used to be known as the Ivory Towers, which in my unfashionable opinion is quite right and proper. They were places where students went to sit at the feet of great scholars. Now they are places where customers go to buy degrees. If they don't get what they think they paid for, they sue. University administrations live in permanent terror of being sued. University life is now dominated by two forms of audit – the Teaching Quality Assurance (TQA) and the Research Assessment Exercise (RAE). Scholarly discussion in common rooms has been replaced by arguments as how best to optimise the RAE or TQA scores. Academics used to recognise three sorts of time, which they tried to keep in balance – research time, teaching time and administration time. At the turn of the decade, however, a new sort of time began to enter the jargon – crap time.

The grovels of academe

The bureaucratic take-over of the university system has already been referred to in the introduction as an exemplar of the technique of The Ratchet. I have a copy of *The University in the Modern World* a collection of speeches made by Lord Robbins in the early 1960s. Symbolically it has a sticker on the front "W H SMITH BARGAIN: ONLY 20p". It is wonderful inspiring stuff, but now has no more relevance to the modern real world than, say, *The Hobbit*. All the things Robbins spoke of as dangers are now implicit parts of the system – unwarrantable bureaucratic interference, the deadening hand of official regulation, expansion by a lowering of standards etc. In those days, university funding was organised on the buffer principle; The University Grants Committee was deliberately put in place to insulate the institutions from bureaucratic interference and maintain academic freedom. This was clearly irksome to the bureaucrats, who seized upon the opportunities presented by the political dislocation around 1982 to begin their long campaign of attrition against the independence of the universities. The process went on for a decade and a half, the bureaucratic stranglehold gradually increasing with each new bill. The culmination of all this was the Teaching and Higher Education Bill of 1997. It was tantamount to nationalisation (*THES*, December 5th 1997) and the Vice Chancellors paid the price for their years of pusillanimity. On second thoughts, the Vice Chancellors were the only ones to do well out of it, as their salaries soared to the levels of industrial chief executives, unlike those of their employees.

It used to be said that managing academics was like herding cats. Now their ovine acquiescence makes the teddy bear's picnic look like a poll tax riot. The bureaucrats have them dancing like puppets on a string.

Measuring Research

> *If we knew what it was we were doing, it would not be*
> *called research, would it?*
> *Albert Einstein*

What is research? Nowadays would-be researchers have to apply for a grant to one of the Government-controlled Research Councils. At one time universities had their own funds to promote research but this is no longer the case. Applicants are required to lay out the project as if it were an industrial development plan, including a (Gantt) chart of what they will be doing in each week of the project. I cannot give a definition of research, but I do know this – if you can draw a Gantt chart of it, research it ain't. In fact, much of what is now labelled as scientific research would not long ago have been called industrial development. Now, I have no objection to universities being involved in industrial development; I have been doing it my entire career, but I do have a strong objection to dishonest labelling. The grant application form even contains a section asking who are the customers and users for the research.

Anyway, like everything else, it was decreed that research had to be measured. Of course, it was immediately discovered that this is unmeasurable, so they measured something else – publication. As we have seen many times over – what you measure is what you get. Publications burgeoned, new journals appeared full of academic papers that virtually nobody reads. Six papers were required of each individual over the four-year period of the survey. Only in the mind of bureaucrats does science conform so readily to a pattern. Darwin's *Origin of Species* gestated for about quarter of a century, while Einstein's first six papers came out in short succession and shook the world of physics to the foundations. These two very different authors, more perhaps than any others, created modern science; but such diversity is inconvenient to the bureaucrat. Who would these two have put down as their customers? Yet, their works impact on our lives hundreds of times a day. There is now no place for the profound study that takes four or five years and produces the definitive book that is used for decades. In fact the bureaucrats of research funding have decreed not only that they have no time for individual researchers, but they do not approve of small research groups, which lets me out. All my career I have derived great pleasure and satisfaction in running small research groups, but I have to accept that my time is over. Having spent most of my life not being a manager, I am not going to start now. Time was when professors were expected to be experts in their own subject. Now they simply have to be good at getting in the money, which means specialising in form filling and grubbing round the bureaucratic establishment to find out which are the in subjects. The successful academic now changes his subject as readily as a flea changes its dog. Ask some of them a detailed question about a paper that bears their name and you will get an embarrassed silence. Deans and Heads of Department were once all noted scholars. Now they tend to be unimaginative, workaholic bean counters who would have been blackballed from the job in days past. Actually wanting the job was once the ultimate disqualification.

Of course it was realised that publications (bibliometry) are not an ideal way to measure research, so some bureaucrats came up with an improvement based on citations (the number of times a paper is quoted by another scientist). The notorious paper by Dr Alfred Steinschneider on Sudden Infant Death Syndrome is a good example of a well cited paper (over 400 citations), but when properly conducted research was performed it proved to be entirely spurious.

As it turns out, a good example of how the form of measurement changes human behaviour is the use of citations to measure the impact of research articles. It is quite clear that little citations circle began to form – "You cite mine and I'll cite yours." It does not even need to be agreed formally. After all, it is only polite to return favours and it does not cost anything. This is also a good example of the Le Chatelier principle. When citation was first used it at least had a tendency to pick out the significant papers, but the system soon restored itself to equilibrium. A late colleague of mine was asked to be an examiner for a candidate for the degree of DSc, which is based on a life's work. He was impressed by the number of papers published and even more when he found out that one of them had dozens of citations. His enthusiasm diminished, however, when he looked at some of the citing papers and found that they were all proving the candidate wrong.

It will be clear to the reader that I have jaundiced views about research assessment, so let me make quite clear that I have no argument with a related process, *accreditation*. This is carried out by professional institutions, such as (in my department) the Institution of Electrical Engineers and the British Computer Society. It is totally free of bureaucratic control and concerned with the quality of graduates and the protection of the public from incompetence, a vital function whose importance is not recognised by the bureaucrats.

Given all this vituperation, I have to accept the an ironic fact that the RAE produced results that were just about right, but not entirely because of the actual research done. What outsiders fail to realise is that the leading university departments are populated by very bright hyperactive paranoids and once they know the rules they play the game hard and for keeps. The new universities wondered what had hit them.

I actually had experience of being on a commission of international specialists making an assessment of research. It was in the Netherlands and just looked at Electrotechnology. As in the British system, we read institutional statements and sample papers published by all the researchers involved, and a demanding task it was too. By the time the commission gathered in a central town in the Netherlands we had formed a remarkably uniform view as to how the various departments ranked. Then we visited them. In a small, but significant, number of cases we changed our minds. The submissions had been angled by the Dean of the Faculty according to his own prejudices, but our independent judgement was different. In all, as such things go, this was a splendid exercise. You can perhaps imagine my distaste when it was announce that the British version would be an exercise on paper only and that the judges would be recruited only from the local establishment. You have probably worked out by now that I do not qualify as a member of the establishment. I was for a short time on a national committee to dispense grants, but they soon got rid of me. Was it something I said?

The programme in question was the LINK scheme, which involved joint research between academia and industry with grants from the research council and the Department of Trade and Industry (DTI). I have held two grants under the scheme, and I still occasionally have a recurrence of the nightmares. First was the process of getting the grant, which lasted two or three years. You had to think up the project and then find industrial collaborators. Then the two different sides had to put in applications to their respective masters. The applications, of course, have to be very detailed. These all go to the committee, which is a large collection of civil servants, industrialists and academics. After much reading and meetings the applications are reduced to a short list (in the case I was involved in from about 100 to about 20). All the industrial applicants are then visited by civil servants and have to establish their technical ability and financial viability. There are then further committee meetings and eventually a small number of grants is allocated. In the year I spent on a committee they had not got round to making any grants at all. The staggering thing is that if you work out the actual cost to industry, universities and government of all the man-hours involved it greatly outweighs the amount of money being granted.

It does not, however, stop there. If you are one of the "lucky" ones to get a grant then the process of management starts. They actually hold you to the Gantt charts you have glibly created. Both my grants were considered to be failures in this respect. The fact that the first one produced a paper that later received the Gold Medal for the best paper at the relevant European conference did not count. The second one was officially designated a disaster. It involved an extremely complex piece of micro-engineering. When it turned out that one of my assumptions in formulating the design was proved wrong by detailed computer simulation, it was clear that a redesign was necessary and that would involve much more complex engineering, involving materials that had never been used in micro-engineering before. Naturally, we asked for an extension to the grant period but this could not be agreed by all the parties involved. We were obliged to have progress meetings every two months, even when we had no progress to speak of. These involved between six and twelve people travelling to a common venue and losing a day. Meanwhile two people were doing the actual work. As I write, we are still waiting for the patent to go through and have been able to publish nothing. The final accolade my project received from a civil servant was "You would not get a grant for it today. It is too researchy."

Now, if you have not skipped on to the next section, you have probably decided that this guy is rattling on about the frustrations of the job that we all have to put up with, but that is not my point. I am trying to give examples of the inordinate amount of waste that is caused by spurious measurement. Far more money is now spent on allocating and monitoring research grants than is spent in doing the actual research. Two decades earlier, a small peer review committee of scientists, with a civil servant in attendance, would allocate the funds available in a particular field according to reports received from a wide range of scientific referees. The cost was minimal and the Britain was pre-eminent in scientific research. Now most of the money is wasted on bureaucratised measurement and the research reputation of the nation has been dissipated. At least we haven't got a Carol Browner. Yet!

The condition of research today illustrates the principle that the audit is the object. Research used to be done for its own sake or for the good of mankind. Now it is done to maximise the results of the audit. In order to ensure that participants toe the line, funding is closely tied to the outcome of the audit.

Measuring Teaching

We used to have quality teaching, now we have Teaching Quality Assurance (TQA). When I was a student I had the good fortune to experience some very good teaching (and some that was very bad too). I remember one Dr Poynton, who would stride into the lecture theatre and give a seemingly impromptu chat on some topic in physics that left me wanting to go to the text books to find out more. I felt that I was really at a university. Nowadays Dr Poynton would be roundly condemned.

When I became a lecturer myself, the pinnacle of the art had been displayed on television, by the likes of Kenneth Clarke with *Civilisation*, Jacob Brunowski with *The ascent of man* and Alistair Cooke with *America*. You could see them thinking. The magnificent pauses, as Harold Pinter was then demonstrating in the theatre, seemed to convey as much knowledge as the words surrounding them. Nowadays, they would have to be filled in by sort-ofs and you-knows, until the next fantastically incredible sentence was ready for pouring out.

Of course, once the bureaucrats finally managed to complete the nationalisation of the universities, they decided that they would have to be subjected to management techniques, and especially measurement. They could not measure teaching so they measured training, and it follows as the night the day that's what they got. The speed with which the TQA destroyed the traditional discursive style of university lecturing was astonishing, even to an old cynic like me. The assumption that students would read the occasional book and value listening to a world class expert talking around the subject was dead and gone almost overnight.

The sort of lecturing that is valued today was not long ago dismissed as Polytechnic style. Polytechnic style lecturing comprised the transfer of revision notes from the lecturer's note pad to the student's notepad via the visual aids. It is not teaching; it is training. It is not even training in the subject; it is training to pass the examination. One of my colleagues was admonished by the TQA inspector because he did not use any notes at all, which was once the mark of the really accomplished lecturer.

Students now fill in questionnaires on what they think about the quality of teaching, which are of great account in quality assessment. The one used at my university made no reference to the reading of textbooks, but asked about how useful "hand-outs" were. Time was when the lecturer had probably written the definitive textbook on the subject and did not expect to have to add handouts. Students being what they are (and I was the same) want to get the maximum marks with the minimum effort. Lecturers used to exploit this desire to turn them into qualified engineers, lawyers or literary critics. Now students have become customers and they expect to receive simple guides on how to pass the exam. A technician reported that she had heard a student coming out of one of my lectures saying "and he expects us to read the book. I didn't come to university to read effing books." A survey of students' opinion of lecturers was carried out at Swansea University and repeated three years after graduation. It was found that many had completely reversed their opinions. This matches my own experience.

Of course, all this measurement is supposed to provide a means of comparison. How do you compare a degree in Physics from Cambridge University with one in Billiard Table Studies of the Metropolitan University of Nether Wallop?

The TQA exercise in my own department generated over 10,000 pieces of paper, which had not been required before. It removed from the teaching process the equivalent of between two and three full time lecturers. Multiply this by the number of university departments in the country and you have tens of millions of pieces of paper and wasted man-hours. Almost none of them will ever be looked at, but they have to be available for sampling.

11.8 Picking Winners

This one is going to be a real winner." said C.J. "I didn't get
where I am today without knowing a real winner when I see one.
David Nobbs — The fall and rise of Reginald Perrin.

Now that the bureaucrats are in control of higher education they are in a position to determine the policy. Even those who are closely involved in a subject have a very poor record at predicting where the breakthroughs will come. In electronics, for example, I do not know of any one who came anywhere near predicting the rate of progress that would actually occur. Yet now committees of self proclaimed experts sit in judgement of what research will actually be funded in future. The system is such that no one with a bright but risky idea can devote time and resources to following it up. Catch phrases are the order of the day. In an idle moment during the Netherlands research assessment exercise we spent a coffee break dreaming up the title of a research programme that would be guaranteed funding anywhere in Europe. We came up with *Mobile neurofuzzy multimedia systems*, which incorporated all the major buzzwords of the time.

One of the technologies that has changed our lives more than most is optical fibres. A few dedicated researchers pursued the possibilities, even though the prevailing official view was that they would never work, because the signal attenuation would be too high. Officialdom was proved wrong, but then researchers had their own resources to follow their own ideas. Today they would not have that opportunity. Who knows what amazing technologies are being suppressed by the prevailing orthodoxy?

11.9 Dear Dr Einstein

Here is a piece I wrote for a University newspaper in 1994. It seemed to strike a resonance with a number of colleagues, many of whom still remember it. It is a matter of interest in the present context that the penultimate paragraph was censored by the editor.

> *Dear Dr Einstein,*
>
> *With reference to your application for the post of Lecturer at this University, I have been asked to write to you to explain why we have been unable to offer you the appointment. You seem to be a little vague about the objectives of a university department. It is quite simple — the objectives are to obtain a five grade in the Research Assessment Exercise and an excellent grade in the Teaching Quality Assessment. Unfortunately the panel felt that appointing you would reduce the prospect of achieving either target.*
>
> *The papers you submitted were most interesting, but sadly they are not the sort of thing that is likely to achieve external funding and therefore improve our norms. The Brownian motion, for example, may be an intriguing little intellectual problem, but its solution is not likely to impress a modern research council committee. As for the photo-electric effect, what possible industrial application could that have, when most of the available funding goes to industrial programmes such as LINK and ROPA? No, I regret to say that the likely outcome of an application by you to EPSRC is an alpha rating but no funding. Again your Special Theory of Relativity may be a pretty little exercise for the brain, but would it attract a CASE award? Even less promising is the fact that you have totally failed to recruit a single research student, which would play havoc with our ratings. Furthermore your persistence in publishing in obscure German journals would no help our ranking at all, since the quality of publications is now solely measured by the journals in which they appear.*
>
> *As for teaching we note your abject failure to produce a set of pre-digested notes to accompany your lectures. Your rambling discourses may well provide intellectual stimulus to your students, but frankly they will not cut much ice with a TQA panel. You seem to have this strange idea that a university is some sort of ivory tower devoted to cerebration, rather than a modern, thrusting organisation dedicated to improving its norms.*

In short, you would be completely out of place at this University and would present insurmountable problems to your Line Manager. I am sure that you will appreciate the difficulty she/he would have in putting anything positive in your staff assessment forms, which would be a record of total lack of achievement.

On a more personal note, it might be helpful to you if I pointed out a couple of tactical errors you made during the interview. In trying to explain your, no doubt interesting, Theory of Relativity, you cited the example of a man on a train. I have to advise you that such gender-specific language is quite unacceptable in this University, and we would fear that the lapse might be repeated before impressionable students. What really put the kibosh on it, however, was that you persisted in smoking that smelly old pipe throughout the interview. The University will tolerate almost any sort of deviance, but up with pipes it will not put.

I know that you will take these remarks in the constructive way they are intended. Meanwhile I would advise you not to resign your post at the Patents Office.

With all good wishes
John Brignell

11.10 A change of state

If anyone had been suddenly been transported through time from the sixties, when I joined the university system, to a university committee now he would be at a complete loss. He would not even understand the language. "What we must do is recruit five-star people. Anyone who does not produce four good papers will cost the department thirty thousand pounds a year. We must be working for the audit after next. We must be pro-active in positioning ourselves in the marketplace." These were all admonitions made at a strategy meeting I attended. In a copy of the *Times Higher Education Supplement* you will typically find the word "marketing" a couple of dozen times. You would be lucky to find the word "scholarship" once. Universities, even quite respectable ones, set up franchised courses at colleges in Malaysia that are little more than ill-equipped private businesses. Students get a British degree without ever visiting Britain. Many, including myself, regard this as a major scandal, but it is impossible to get such a view published in the academic press, who take the view that this is a fine piece of marketing. Honorary degrees are openly up for sale. I don't know about our time-traveller, but I feel pretty much an alien myself. Now there are not only audits, there are rehearsals for audits. One of the saddest remarks that summarises the situation was made by a bright young man I recruited some years ago – the job is just routine really.

Heads of Department and Deans used to be chosen for their scholastic standing. Now they are chosen for their ability at bean counting and form filling. Consider, for example, Engineering at Warwick University – anyone in the trade will tell you that they are a world class research department. Yet they were awarded a meagre grade four in the RAE. Assuming there is no skulduggery, the only explanation is that someone made a mess of filling in the forms. As a result one of our leading engineering departments has had its funding significantly reduced.

It is probably almost impossible for anyone under fifty to understand just how alien the modern university scene seems to oldies. In the early seventies I used to write an occasional spoof column for the University newspaper called *Senate Record 2000* in the style of the official record. It was supposed to be a ridiculous extrapolation of the trends of the time with silly degrees and foolish research projects. I was far from the truth. If I had included honours degrees in golf and tourism, which we now have, or heavily-funded research into which wine gives the greatest protection against heart attacks, there would have been demands for the column to be censored on the grounds of being embarrassingly fatuous. How innocent we were in those distant days!

One of the starkest changes in universities is a companion to the compensation culture, which is the "excuse culture". As usual it is Frank Furedi (*THES* October 16, 1999) who puts numbers to the trend of which we have all been aware. In 1978 2.6% of American first-year students reported some form of disability. By 1991 it had risen to 8.8%. In the five years to 1996 the number of SAT candidates receiving special treatment doubled to 40,000. In the UK, boards of examiners now spend more time weighing the "medical" evidence than all the rest of their business. I myself have observed that "dyslexia" is almost an epidemic among modern students. What used to be attributed to idleness and insouciance is now given a variety of new disability names. There is a powerful learning disability lobby that is dedicated to expanding the numbers involved. So-called learning support tutors can overrule attempts by examiners to fail students who write incomprehensible papers. Students of my era would have regarded it all as a great joke, until the unfairness of it all registered. What nobody seems to care about is that these people will become graduates with entry into various professions; unless, of course the professions decide to put their own house in order.

11.11 Hospitals

Just as I was trying to wind up the research for this book, yet more new figures were published for the performance of National health hospitals. The Minister declared that he did not wish them to be used to create league tables. Oh yeah? What else did he expect journalists to do with them? Figures were given for the number of deaths occurring during and after operation. I asked a medical friend what he thought the effect of publishing these would be. In the first place, he said, surgeons would be under pressure to avoid risky operations that might just save a patient from certain death. Secondly hospitals will begin to move out of risky areas altogether and concentrate on safe ones.

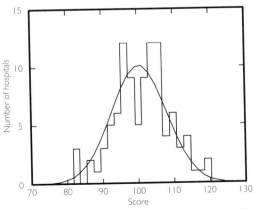

Figure 11.1 Breast cancer mortalities for NHS hospitals

Even before the Government started publishing mortality tables it had long been giving detailed tables of performance in such factors as waiting times for the first appointment. Lo and behold, some of the country's most famous hospitals were among the worst performers. The moral of the story is – if you want to get your hospital higher up the league tables make sure that it is one that patients do not wish to go to. What you measure is what you get!

For a really banal table from an emotive source, the one for breast cancer mortality ratios takes a bit of beating (*The Times* December 10 1998). These were presented as a percentage of the national average. I took the trouble to plot the results for 99 areas as a histogram and fitted a normal curve. It is clearly an unexciting normal distribution. The relative scatter (standard deviation as percentage of mean) is 7.63. This is a fairly commonplace sort of value. For example, one of the early 1999 silly season stories, of a policeman who related the number of car thefts to the birth signs of the owners, produces a figure of 7.44; while the heights of my identically treated tomato plants produced 8.1. It is just random variation from which nothing can be deduced. There are no startling high or low values (three standard deviations away from the mean). The Minister, Frank Dobson, regards such lists as a crucial indicator of the performance of hospitals. They are nothing of the sort. There might be underlying factors contributing to the variation, but they could be anything and everything (awareness among patients leading to early presentation, life expectancy leading to an older population, number of policemen per thousand etc.) and there are not necessarily any at all. This sort of number abuse produces nothing but a great deal of stress and anxiety. You might as well say "Oh my God! All the people in this town are of different heights." and launch a Procrustean programme to rectify the evil. Because this table is normalised to an average of 100, there is no information in it at all. It might as well have been created by a random number generating program. It is yet another waste of column inches and a needless sacrifice of trees.

I will refrain from going through another modelling exercise, but for an amusing example see the league table in *Why do buses come in threes?* (Bibliography) and answer the question "Which manager would you sack?" It is no longer amusing, however, when not only SIFs and journalists create anxiety and despondency out of the nothing of normal random variation, but Government ministers do it too. There has been a sea change in the whole business of government.

How did these disasters come about, and so quickly? Obviously the origin must be political, so let us have a look at the politics.

Chapter 12
Politicians, bureaucrats
and other animals

*The whole aim of practical politics is to keep the populace alarmed –
and hence clamorous to be led to safety – by menacing it with an
endless series of hobgoblins, all of them imaginary.*
H.L. Mencken

Politics has been a constant theme throughout this book. The massive outbreak of wrong
numbers is more a political and social phenomenon than a scientific one. Time was when the
doings of politicians had very little impact on the everyday life of the ordinary person. Now, in
the information age, they can implement a compulsion or ban, often without even resorting to
the normal processes of Parliament, and every citizen in the land feels the impact almost
immediately. Governments are put in place by party machines, spin doctors and media moguls,
using all the power of modern communications and persuasion, and are then able to ignore the
aspirations of the electors who, in theory, put them there. Ministers rapidly become isolated,
swanning luxuriously around the world accompanied by their concubines and minions,
manipulated by their beavering bureaucrats; and all the time absorbing and spewing out wrong
numbers. Back-benchers, who ought to be acting as our agents to curb the worst excesses of the
executive, are selected by the machine to be passive clones.

12.1 A brief history of bureaucracy

Sed quis custodiet ipsos Custodes?
(But who is to guard the guards themselves?)
Juvenal

Of the many gifts bestowed by the French on the Anglo-Saxons, bureaucracy must be the most
potent. In Saxon times the learned and beneficent Alfred the Great could decree that half the
revenues would go to education, and it was done. When the first English Kings reigned, the
Treasury was just another department of the royal household, like the Wardrobe. Subsequent
centuries would see a growth in the power and influence of the Treasury that is still continuing
today. It was, however, the Norman Conquest that brought effective bureaucracy to England. As
Winston Churchill points out in *The Island Race*, the Normans were administrators and lawyers
rather than legislators.

Domesday, a written record of a statistical survey of England ordered by William the Conqueror
in 1086 but completed by William Rufus, was designed to register the landed wealth of the
country in a systematic fashion, and determine the revenues due to the king. Its scale was
unparalleled in medieval Europe. The old system of taxation had become ineffective. By listing all
feudal estates, both lay and ecclesiastical, it enabled the king to strengthen his authority and exact

oaths of allegiance from all tenants, nobles and churchmen. The survey was executed by groups of officers called *legati*, who visited each county and conducted a public inquiry.

Henry I (Beauclerk) was the great administrator king, who used his feudal court and household as a base to organise the government. He reorganised the judiciary and created the *Curia Regis* act as a court of law and to supervise taxation. The Exchequer (the Royal Treasury) was established at this time. After a slight hiccup under the weak king Stephen, Henry II resumed this work and it was largely completed by Edward I. Despite the turmoil of the Hundred Years War and the Wars of the Roses, English government, society and law had taken on a permanent form. The final usurpation that brought in the first of the Tudors, Henry VII, led to a period of stable (if avaricious) government

A great engine of growth for bureaucracy in the Middle Ages was the church. Its *curia* or court was the centre of administration. A rising tide of parchment and then paper flowed along the roads that all led to Rome, and they were in the common international language, Latin. The church had an iron grip on education, including the new universities that began to appear in the thirteenth century. Yet, uniquely in Europe, there was also a respect for the individual that was strengthened by the Protestant revolution.

There was further great turmoil until Elizabeth I, when England was to see the flowering of its learning. It was also the age of colonisation and the British form of bureaucracy became the model for a large part of the world, including America. It also marked the end of absolute monarchy and Parliament began to take on the mantle of control. The inevitable clash produced the Civil War. The restoration produced a weak king, Charles II, who had the one great merit of an interest in science, founding The Royal Society in 1662. The scientific era and the party political era had simultaneously been given birth. George III made a brief attempt to wrench power back from Parliament, but his reign was a disaster, including the loss of the American colonies.

Political parties had emerged during the restoration, when politicians divided into the conservatives (Tories) and radicals (Whigs). In the subsequent three centuries a continuous process has occurred in which the party machines have gradually taken control. This process accelerated towards the end of the millennium, so that the machines are now in firmly at the helm. Throughout all these centuries of development bureaucracy was growing in fits and starts. But it was yet to see its finest hour. The general election of 1945 gave the Labour Party for the first time a majority of the popular vote and an overwhelming parliamentary majority.

The new Government, led by Clement Richard Attlee, sought to promote social equality in Britain. The two measures that established a welfare state in Britain, the National Insurance Act of 1946 and the National Health Service, set up in 1948, were widely popular. Both were the result of wartime reports by William Beveridge, a Liberal. The nationalisation of the Bank of England, the coal industry, gas and electricity, the railways, and most airlines had popular support, but the Conservatives vigorously if vainly opposed the nationalisation of the road-freight, and the iron and steel industries. These changes were made in the midst of a post-war era of austerity. As a result of the war, the national debt had tripled, and for the first time since the 18th century Britain had become a debtor nation. Wartime regulations, therefore, had been kept; food-rationing in 1946 and 1947 was more restrictive than during the war. I still have my sweet coupons from my primary school days. Labour had taken power over the commanding heights of the economy, but it had created a great army of bureaucrats and snoopers in order to administer it.

The combination of this deadening bureaucracy, savage taxation and the absence of any signs of returning prosperity enabled the Conservatives under Winston Churchill to regain power in the election of 1951. Except for denationalising iron and steel, the Conservatives made no attempt to reverse the legislation or the welfare-state programme enacted by Labour, but the early 1950s brought steady economic recovery. As income tax rates were reduced and the framework of wartime and post-war regulation largely dismantled, housing construction boomed and international trade flourished. Britain was on a rising tide of economic success.

By the 1964, however, there was a mood of rebellion against the traditions of society and the Labour Party was restored to power. This was the age of the swinging sixties, when a whole society kicked over the traces. It was also the age of inflation, which was to peak at 25% per annum in 1975. The struggle against inflation produced a great deal of trade union unrest and the Labour Government collapsed to allow the Thatcherite era to begin. Margaret Thatcher had the one thing that every political leader needs – luck. The opposition committed electoral suicide by espousing unpopular left wing doctrines, while the Falklands war came along at the crucial moment. The oil crisis was replaced by an oil bonanza. The new Government rapidly lost touch with its grass roots. In our constituency the code word for them was the CIA (Complacent, Insensitive, Arrogant). Having promised to get Government off the backs of the people, the Thatcher Government instituted a process of increasing centralisation of control. The Westminster bureaucrats began to exercise control over local government, education, science and many other areas of public life, though a massive privatisation programme liberated whole sections of industry. This, however, led to a whole new raft of regulatory bodies. Inflation returned in a consumer led boom. This and the grossly unpopular poll tax brought to an end the longest premiership since the end of the Napoleonic wars. The English, unlike their Celtic neighbours a deeply conservative people, had been virtually disenfranchised by being presented with a choice of three radical parties. John Major virtually single-handedly won an election in 1992 that his party was ready to lose. The subsequent debacle was all the more severe for its postponement.

Meanwhile, the Labour party was beginning its hard road to recovery. Reforms painfully forced through by Neil Kinnock laid the path for "the project" by which Tony Blair was able to create the ultimate party machine, ditching socialism in the process. The Conservative party split, mainly over European policy, and amid charges of sleaze was demolished at the 1997 election, which New Labour won with a massive majority, with Tony Blair as Prime Manager. The Conservatives had lost the core of their membership, who were not only the moderates, but also the party workers. They had thrown away the most efficient electoral machine in modern history and lost the skills even to organise and exploit a canvass. In Parliament and in the country they were an unrepresentative and irrelevant extremist rump, much as Labour had been in the previous decade, and doomed to act out the same Greek tragedy. The new Government majority was so great that it was able to act on little thought and with impunity. It savaged the constitution, emasculating the House of Lords, which had ironically proved more in tune with the aspirations of ordinary people than the Commons, and was the only restraint on the unbridled excess of the Government, to replace it with a House of Cronies. Bureaucracy reigned supreme. Bans were imposed frequently and at whim. They were empowered by the myth of the manifesto, which gave them a mandate to carry out all of their policies. The British, in particular, do not vote for things, they vote against them. The key policy was change, under the code word of "modernisation". Change, however mindless, was seen as A Good Thing in its own right. The New Left had also seized power in the USA and Europe, so SIFs became a prominent engine of policy throughout the western world.

Elections are supposed to be a form of measurement, of the will of the people. Dewdney shows how important the abuse of numbers can be in getting elected and staying elected. The British electoral system has the theoretical advantage that it produces members who individually represent their constituents. The increasing dominance of the party machines and the pusillanimity of MPs made this no more than theoretical. The system instead gave large majorities to one party or another, even sometimes on a minority vote. The resulting violent oscillations of policy caused a great deal of mindless destruction. In the European election of 1999, the country went from one extreme to the other and introduced that travesty of democracy, the closed party list, which was the ultimate triumph of the party machine. As party membership sagged in the country, tens of millions of pounds of taxpayer funds were diverted directly to the party machines.

As it had done from early in the millennium, the Treasury continued its growth and extended its hegemony. It seized control of more areas of national policy, raided pension funds, the National Lottery and many other sources. Its bureaucracy was the fastest growing section of government. It sets audit targets, hundreds of them, for all the other departments of Government, which produced all sorts of stresses and strains throughout the nation. All political parties while in opposition promise less bureaucracy and more openness. In government they deliver more bureaucracy and more secrecy. A small compensation to the British was that, however bad its level of bureaucratic intervention, it could not match that of the Franco-German alliance that was tying Europe up in knots of red tape. While I was writing this book quangos were breeding at an alarming rate, but they now had nice friendly names such as "task forces", so that was all right.

12.2 Great computer disasters

To err is human but to really foul things up requires a computer.
Farmer's Almanac for 1978

What is this section title doing in a chapter on politicians and bureaucrats? Surely the author has got it in the wrong place. It is well known that computer disasters are caused by pushy salesmen and incompetent programmers and systems analysts.

We are not talking about peanuts here. In Britain billions of pounds have been lost on computer systems that were scrapped before they were ever put into operation. It happened notoriously in my local (Wessex) area health authority. I have been involved on the fringes of the bidding for such contracts as a minor consultant, so have seen what happens at first hand. The first big problem, as in so many aspects of modern life, is the involvement of the Treasury. Because of Treasury rules, the way these things are done is that several potential suppliers are invited to make bids. The one chosen is the one that appears to offer the most performance for the least money. The dreaded auditors will pounce on anyone who fails to squeeze the best value for money out of a supplier.

If you want to find someone to paint your house, the worst way to go about it is to seek a number of bids and pick the cheapest. You would virtually be guaranteeing that you would latch on to the one cowboy among the candidates. The way sensible people go about it is to ask friends and neighbours who locally does a reasonable job at a reasonable price and go along to look at the results. Some will seem very cheap, but a year later the job needs redoing; while some that seem expensive produce a finish that lasts for years.

The great flaw in the Government purchasing system is that it provokes a spirit of derring-do. Normally sane salesmen, engineers and programmers get together to discuss their bid, but they are haunted by the shadows of their rivals who are going through the same process. They egg each other on to higher and higher excesses of performance over price. This all takes place over periods of weeks or months and, in the hot house atmosphere of the competitive bidding process, people fail to notice the point at which they slip over the edge of reason. They are also haunted by the prospect that failure could mean many of their colleagues, and even themselves, becoming unemployed. Thus most of the bids end up being silly, and the prize goes to the one that is silliest of all.

It does not stop there, of course. Almost as soon as the contract is signed, the bureaucrats, who are the customer, start to think up variations on the design that would make it even better. Then they start demanding impossible timetables. The rest of the process is such a mess that it is indescribable.

The contract I was on the fringes of involved an airborne computer system. The firm I was retained by lost the contract and it went to another bigger company. I remember saying to one of the sales engineers "This is a national disaster. They have not even got a working airborne computer. How could they possibly get the contract?" He replied "Nobody knows, but it is rumoured in the industry that they threatened the government that they would put the whole of the town of ------- out of work if they did not get it." £800 million later the contract was declared a failure as the computers were too heavy and the government were obliged to buy an American substitute system.

After I had written the above, the great passport scandal occurred. Thousands of would-be travellers were queuing at passport offices around the UK, frustrated because they could not get their passports in time for the holidays and business trips they had booked. The contract, awarded to Siemens for £230 million over 10 years, was to supply a computer system that would speed up the passport system and increase its security. It did neither. Then students might not get their loans in time for the start of term, because of computer problems. The next one boiling up nicely was the NHS computer network. The contrast between public and private enterprise has no more graphic illustration than in the implementation of information technology.

I must confess that these never-to-be computer systems did not produce any wrong numbers. In fact they did not produce any numbers at all, apart from the billions of pounds of losses, but they are an interesting sidelight on the main themes of this book.

12.3 SIFs the lawmakers

Feel-good causes seem to morph into mindless crusades at just the moment when the original reasons for the cause have been lost sight. Eric Peters, The Washington Times (September 30, 1997)

We have seen many instances where Single Issue Fanatics have brought about changes in the law to the detriment of most of their fellow citizens. They do not always succeed, but they never give up. Take a typical case of members of the European Parliament trying to force through legislation to make drivers face repeated driving tests throughout their lives. It started, of course, with a number, a claim that there were 45,000 road deaths every year and it was **hoped** that re-testing would reduce that number. MEPs were also worried about a recent upsurge in aggressive driving, such as incidents of so-called road rage. Note the characteristic features of this putsch. It starts from number, then there is a missing link and it finishes up with draconian legislation. The case is quite unsupportable in reality. In my experience, aggressive drivers tend to pass their test first time. They easily modify their behaviour for examination, which is a great inconvenience for all and misery for an innocent minority, who find examination of physicals skills a nightmare. It was yet another excuse for intruding on the lives of people, causing billions of pounds worth of unproductive activity. All based on a hope. Fortunately, in this case common sense prevailed.

Education is a field in which SIFs flourish. In Britain the grammar schools, some of the finest in the world, were deliberately destroyed in the quest for equality. The people who lost out were those like me, academically inclined but living in a poor area. They are the ones who tend to get bullied in comprehensive schools. The rich were still able to buy good education and they did not even have to pay fees. Today, if you want to buy a good education for your children you do not spend money on school fees; you spend it on a bigger mortgage to move into the right area, which is a better long-term investment, anyway. It takes generations to create an institution such as a fine school, but only months to destroy it.

As I have passed through the ages of man I observe that the operation of society takes the form of a war between the middle aged on one side and the young and old on the other. As each generation passes through the stages of development it carries its own flag from subjugation to triumph and back again. The oppressed of one decade become the oppressors of the next. In my youth, a particular trade unionist, Vic Feather, was decreed by popular vote to be the most powerful man in the country. In my father's youth, such people represented the exploited. Now, they are regarded as negligible, even by the party they founded. Towards the end of the century the dominant caste are the New Left. Their icons and chimeras dominate the media. Their propaganda rains down upon the young and the old, who respond with a yawning "Oh, yeah?"

The SIFs have now established a dominant position. They are the drivers for a number of policies that are forced through, often without debate in an emasculated parliament. They manufacture the justification for ever more burdensome taxation. Drivers, drinkers and smokers provide ten percent (and rising) of Government revenue on top of their other taxes. The mounting imposts are presented as not being real taxes at all, but environmental and social measures. New draconian regulations, compulsions and bans on things of which the SIFs disapprove pour out of the bureaucracy at increasingly frequent intervals. Outfits like DEMOS, pressure groups masquerading as so-called think tanks, have a direct line into Government. Policies are formed with the aid of focus groups, who tend to reflect the current media hype rather than the long-term interests of the country. Wrong numbers are the foundation of these policy structures.

Unfortunately there are no SIF groups dealing with the real concerns of most people, such as the flourishing of burglary, muggings and vandalism, with little apparent official action to reduce them.

12.4 The ratchet

Here lay the tragedy. Western man is so constituted that he cannot abide contentment. It is the unforgivable sin. He must strive towards some unseen goal, whether it be material comfort, a greater or purer God, or some weapon that will make him master of the universe. As he becomes more conscious he becomes more restless, more grasping, forever finding fault with the warm dust from which he sprang and to which he must return, forever desirous of improving and so enslaving his fellow-men.

Daphne du Maurier, The Archduchess

Like the spider weaving her web, the bureaucrat exhibits infinite patience. A dozen small steps in the desired direction, each imperceptible to the unsuspecting bystander, can achieve the objective. It is merely necessary to ensure that there are no steps backward. The classical case, as we have observed, is the nationalisation of the British universities. It took decades – just one small step in each successive education bill. The same process is going on throughout our society. The dead hand of bureaucracy is on almost everything we do. The Health and Safety at Work regulations alone have created a vast bureaucracy, within and without organisations. Bureaucrats can now find some regulation or other that will give them an excuse to probe into any corner of an organisation or the life of an individual or a corporation.

A particularly unpleasant aspect of the relationship between politicians, bureaucrats and ordinary people is the one-sided nature of it. We are expected to reveal all about our lives and work on demand, yet our masters insist on the right of lying, or at best withholding the truth.

The British bureaucrat is in a class of his own. An engineer involved in the movement of heavy equipment around Europe summarised it – "The British take each piece of health and safety legislation and gold-plate it. In a thousand small ways they trim the sense of each rule and make it just that little bit more onerous. For example, *repeated offences* becomes translated as a *second offence*." The end result is that British industry, on top of all the burdens it carries because of monomaniac economic policy, is saddled with onerous and rigorously applied legislation, which results in manufacturing industry moving elsewhere.

12.5 Budgetary bluff

It contains a misleading impression, not a lie. It was being economical with the truth.

Sir Robert Armstrong

The British Chancellor's budget of 1999 was a masterpiece of deception with numbers. **Everyone's a winner** yelled the tabloid headlines. In fact, while appearing to be reducing taxation, the Chancellor was substantially increasing it. The budget itself was the usual sort of mishmash of tinkering, with adjustments here and there, having the main effect of making life more complicated and stressful for the average citizen. What was unusual was the budget speech, which went beyond the usual sleight of hand. It was turned into a triumph of reason and generosity by simply leaving out the nasty bits, which were consigned to the small print of the follow-up documentation. Much was made, for example of the introduction of a new 10% tax band, but the fact that the 20% tax band had been eliminated in favour of a higher band was conveniently ignored. The abandonment of mortgage tax relief was presented as a reduction in public spending rather than an increase in taxation. The end of relief for maintenance payments for children of broken marriages was simply kept secret. A further savage increment in motor fuel duties was presented, thanks to the preparatory work by environmental SIFs, as an "environmental tax" and therefore not really a tax at all. With similar fore-ordination, duties on tobacco were inflated, and the inevitable boost to smuggling activities was to be solved by the introduction of yet more numerous and powerful snoopers (in actuality, they cut Customs and Excise, but that's another story). The chief victims were, as usual, found by rounding up the usual suspects, such as the married and rural communities. The removal of the married persons' allowance was justified by an introduction of a children's tax credit, but it was somehow forgotten to be mentioned that there would be a gap of a year between the two.

When you look at the overall effect of the budget, the triumphalism of the speech is quite astonishing. The contempt of Parliament, to say nothing of the ordinary taxpayer, is almost beyond belief. Yet it all passed with scarcely a ripple. Only the headlines endured, and the subsequent questioning was ignored as quibbling. As reality dawned, it only appeared in the form of comments in the broadsheets and the original impression remained intact. I still meet people who are mystified that they are so much harder up when taxes are being cut. It was months before people discovered that, for example, VAT was to be charged on care for the elderly (*The Times*, Letters, July 22, 1999).

12.6 The Nanny State

And always keep a-hold of Nurse
For fear of finding something worse.
Hilaire Belloc, Cautionary Tales

One of the less endearing characteristics of government in the modern age is what has been termed Nannyism. This is the tendency of bureaucrats to take away from individuals their decisions as to what risks they wish to take and keep it for themselves. During the first week of December 1997, alone, the Nanny Government of Britain announced three bans – tobacco advertising, vitamin B6 and beef on the bone. I used to wear a seat belt before they became compulsory because I made the highly personal judgement that it was more likely to save my life than kill me. Nevertheless I was angry when nanny took away that choice and made it compulsory. Anyone who has a relative killed by a seat belt should have the right to sue the Government for compensation.

The Ministry of Agriculture, Fisheries and Food (MAFF) has the most appalling record of nannyism. They would rather do anything rather than let people make their own decisions about risk. For example, they censored the papers of their own researchers to suppress the early evidence that BSE was a risk to humans. Then they swung in the opposite direction and banned beef on the bone. They banned Roseclear, a valuable product for the gardener, because of risks that were already clearly stated on the bottle label. What did Nanny think we were going to do – read the warning "Keep away from eyes" and then say " I think I will spray some of this into my eyes"?

The height of British Nannyism was reached in December, 1997, when Super-Nanny, Jack Cunningham, decreed a ban on the sale of beef on the bone. He saw it as his duty to protect the public from a risk of BSE that was so minuscule that the probable death rate was less than one person in the whole population in a period of ten years. Even organic butchers and abattoirs, with no record of BSE, were denied the right to provide their customers with what they wanted. The British public showed what it thought of this travesty of democracy by rushing out and buying up all the T-bone steaks, ribs and oxtail in the shops. I know because I was too late and they had sold out by the time I got there. There was no problem though – one just went to the local butcher and repeated the mantra "It's for catering" and the deadly stuff was supplied without demur. However, Jack Cunningham only kept the title Super-Nanny for a week. Along came a committee of EU "scientists" proposing a ban on lamb on the bone, from which there was no known risk at all.

Frank Furedi pithily summed up the situation in an article in *The Wall Street Journal Europe* (March 30, 1998) entitled "New Britain: A Regulator's Paradise".

> *It is not surprising that Labour's recent budget claims that environmental protection and safety concerns motivated its attack on car owners. Safety has become the fundamental value of the New Britain, perhaps because it can be used to justify almost anything given a sufficiently expansive definition. The meaning of health now seems to encompass virtually every human experience. The recent government green paper "Our Healthier Nation" aims to supplement exhortations to behave correctly – stop drinking, take exercise, drive slowly, don't smoke, eat salads, forget about meat – with an effective system for regulating behaviour.*

> *Labour's determination to impose a safe lifestyle on society has reached ludicrous proportions. The outcome of this nannying impulse has been to create the impression that the very act of eating has become a highly dangerous experience. Since last December, when it banned the consumption of beef on the bone, New Labour has helped create a climate where food panic is the norm. In January, the British Medical Association declared that the raw meat in your fridge should be treated as if it is infected and could give you food poisoning. This statement was clearly in line with Health Secretary Frank Dobson's previous advice that even those eating average amounts of meat should "consider a reduction."*

> *In February, the use of raw eggs in restaurant dishes was targeted by the Orwellian-sounding Local Authorities' Coordinating Body on Food and Trading Standards. This body called on the government to consider a ban on the use of raw eggs. A few days later it was announced that ministers planned to ban unpasteurised milk in England, since a fifth of the sample tested by the government's laboratory was deemed to be of an unacceptable quality. With one food panic leading to another, it was only a matter of time before British food production itself became the target. A recent report by the self-described National Consumer Council declared that intensive farming methods in Britain represented a growing risk to the consumer. The report warned of "life-threatening illnesses" and noted that the "risk to consumers is incalculable." Next in line for punishment were American agribusiness interests. The frozen food chain Iceland indicated that its 770 stores will reject food which may have been made with genetically modified soya from the United States.*

The recent escalation of the British food panic has coincided with an outbreak of hysteria about the peril of passive smoking. Contrary to all reliable evidence, a government-appointed committee of medical experts declared this month that there was a "definitive link" between a variety of killer diseases and passive smoking. Sensationalist headlines claimed that babies run twice the risk of cot death if their mother smokes and that tens of thousands of non-smokers faced death from environmental smoke. Naturally, the report led to calls for the banning of smoking in public... places. It seems that in British political life, regulation has become even more addictive than smoking cigarettes.

The most grotesque manifestation of the regulatory impulse has been New Labour's attempt to stigmatize car ownership. Numerous ministers have indicated that the "car culture" should be curbed. They have argued for imposing new speed limits, taxing firms who provide parking space to their employees and customers, and penalizing people who drive large cars............

The current obsession with safety seems to have overwhelmed the entire British political class. It is worth noting that one of the final bills passed by the last Conservative government was the Road Traffic Reduction Act. This stigmatization of the car culture has given New Labour a wonderful excuse to raise road taxes.

Likewise, the lack of a forceful opposition to the government's zeal to regulate the production and consumption of food is a worrying symptom of the times. Although an outburst of indignation followed the government ban on sales of T-bone steaks, the opposition has been reluctant to challenge the claim that British food represents a major danger to the population. The fact that British people live longer, lead a healthier life, and eat better food than ever before is rarely acknowledged by public figures. The very mention of a possibility of health risk has the effect of silencing otherwise critical voices.

Risk avoidance has become a major counter-productive industry nurtured by the bureaucrats. The Management of Health and Safety at Work regulations of 1992 imposed an enormous burden on public and private organisations. They were all required to write "risk assessments" covering all their activities, amounting to hundreds of pages a time. Besides the inordinate cost of all this, it eradicated school adventure holidays, crippled sport and added to the bureaucratic nightmare endured by workers at all levels. The country is being strangled in red tape. The rituals of risk avoidance dominate our lives.

12.7 The snoopers

On each landing, opposite the lift shaft, the poster with the enormous face gazed from the wall. It was one of those pictures so contrived that the eyes follow you about when you move.
BIG BROTHER IS WATCHING YOU, the caption beneath it ran.
George Orwell, Nineteen eighty-four

My generation turned against the post-war socialist government for many reasons, but a major one was the successful Tory campaign against *the snoopers*. These were Government officials, paid for by the taxpayer, who snooped around looking for people carrying out trade that would now (but always?) be regarded as normal. So it is with a sense of *déjà vu* that we see it all happening again. The growing army of state sneaks is combing the country for newsagents selling cigarettes to youngsters, butchers selling T-bone steaks or travellers selling legally bought continental wine to a friend. The more the irrational bans and imposts multiply, the more the army of state agents swells. The annual cost of the parasitic regulation industry is about £3 billion. If you think I am straying from the point, just remember how each of these impositions was justified, and ponder what will be next.

The erosions of freedom continue. Next comes roadside drug testing. The vast majority of innocent travellers will have to live with the threat of temporary arrest and ritual humiliation in order that the offending few might be caught. The pawl gives the ratchet another tug. Ordinary people contrast their own harassment with the leniency handed out to real villains by the courts.

When we are outside our homes we are unwittingly under observation much of the time. Television cameras have become so small and cheap that they can be installed all over buildings and town centres. There are now well over a million in Britain. All in a good cause, you might say, but they will also be there if the cause is not so good. The first major television drama I saw was *Nineteen eighty-four,* with Peter Cushing playing the part of Winston Smith. It had a profound effect on me, though some of it seemed a little far-fetched. For example, that people could be under television surveillance everywhere they went. Yet, at the other end of my lifetime it has all happened. When the intrusions of the police get to the point where citizens find them unreasonable, disorder is promoted, as was amply demonstrated during prohibition.

One of the most profound changes I have noticed from my childhood is in the attitudes of ordinary people to the police. I recently went to collect my newspaper in the next village at 8 o'clock one beautiful quiet summer Sunday morning and there were police officers in the middle of the village operating a speed trap. I had a sudden mental throwback to a visit to Czechoslovakia just after the Russian invasion. There was a pompous peak-capped officer holding up his "gun" by the side of the road, watched by a sullen population muttering things like "Haven't they got anything better to do?" Why is there so much hostility to the police when they are only doing their duty and preventing dangerous antisocial behaviour? The old British Bobby, however much now caricatured, was genuinely admired, even loved. It was a cliché that Americans used to say "Your policemen are wonderful", but one the British revelled in. Why has all this died so completely? I think is because they were once Us and are now Them.

The familiar, friendly police of my childhood had one duty, to maintain the rule of law and order. Now the politicians have turned them into anonymous tax-collectors, traffic wardens, snoopers, number-crunchers and petty bureaucrats. Their main duty is to maximise their computer norms. Even when I moved into my present village twenty years ago, we had a village Bobby, who knew everybody in the village (which he patrolled on foot) and all the villains in the surrounding area. He often dealt with minor offences, or prevented them from occurring, by means of a quiet word. Most importantly of all, he knew immediately if there were strangers on his patch. If we see policemen now, they are total strangers from a nick miles away, skulking in a car in a back street near the village pub. If a burglary is reported, you are lucky to receive a visit in less than two hours, and that will be desultory, discouraged and discouraging. There is a telephone number to ring if you see anything suspicious, but usually nobody at the other end. A publican reported suspected poachers on the river Test. When the police eventually arrived, they asked "Can you tell us where the river is?" You have to feel sorry for the individual policemen. Policing, like so many modern activities is done by numbers. The simplest arrest generates hundreds of pieces of paper.

Crime prevention produces no computer data and therefore no brownie points. As the police withdraw from crime prevention, private organisations take over the task. Even run-down estates in London now employ security guards and television cameras, sometimes with dramatic effect, so the villains simply commute to rural areas, where they ply their trade with impunity.

12.8 Putliar and Daisnaid

I'm the king of the castle and you're a dirty rascal.
Traditional children's rhyme

One of the least amiable characteristics of politicians is the change of attitude they reveal when they at last manage to seize the levers of power. This can be summed up in two slogans *Pull Up The Ladder, I'm All Right* and *Do As I Say, Not As I Do*. The Minister of Transport with two Jaguars not only urges everyone else to cut their driving but penalises them so much that they cannot afford to keep their cars. Anyway, what does he do with two Jaguars, use them like roller skates? He makes heavy jokes about this that do not go down too well in rural areas, where people are desperately trying to hang on to their ancient cars as their last contact with civilisation. He often travels to his engagements by helicopter at the public expense. Most people don't mind that the Prime Minister sends his children to the most select schools, but they do mind when he supports legislation to prevent them from doing the same. The whole government enacts SIF inspired legislation, but make damned sure it does not afflict their personal comfort. How much greenhouse gas was released by the hundreds of aeroplanes that flew all the nobs and SIFs to Kyoto? Does the Deputy Prime Minister really religiously turn off the stand-by on his video recorder every day and then grovel around to reprogram the time and date when he wants to use it? What has all this to do with wrong numbers? Think about it.

12.9 The Ben Turpin syndrome

Very interesting – but stupid.
Rowan and Martin's Laugh-In

Ben Turpin was a character who turned up in a number of silent films. He was seriously cross-eyed, and a running joke was his tendency to aim at a target and hit something completely different. He is a good metaphor for a lot of modern politics.

Heroin and crack-cocaine addicts face a ruined life and probably a sordid death. To feed their habit they need an annual income greater than the Prime Minister's. They are responsible for fifty billion pounds worth of crime per year. The pushers openly trade on the streets of cities and even villages. Meanwhile the Government directs vast resources to the pursuit of drivers who have had a couple of drinks and are demonstrably a negligible risk to their fellow man, shopkeepers who sell cigarettes to youngsters and butchers who sell T-bone steaks.

When I ask my neighbours what they worry about most, the answer is almost always "being burgled". Many of them have had this dreadful experience, some more than once. I know couples who never go out together because of the fear of leaving the home unattended. When did you last hear a Government spokesman talking about burglary and what they are going to do about it? Where are the single issue fanatics pressing for action on this or other crimes that ordinary people live in dread of? Where are the big newspaper headlines or TV spectaculars? Chief Constables boast of falling crime rates, yet in many areas over 90% of burglaries remain unsolved. Having roundly abused them and their ilk, let me put in a good word for the Audit Commission. They spotted the fact that police authorities were cooking the books on the rates of solving crime (*The Sunday Times*, June 21 1999) which are, in fact, even lower than published. We are supposed to have forgotten that there was to be the government that was **tough on crime and tough on the causes of crime**. In some areas the rate of crime detection is as low as five per officer per year. It would be bootless to ask what they are doing with their time; we have already covered that. Their priorities are decided by SIFs and bureaucrats, not by the ordinary people who pay some £200 a year for the privilege of having them around.

It might seem by this stage that the author has a bit of a bee in his bonnet about burglary. Too right! Here is a number for you – according to the British Crime Survey of 1997, just under 6 per cent of households in England and Wales experienced at least one burglary (either attempted or successful). Many people have their lives completely shattered by this experience. No amount of insurance money can compensate for the loss of precious personal items or the invasion of one's home.

Animal rights campaigners were responsible for more deaths than all the hunters put together. They released captive mink, which have infested large stretches of our riverbanks, killing millions of creatures and causing the extinction of species in many areas, including the one in which I live. I used to spend hours watching water voles at work and play. Why is it these people direct their affections towards ruthless and indiscriminate killers, such as foxes, mink and swans? Alas, my beloved voles are no more. The vandalisers of GM crops are causing farmers to carry on using excessive amounts of pesticides and nitrogen, which they claim to oppose.

12.10 Rationing by Price

> *It's the same the whole world over,*
> *It's the poor what gets the blame,*
> *It's the rich what gets the gravy.*
> *Ain't it all a bleedin shame?*
> *World War I army song*

As we mentioned earlier, money represents a form of measurement. It gives a way of comparing, say, a new car with a life insurance policy. It is how we know that a footballer is worth fifty professors. If we went back to bartering, the complexity of our dealings would be unsustainable. The usual means of applying measurement to goods and services is the market. When it comes to dealing with the market modern societies tend swing from one dangerous extreme to another – rampant market fundamentalism and rigid central control.

The problem with market fundamentalism is that is based on the Darwinian principle of survival of the fittest. Under such a system extinctions are bound to occur. In the market-dominated eighties, for example, Britain allowed many of its indigenous industries to die (electronics, ship-building etc.). It was doing it all again with the few remaining manufacturing industries while I was writing this book. The problem with this is that you make yourselves a permanent client state. All is well as long as someone else is prepared to sell you the ships and chips that you need and is willing to buy your services in return, but you have given a hostage to fortune. The current philosophy is that a modern state can exist on service industries alone. At best this is unproven. Whether, when times are bad, we can exist by taking in each other's washing remains to be seen.

The alternative to the rampant market is rigid centralism. This was carried out quite successfully in the former Soviet Union until the competition of Star Wars provided a breaking point and the whole thing collapsed. It was not a pleasant system to live under, but it worked, and there is even some nostalgia for it in places where the market mechanism has proved even less comfortable. There is nothing unconservative in appreciating the valued of state provision. The free health service in Britain was a wonderful achievement that has gradually been whittled away. Spending on health, as on other infrastructure, is lower than in the rest of Europe. Dentistry in particular has seen a covert privatisation and what now passes for a National Health provision rations by price so severely that rotten teeth have once again returned to the British scene. Many people who are not officially poor do not take their prescribed medications because of the rising prescription charges.

The current system commonly adopted is the free market subject to tampering by governments and one of the control mechanisms is rationing by price. Governments manipulate access to goods and services they wish to control by means of taxes and duties. This is quite a separate activity from raising revenue, though of course it does help. It is one area where SIFs exercise and inordinate degree of influence. Your access to cars, tobacco, alcohol, parking, motorways etc. is increasingly being determined by how rich you are. Some people regard fines for illegal parking as an everyday business expense that is routinely dealt with by the secretary. There are many others for whom a parking fine incurred in an emergency represents a major family financial disaster. The parking tax is a lucrative form of income for local councils and it is justified on ecological grounds. All goods and services have a natural number attached to them, their market price. As soon as this mechanism is interfered with problems begin to occur.

Apart from the fact that they are so manifestly unfair, the real worry about such methods is the incentive they give to crime. Young men, already feeling excluded from society, desire the goods and services that are so widely advertised and available to those with money. They cannot earn it, so they turn to crime as a means of achieving their desires. Excessive duties also give rise to a dramatic growth of smuggling and its associated crimes of violence. SIFs give governments the means to cloak these imposts in the form of "environmental" or "health" taxes. Not only does the Nanny State withdraw access to the things of which it disapproves, it does so selectively. Why poor people should be held proportionately more responsible for health and the environment, while relatively the rich are relatively excused, is not explained. The people who suffer most are the moderately poor in rural communities. They beggar themselves to keep hold of the ancient car that is their only protection against total isolation, and year after year the Government piles taxes on vehicles and fuel in the name of environmentalism.

One of the worst examples of rationing by price that I came across brought tears to my eyes. It was when I attended an awards dinner held at the Science Museum. At the entrance I saw the list of admission prices, including those for children, and they were not modest. When I was a schoolboy, living in a poor part of North London, our parents would give us our tube fare and some sandwiches and we would spend the day in the museums around Exhibition Row. We went from museum to museum educating ourselves while having fun. That this experience should become a commodity restricted by price seems to me one of the saddest manifestations of the rigours of market fundamentalism.

It has not ended. Much of the legislation in the pipeline is concerned with provisions to charge for access to various amenities.

12.11 The means test

When I was young I heard a lot about the means test. It did not have any significance to me and, as it was mostly spouted about by socialists, I dismissed it as an irrelevant piece of propaganda. It first made a serious impact on me in the mid 1980s, when I had to counsel students, and even their parents. Many middle class families had started businesses, largely at the prompting of the party I then espoused, only to have them destroyed by the draconian budgets of Geoffrey Howe and the recession they induced. In practice there is no such thing as limited liability for small businesses, and they found themselves deeply in debt over personal guarantees. With the instinct of their class to keep the family home many of them took on onerous mortgages. This was hard enough to endure, but when their children became old enough to go to university the discovered that, not only had they inflicted real poverty on their families, but they had virtually deprived their children of higher education. The student support grant for higher education was means tested, and only the tax allowable part of a mortgage was permitted to be included. Fortunately there were a number of educational charities, some of which I got to know quite well, and they were often able to fill the gap.

The means test is one of the most offensive forms of measurement. It purports to measure wealth, but in fact only measures income. These parents often had high incomes, but the net amount they had to live on was often less than that of people who were officially poor. The means test only allowed them to offset the amount of mortgage that was tax deductible, which was often a small and decreasing proportion. Those who benefited most were the feckless, who had not even tried to provide a stable family home. Many unmarried couples only declared the mother's income on the form. Now the means test is becoming more and more prevalent. Student loans, payments for prescriptions and more and more impositions are determined by this spurious form of measurement. It is just another form of line drawing, and a damned unfair one.

12.12 Economic (Mis)Management

If it ain't broke, don't fix it.
That's the trouble with government. Fixing things that aren't broken
and not fixing things that are broken.
Bert Lance

I may well be wrong, but I feel that I am as well qualified as anyone to comment on the state of British industry. I have been an apprentice. I have swept, turned, milled, soldered, tried to interpret impossible engineering drawings – even issued impossible engineering drawings. I have run my own company through the recession of the early eighties, an experience I would not like to repeat. I have also lunched in boardrooms of major companies and acted as consultant to some of the biggest and smallest companies in the UK.

Nevertheless, the idea of a simple engineer commenting on such weighty matters as the world economy will be ridiculed by those who have appointed themselves as the experts in the field. However, we only have their word that they are any more qualified than, say, a fish market trader to make such pronouncements. Since the dawn of civilisation men have tried to confuse others with various forms of hocus pocus. Economics, like psychiatry, is no more than a series of untested hypotheses, and has made an equal contribution to the sum of human misery. Yet these self-appointed gurus have the ear of the world's leaders. They call economics the dismal science. Dismal it certainly is, but science it ain't. Like Freudian psychology, it is no more than a train of unsubstantiated conjectures. Take any two economists and they will give you different prognostications, but events will prove both of them wrong.

A fashionable branch of economics is macro-economics. A macro-economist is like a physician who only looks at one measure, say weight, to determine bodily health. So, though the right arm might be withered and there is a massive tumour in the gut, as long as these things balance each other everything is satisfactory. One of the greatest dangers faced by the world economy is that posed by doctrinaire finance ministers. They get fixed ideas into their heads, usually picked up from remote academics, and no amount of input from the real world will displace them. If such a minister is in control of the finances one of the leading economies, then the whole world is in trouble. By the mid-nineties the world economy had become a relatively tranquil millpond, waiting for someone to throw a rock into it.

At this point in the narrative I had planned to insert a historical discussion of the consequences of numerical monomania (q.v.) in ruling politicians. It was to be largely based on two incidents in recent British experience. The first was the disastrous Chancellorship of Geoffrey Howe at the beginning of the eighties. The number in question was inflation, which to be fair had been hopelessly mismanaged in the previous decades. The result of the ensuing monomania, however, was that the world's first industrial nation committed industrial suicide. Admittedly the prime enemies of national prosperity, the trade union bosses, had been defeated, but it was what is known in the trade as a Phyrric victory, since the people destroying British industry were defeated by destroying British industry. The worst aspect of this debacle was that the only piece of economic luck that Britain had experienced in living memory went completely to waste. After years of having to cope with oil crises, Britain suddenly had an oil bonanza. The rational outcome of this should have been that the nation would enter the twenty first century with the finest infrastructure (transport, education etc.) in the world. Instead it would have an infrastructure that was seriously run down, to say the least. All that extra money was spent on paying people to do nothing. It is a remarkable testament to the power of political propaganda that there are still people who look back to that period as the golden age.

The second incident involved obsession with a different number, the exchange rate. At the end of the eighties Britain had joined the European exchange rate mechanism (ERM). There was nothing wrong with this decision in principle, but it was a case of "Sorry, wrong number!" The level at which the Government chose to defend the pound at all costs was known by everyone who travelled around Europe to be absurd. To cut a long story short, we had Black Wednesday. George Soros and Co made a lot of money and the British taxpayer lost a lot.

I was, however, moved to abandon all my notes and copious press cuttings on these matters, as, while I was half way through writing this book, the new Labour Government created an experiment in numerical monomania in its most pristine form, one that I could monitor as it happened. It decided to abandon political control over interest rates (and who can argue against that?) but it appointed an academic body of people (the Bank of England's Monetary Policy Committee) to take control. Most remarkable of all, however, was that this body was charged with controlling only one number, the rate of inflation. Never mind unemployment, industrial output, bankruptcies, trade balance, homelessness and general misery; as long as this one number was maintained within the prescribed limits the had done its job. I could not have wished a better test of my hypothesis that numerical monomania was an inevitable route to disaster, but I would dearly like not to have been part of the experiment. I decided to monitor the progress of what I thought would be the inevitable recession.

One of the classic forms of measurement abuse mentioned earlier is the use of out-dated information, and this is the one adopted by government in trying to run the economy. As we have observed, this is a complex, non-linear system which presents what engineers call a multivariate control problem. The chart of interest rates under control of the MPC looked exactly like the results of the demonstration mentioned in chapter 2; first steering violently in one direction and then equally violently in the other.

The recession that never was

Unfortunately, my pristine experiment in economics came to the grief that always occurs in this field of human endeavour. External events came to dominate the scene. This situation, however, only served to highlight the absurdity of the British situation.

I became finally convinced that a major recession was inevitable in January of 1998. This was on a mission to Singapore and Malaysia I had undertaken on behalf of my University, one of a number I had been on over a period of six years. It was clear that the economies of those countries were declining rapidly. More so in Malaysia, where grandiose schemes of development had produced a weakness that was far less evident in Singapore. On my return I alerted as many people as would listen to me of what was coming. In particular, I advised my small business contacts to get liquid and avoid extending themselves. I resolved to monitor the progress of the recession as it developed. To my astonishment the whole establishment, Government, the City and the media were behaving as though everything in the garden was lovely. The stock market continued to climb. The Bank of England Monetary Policy Committee were still talking about inflation as the major problem. I thought it self-evident that it would be the least of our problems by the turn of the century. Unbelievably, they continued to hike interest rates. The Government, basking in the illusion that a strong currency signified a strong economy, adopted a complacent attitude.

The official definition of a recession is two quarters of negative growth of the economy. What possible value is there in a measure like that? You don't know you have had it until nine months later. It is like making giving birth the definition of pregnancy. The only merit it has is indisputable accuracy, which hardly makes up for a total lack of usefulness as a measurement tool.

In April 1998 the first signs began to show. Small businessmen gathering in village pubs were exchanging experiences of the difficulty of getting money out of customers. For Sale signs were beginning to hang about outside houses in sought after areas, where they would normally be snapped up as soon as they were put on the market. I knew that the recession had really begun to bite by May. It was when I heard a group of salesmen, propping up the bar in the village pub, all agree that "It is getting hard out there." Now salesmen are the most optimistic people on earth. They have to be, to cope with the indignities of their calling. When they say things are getting bad, things really are getting bad. The news filters slowly up through the industrial hierarchy and six months later appears as a downturn in an index of industrial optimism, yet another hopelessly delayed measure.

How did it all start? As I have stated, the world economy is like a pool with its surface gently undulating, until someone throws a rock into it. It was all down to one man, Ryutaro Hashimoto, Prime Minister of Japan. The perceptive Anatole Kaletsky pinpointed the exact moment in an article entitled "*Another fine mess Japan's got Asia into*" (*The Times* 13th January, 1997):

> *The catalyst for the chain reaction of financial panic across Asia was the enormous tax increase imposed by Mr Hashimoto last April. This tax increase may have been the stupidest and most pointlessly destructive economic action undertaken by any advanced capitalist country since America's Smoot-Hawley Tariff act of 1930.*

We in Britain had seen before the consequences of a sudden deflation of the economy for reasons of dogma under Chancellors Healey and Howe. Within weeks the Japanese economy suffered the only too predictable collapse. The world's second largest industrial complex began to dump its products in Asian and world markets, just as protectionist America had done in the great depression sixty years previously. Japan's banks were highly exposed in the burgeoning economies of East Asia, and a vicious cycle of deflation ensued. The over-protected and rigid Japanese financial system faced collapse. One by one the dominoes fell: Thailand, Korea, Hong Kong, Indonesia, Malaysia, and Singapore. The rest of the world looked on complacently, as there was a pause in the spread of the contagion. Then Russia, beset by horrendous internal political problems took a massive economic nosedive, leaving a large number of Western banks exposed. The contagion spread to Brazil (though economic orthodoxy maintains that there is no contagion).

In the face of all this, the complacency shown in the West beggars belief. As late as September 1998, when I sat down to edit this section, Wim Duisenberg, the President of the European Central Bank, declared that Europe would remain "an oasis of peace". The Bank of England's Monetary Policy Committee declined to reduce interest rates, which were at a destructive 5% above inflation. Meanwhile consumer confidence dived to a new low, house prices had begun to fall, with for-sale signs accumulating in the streets, and business failures were rising. Manufacturing, which after two decades of neglect had been reduced to a mere 20% of GDP, but still represented 60% of exports, was entering a downward spiral, with exports at a 15 year low.

People like me, who declined to celebrate the phenomenon of inward investment, the arrival of foreign companies keen to exploit the docility and cheapness of British labour to create offshore manufactories, were as usual labelled as cynics and pessimists. This phenomenon was supposed to compensate us for the loss of indigenous industries during the artificially created recession of the early eighties. The developing recession of the late nineties fully justified the cynical view. In the face of shrinking markets companies naturally closed down their overseas operations rather than home ones. All the subsidies and perks that attracted them went for nought: still, it's only taxpayers' money.

It was on June 4th, 1998, however, that there occurred one of the most bizarre episodes in the annals of economic mismanagement. It had become clear that the recession was no longer just an approaching threat. All the classic signs were there – falling order books, delayed payments, gloom from every industrialist to whom I spoke. Yet the remote, ineffectual dons of the MPC met and voted to **increase** interest rates from 7.25% to 7.5%. It was not just the wrongnesss of the decision that was mind boggling, but more its sheer irrelevance. Almost to a man, the journalistic economic establishment applauded their action. Even the normally percipient Anatole Kaletsky, who had alone spotted the trigger event in Japan, wrote that the MPC did the right thing. The honourable exception was David Smith of the *Sunday Times*. The excuse for this extraordinary lurch was that the Office for National Statistics had produced figures to show that the rise in earnings had jumped to 5%. Talk about the abuse of measurement! Anyone living in the real world knew that this was nonsense. The only people getting serious pay rises were those living in the fool's paradise of the City of London. As it transpired the estimate was later reduced to less than 4%.

Did anyone outside the coterie of the economic establishment seriously believe that this putative wage inflation had the slightest bearing on what was going to happen to the economy over the coming year? The MPC were like children on a beach hastily digging a moat round their sandcastle while a tsunami loomed over them. An apt simile, in that it all started in Japan, inapt in that they would not be but the ones to be engulfed, and would remain in their comfortable salaried positions while the unemployed and the bankrupted entrepreneurs bore the brunt of their dereliction.

It is necessary here to pay tribute to another honourable exception. DeAnne Julius, the only women on the committee and the only one with experience of the real world, was the solitary vote for a cut in interest rates. How did this bunch of buffoons come to be appointed? Apparently it was delegated by the Chancellor to his economic advisor, Ed Balls, another name of strangely Dickensian aptness, who managed to dig up a weird collection of Bank of England insiders and theoretical economists. No wonder "academic" has come to be a pejorative term! There were four professors on this committee, two from the LSE, one from Cambridge and one from All Souls, Oxford. They were all adherents of macro-economic theory, pure academics with no experience of the real world between them. It is doubtful whether any of them even had a mortgage, and if he did it was probably on favourable insider terms. As they made a cool £125,000 a year for attending the committee on top of their secure academic jobs they are unlikely to experience the misery they inflict on their fellow countrymen. Of course, when the time comes to pass the buck "unexpected" external influences will be to blame.

As the recession developed, so the foreign investors in the UK withdrew their favours. One by one they closed down or postponed factory developments: Seimens, Fujitsu, Philips and many others retracted into their home bases. Nevertheless the stock market carried on booming, the 1999 budget was built on optimistic assumptions about economic growth. The stock market rose from one record level to the next week after week. The internet stock bubble was a particularly dominant feature. The official line was that there was no recession and there was not going to be one. Indeed, in macro-economic terms there was no recession. Manufacturing industry might be closing down, throwing people onto the streets, but the service industries were booming, the City was awash with money, fuelling an explosion of share prices that belied the actual value of the companies involved. The same thing was happening in the USA.

The thing I still find most extraordinary about all this is that the recession still never officially happened. Entrepreneurs in the north might have gone bankrupt and skilled manufacturing workers lose their jobs, but to the macro-economists everything in the garden was lovely.

Financiers and journalists who based their activities on the City of London, Government ministers and academic economists celebrated the success of the macro-economy in avoiding the precipice. Nevertheless, however good the party, the time comes when you have to pay the bill. Of course inflation did fall, but it might be argued that this was a world rather than a national phenomenon. Britain was once again dividing into two nations, as marked out by house prices, which were booming in some places and stagnant in others. You could by a whole street in certain northern towns for less than the price of a small semi in London, but that is macro-economics for you.

12.13 The Department of pointless gestures

One of the many irritating characteristics of politicians is their tendency to harangue the public with meaningless truisms and gestures of mind-blowing triviality. Much of the advice they give to a weary electorate is the equivalent of saying "If you never get wet, you will never be attacked by sharks." But there is another newer variant that is equally trivial and irrelevant. This gesture politics is usually aimed at appeasing some SIF pressure group or other.

Consider, for example, the great no-stand-by crusade. Initiated by Gore (who else?) but embraced by his British double, this was a campaign against the tiny trickle of electricity used by devices like television sets, whether they are on or not, because it results indirectly in a steady emission of carbon dioxide. On the corner of School Lane, near where I live, the bureaucrats decided to install a mercury light. It was meant to add to the safety of children coming home from school in the winter, but it burns away all night. It has taken away one of the great pleasures of my life – admiring the night sky as I walk back from the village pub – a pleasure I learned as a child during wartime blackout London. When you fly across the world at night, you can see the residential areas picked out by sodium lights, even in some of the poorest countries. They are largely there to provide an element of security. Astronomical observation has become all but impossible in these areas, as billions of watts in energy pour out into space. Yet we are enjoined to turn off the stand-by on our television sets and video recorders in order to make a contribution to the war against global warming.

From the same motivation a bus lane was instituted on one of Britain's busiest motorways. Press photographs showed this lane entirely empty while the other three were blocked by stationary traffic, all belching out fumes and the dreaded carbon dioxide. This gesture was not only pointless; it had a negative effect by increasing journey times, thereby increasing fuel consumption and pollution, to say nothing of the added economic costs. The responsible minister, known as "Two Jags" ostentatiously leaves his cars and helicopter behind and travels to a by-election by train and bus.

A leaflet issued with aerosol inhalers explained that they had been changed to a less efficient form. CFCs were removed as a carrier in order to protect the environment. How the tiny amounts of this dreaded material in children's lungs managed to get into the ozone layer and disrupt it was not explained.

A related phenomenon is the modern form of Bowdlerisation. A statue of Harold Wilson was unveiled without his trademark pipe. A famous photograph of Isambard Kingdom Brunel was doctored to remove his ever-present cigar. The comic book hero of my childhood, Desperate Dan, was deprived of his beloved cow pie. Everywhere signs of politically incorrect activity were quietly erased.

12.14 The Rubber Ruler

In many areas of life we are obliged to adopt a measure that is far from ideal, particularly in social matters. Nevertheless, however limited in value it might be, such a measure enables us to monitor change. One of the most inexcusable forms of political number abuse is the change of measure in mid-stream. The classical example was the unemployment figures of the 1980s, which were soaring out of control as a result of draconian financial policies based on the dogma of the time. The Government simply changed the definition of unemployment, and more than once. This not only reduced the embarrassing numbers dramatically, but it made comparisons with the past impossible. A subsequent Government, embarrassed that their audit failed to show an improvement in hospital waiting lists, changed the definition. You had to go on a waiting list to get on the waiting list. Tobacco became officially addictive because the official definition of addiction was changed. The embarrassing figures on university participation were cancelled overnight by a change in the definition of a university.

These elastic measures are just another example of the asymmetry in the contract between government and the governed. If a pub landlord suddenly changed the size of his glasses, the weights and measures snoopers would be down on him like a ton of bricks. Governments simply change the length of the ruler to suit their purposes. The modern politician is an illusionist – like the comedy tailor who grabs the surplus material at the back of the jacket, so that the client can see in the mirror that it is a perfect fit. Presentation is everything. Up against a wall, politicians cry "We are not getting our policies over" when they should be admitting "Our policies are crap." What chance does real science stand in this world of smoke, mirrors and rubber rulers?

12.15 Politics and Science

In the mid-eighties I was so concerned about the neglect of science that I got involved with a movement called Save British Science and was on the committee for a while. We had a meeting with a few sympathetic MPs at the Athenaeum. I remember trying to make the point that one reason that a wide range of science was necessary was because, for example, the next health crisis would involve areas of expertise that could not be predicted. It was therefore with a sense of *déjà vu* that I read more than a decade later of the evidence of Professor Anthony Epstein to the BSE enquiry (*Research Fortnight*, 11th March, 1998):

> Support for basic scientific research has been consistently run down and restricted in the UK since the early 1980s and the sudden unexpected emergence of BSE at a time when work in the field was minimal and experts few, provides a grim warning of the dangers of letting many aspects of basic science wither for lack of funds.

The problem, however, is not simply one of neglect. What science there is has become increasingly shackled by the mounting bureaucratic obstruction. The Health and Safety at Work Act alone has inflicted enormous damage on science and scientific education. As Professor Jack Pridham (*The Times* July 5 1999) points out:

> It has created a climate of excessive caution, which has taken chemicals deemed to be dangerous from our shelves, reduced the quality of laboratory exercises, disrupted field studies and spawned endless paper work.
> It can be claimed that "health and safety" offers a degree of protection against litigation but, all in all, it has reduced professionalism, enthusiasm and spontaneity in science.

This last sentence really sums up what the dead weight of bureaucracy is doing to all of human activity. You could apply it to almost anything – children's playgrounds, restaurants, cheesemaking etc.

An unfortunate aspect of the politics of science is the fact that the junk science debate has become polarised to a left-right one. This means that the fragile anti-junk movement gets caught up in so-called conservative causes. Just one example is the gun lobby in America, which contaminates even the Junk Science Home Page. The murder rate in England has been falling for 800 years (*The Times*, June 24, 1999); from 200 per million to 14 per million. In this respect America, with 100 per million is still stuck in the 17th Century. 60% of those are committed with guns, as compared with 8% in Britain. According to CNN (April 30, 1999) 13 child deaths are caused by firearms in the USA every day. Half a million guns are stolen there every year. Wary as I am of body-count politics, I find it difficult to resist the proposition that British-style gun control could save 10,000 American lives a year. The gun lobby, however, tells us that *it's people who kill, not guns*.

12.16 Television

Everybody's got an angle
Anon

TV has become, within a few decades, the most powerful influence in our lives. More than any other part of society it sets the political agenda. Most of us spend some hours watching it every day. Politicians use it as their main tool to obtain and maintain power. One who has the misfortune to have a bad TV image (such as the unfortunate and brilliant Alec Douglas Hume) is destined to be a non-starter. Sound bites are honed to perfection and carefully placed where they will be picked up by hungry news-hounds.

The first time I got involved in a major TV presentation, the director gathered all the participants together to address them, His first words have always stuck in my mind – "What you have to understand is that television is an illusion." Unfortunately most people do not understand this, or they forget it. A series of scandals broke out in early 1999 about the use of actors pretending to be genuine participants in those grisly confessional shows, but this was only the tip of an iceberg (to coin a phrase).

On Saturday 13th February 1999 I looked in the *Radio Times* to see whether there was anything worth watching. There was a BBC programme in the series *Correspondent* called *Arctic Warning* which sounded as though it might be interesting, so I turned it on. You have probably guessed that it was our old friend Global Warming again. The programme was forty-five minutes long. Forty of them were taken up with evidence that the Arctic is warming up, which was hardly surprising since, as I am sure you are tired of reading, the planet has been warming up for over four hundred years. The other five minutes comprised interjections by various people about what **we** were doing to our planet, the climate scientists are right when they say... Experts on the climate were holding forth with the usual warnings about floods, diseases, tornadoes etc. There was not one sceptical scientific voice in the programme. The only opposition came from an oilman, who, as was heavily implied, had an axe to grind. BP were introduced as a welcome and selfless convert to the global warming family (see the cynical old Junkman for an analysis of how BP would obtain economic advantage over its American rivals if emissions were cut). No one would dream that far more qualified scientists had objected to the Kyoto agreement than had supported it. It was all stuff we had heard before (the BBC, for example, did it in the January of the previous year) but it was accompanied by emotive scenes of melting ice and Inuit who were desperate because their way of life was changing. The Norse Greenlanders who were forced out half a millennium ago by the advancing ice (which is still there) were pretty pissed off too.

It is not, however, the fact that this programme was the same hoary old stuff that I wish to address. It is the fact that it typifies the genre. The director starts out with an angle and gathers material (usually of a striking visual form) that confirms his thesis. Any dissenting voices are crudely suppressed, unless they can be held up to ridicule or shown to be venally self-interested. Thus the political orthodoxy is built up and maintained. You will see whistle blowers from the tobacco industry but never those from the EPA. The proponents of the two sides of the argument are equally mendacious, but one side is treated with kid gloves.

The average American sees 10,000 deaths on TV by the time they reach the age of 15, but most of them have never seen a dead body in reality. It is all a part of the fantasy world that is television. There is a continuum of program types from pure fantasy to apparent fact. The public largely form their view of the world from these programs and are often unable to unravel fact from fancy. I was sitting in a Dallas hotel recovering from jet lag and turned on the afternoon children's television. It was a Hollywood film. By the time the boy hero had disposed of one of the villains by turning him into a human torch with an improvised flame-thrower I could not take any more, so I switched off and picked up the local paper. The story was of yet another mass school shooting. **How could it happen here?** was the headline. It is in the media, however, that the political agenda are set. In particular, scares get audiences. An inside story in that paper was another fatuous carcinogenic substance scare, which was repeated when I turned back to the TV news. Watching television today it is hard to believe that life expectancy is higher than it has ever been in human history and still increasing; that health and wealth among the populace are at levels undreamed of a lifetime ago.

As a result of all this media hype, people develop a totally distorted view of the nature of risk. As often happens, the worst sufferers are the children. They are now virtually housebound and have no opportunity to develop the capacity to cope with the world on their own. Cocooned, for fear of the terrible diseases their parents hear about, they do not even have the opportunity to build up their immune systems. There is a paedophile on every street corner and a drunken driver round it. When, at last, they get some liberty as teenagers, is it surprising that so many of them seem to go off the rails. Clearly, this misperception of risk is a fundamental weakness in our society. How does it come about? By wrong numbers!

Chapter 13

Living with risk

Whose life is it anyway?
Title of a play by Brian Clark

Life is risk. As soon as you get out of bed you take a risk. If you decide to stay in bed you take a risk. About twenty Britons die every year as a result of falling out of bed, while thirty die in their bath. Around 600 die on their own stairs. You can choke to death on a lump of health food. A successful life consists in calculating the risk-reward ratios and acting accordingly. You might win, you might lose. It should be regarded as a fundamental human right to be able to make such calculations without being lied to about the risks, or the rewards, but it is not.

The Puritans of the past worried about their immortal souls, and they saved the immortal souls of others by burning them to death. The modern Puritans are more concerned with the immortality of their bodies. People have always found it difficult to accept that they are going to die and it seems to be in human nature to believe that the avoidance of certain sins will ensure immortality. Only the sins change with fashion, so as adultery and sodomy become acceptable they are replaced with drinking and smoking as the mortal sins. Saving people from themselves has always been a source of noble satisfaction.

13.1 The Nature of Risk

The days of man are but as grass: for he flourisheth as the flower of the field.
For as soon as the wind goeth over it, it is gone; and the place thereof shall know it no more.
Psalm 103

It is, of course, impossible to extract human emotion from the risk/reward calculation. Statistically, air travel is one of the safest forms, yet a large proportion of the population is terrified of it. I know people who will not go near a plane but drive their cars like suicidal maniacs. The chances of being killed in an air crash are about three in a million journeys. If this seems a big risk, put it in context by imagining that you fly every day of your life. You would have to do this for over 900 years before your reached an evens chance of being killed. In any given area of activity there is a tendency for the risk-effect product to remain constant. Thus, when the Americans built the levees, they exchanged a large risk of small floods for a small risk of large floods. Similar rules apply to energy production or transport. It is in the field of health, however, that the greatest amount of anxiety is generated, often deliberately.

About one third of us are going to get cancer and a quarter of us will die from it. This is an uncomfortable thought and one we prefer to put at the back of our minds. We might increase the risk by coming into contact with carcinogens, known and unknown, but the main reason for the dramatic increase in deaths from cancer is that people used to die of cholera, TB, bubonic plague etc and did not live long enough to get round to contracting it. What people are entitled to know is how any action will affect their life expectancy, or to be more accurate the expectancy of a tolerable life. What the pressure groups were telling us was the maximum intake of alcohol the actuaries were telling us was the optimum for life expectancy. In fact, life expectancy is not enough information on which to make a reasonable choice; an extra ten years in a state of senile dementia is not an appealing prospect. What we are entitled to be told how our actions a likely to effect both our length and quality of life. We need to get this information from a disinterested source, and there is none.

Mortality statistics hide a lot of risk that is relevant to most of us. Suppose you die of heart failure after ten years of dementia? You contribute one unit to the statistics of mortality. They say nothing about the quality of life you had. The causes that medics write on death certificates are really quite arbitrary. Someone who has had ten years as a human vegetable with Alzheimer's is quite likely to be recorded as having died of heart failure, which most of us die of in the long run.

13.2 The facts of death

The days of our age are threescore years and ten; and though men may be strong that they come to fourscore year: yet is their strength then but labour and sorrow; so soon passeth it away and we are gone. The Book of Common Prayer

As Benjamin Franklin said, death, like taxes, is a certainty in life. It is something most of us would rather not think about. Indeed, dwelling on it is a rather pointless activity and an indication of a morbid mental state. As we grow older we experience the trauma of bereavement, totally devastating, however much we prepare for it. Exploitation of our fear of death is one of the nastier practices of the zealots and entrepreneurs who seek to influence us with their wrong numbers. In order to understand what they are up to it is necessary to appreciate some of the basic statistical facts. First, what is the normal state of affairs?

The diagram of figure 13.1 shows the probability of death plotted against age. The curve is a well known (Gompertz) form fitted to data obtained from taken from UN Demographic Yearbook 1996 for UK males. This shape appears frequently in science and engineering, especially in the theory of failure (such as the voltage at which insulation breaks down). It is a close fit except for the very young and the very old.

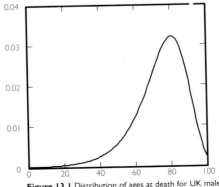

Figure 13.1 Distribution of ages at death for UK males

195

It will be seen that the most probable age at death (the mode) occurs at about 80 years. Because the distribution is skewed to the left, the average age at death (the mean) is lower at 73.7. This correlates closely with the figure given in *Whitakers Almanac* for 1998, which is 74.1. For females the figure is 79.4.

As an individual there is a limited amount of information that you can glean from such a curve. For example, if you reach 60 say, how many more years can you expect to live on average? If some circumstance increases your chance of death at one age, how will it affect it at a later age? The latter is not a simple question as the sum of all the probabilities (the area under the curve) has to add up to one, since we all die, and a change at one age affects all the others. We obviously need a different and more useful curve.

The case of the senile statistician

An elderly statistician looked at the above curve and was thrilled to find it going down rapidly at the point corresponding to his age. If I can stay alive a bit longer, he thought, I will be practically immortal. What is the fallacy in his reasoning? It is the fact that he has already passed through all the hazards of life at earlier ages. The only part of the distribution that affects him is the area to the right of his present age. In order to adjust for this defect we have to divide the probability by that area. The result is an important sort of curve that appears under various names. Engineers call it the conditional failure rate, while biologists call it the force of mortality. For simplicity we will call it mortality and define it as the probability of dying in the next year on condition that death has not already occurred. This gives us a completely diffeent sort of curve.

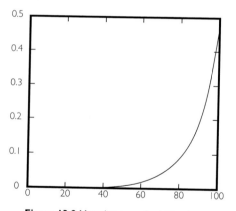

Figure 13.2 Mortality curve for UK males

This curve is the well-known exponential function. It is a powerful tool as we can add in probabilities of death at particular ages and they will not get mixed up with other ages. In order to calculate things like averages, however, we have to get back to the distribution as above, by reversing the process with an integral transform that is not suitable for the present text; so I hope you will take my word for it. We can now see where our aged statistician went wrong. Each year his probability of death is going up, because we have unravelled it from the earlier years.

Life expectancy

One of the things we can calculate from the above curve is how many years he average person has left at a particular age. In order to do so we have to throw away all the data for earlier ages and calculate the distribution and then the average for the remaining data. We can then create a curve of life expectancy (how many years we have left) against age.

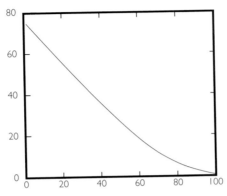

Figure 13.3 Life expectancy against age

Always remember that these are all just averages. Life does not come with any guarantees.

13.3 Testing the numbers

With the tools introduced above we can examine more closely some of the numbers that are given to us, which we would normally have to take at face value. Here is one of the most famous risk tables:

Cause	Mortality
Smoking 10 cigarettes a day	1 in 200
All natural causes age 40	1 in 850
Any kind of poisoning	1 in 3300
Influenza	1 in 5000
Accident on road	1 in 8000
Leukaemia	1 in 12 500
Playing soccer	1 in 25 000
Accident at home	1 in 26 000
Accident at work	1 in 43 000
Radiation working in radiation industry	1 in 57 000
Homicide	1 in 100 000
Hit by lightning	1 in 10 000 000
Radiation from nuclear power station	1 in 10 000 000

This celebrated table has been repeatedly published since it was produced by the BMA. I have seen it in at least a dozen different books and television programmes.

Most of these numbers are pretty small. In fact, only the first two are big enough to be even visible on our mortality curve. There are, of course, some interesting comparisons, e.g. between influenza and road accidents, when you look at the relative political stir they create. Nevertheless, to two individuals, say a young motor cycle enthusiast and a housebound asthmatic old lady, the actual risks might be quite different. There are also even far smaller numbers not in the table, such as the risk of eating beef on the bone. The second number has two immediate uses. First, it allows us to check the calibration of our own curve. The table gives a probability of 0.0018 per year, while our curve at the same age gives 0.0025 per year. The difference might be due to the definition of natural causes, but it is not great in statistical terms. Second, it tells us something about the first number, that it is intended to be independent of age. Let us, then, see what we can derive from the first number.

I have never been a cigarette smoker, but from my observations ten a day seems a modest dose. Nevertheless we will accept it as representative. I also observe that cigarette smokers tend to start in their early teens. Having decided that, we can now create a testable hypothesis: cigarette *smoking increases mortality by 0.005 per year.* We can now generate a plausible mortality function:

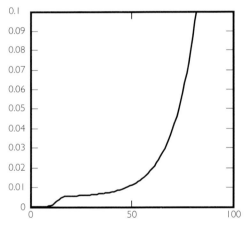

Figure 13.3 Hypothetical mortality of smokers

The assumption in this is that smoking is gradually taken up in the early teens, adding an amount of 0.005 to our mortality thereafter. We can now derive a mortality function and hence a distribution of ages at death from this data:

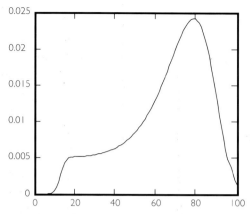

Figure 13.4 Hypothetical age at death of smokers

Even if you do not follow the precise mathematical transformations on the imprecise statistical data, I hope you will accept that the distribution is a reasonable representation of the implications of the hypothesis. The added risk produces a plateau in the early adult years until the point where the natural risks take over. In consequence the total probability (area) at higher levels is reduced to make the total one.

We are now in a position to generate some simple numbers that provide a test of the hypothesis. First the average age at death is reduced from 73.4 to 65, an impressive, even devastating, number. It is not, however, one that the ordinary person can put to the test for himself. Consider instead the proportion of people that would die before the age of 40. For our normal population it would be less than 3%, while for our hypothetical population of smokers it would be more than 15 %. This is a number most of us can put to the test from our own experience, since we have all known a hundred cigarette smokers. The question is "have fifteen of them died before they are forty?" If they have then the hypothesis is supported but not proven. If they have not, the hypothesis is falsified and disproven. To be "scientific" about it we should take the level at which there is a one in twenty chance of being wrong, which would make the number nine. Thus, if you have known one hundred cigarette smokers and nine or more have died before they were forty, you are able to confirm the hypothesis and not just accept a number that was thrown at you. On the other hand you might be inclined to take the view that all the numbers in the table except the first are Trojan numbers *(q.v.)*.

The glaring fact is that most of the risks we are invited to panic about involve probabilities so small that they are invisible in the mortality curves. Life expectancy, which is just an average, has increased mainly because of the massive reduction in infant mortality. The days of our age were threescore years and ten and they still are three score years and ten. Examine the tombstones in any ancient churchyard and you will find that there is nothing new in longevity, but you will be struck by the high mortality among children.

13.4 The science of pollution or the pollution of science?

It isn't pollution that's harming the environment. It's the impurities in our air and water that are doing it.

Dan Quayle

Headline in *The Times* March 2, 1999

Car fumes make Los Angeles the cancer capital

Cancer-causing chemicals in car exhaust fumes have left residents of Los Angeles hundreds of times more at risk of fatal disease than the federal Clean Air Act allows, according to a government study that is likely to send shock-waves through the healthcare and motor industries.

The congressional study of air quality in America's second-largest city, published yesterday, reveals airborne carcinogens at levels 426 times higher than those established as safe nine years ago.

The alarming figures "should give a jolt" to the city, a spokeswoman for the Natural Resources Defence Council in Washington said. "We know our air is dirty, but now we know in black and white that it's toxic too," she added

Now, if you remember from our remarks about precision *(q.v.)* as an indicator of junk science, the number 426 should have started the alarm bells ringing. This stuff, however, is beginning to have a familiar ring to it. That was from the London *Times*, but we can get nearer to home by following up the same story in the *Los Angeles Times*.

Here we find that the source of the figures is the California EPA. As we see throughout this book, *California* and *EPA* are both terms that should cause our junk antennae to twitch. Bring them together and you have the junk science equivalent of Godzilla meets King Kong. Reading between the lines we deduce that the number are based on the fact that concentration of "carcinogenic" substances is 426 times the level arbitrarily established by the EPA in the 1990 federal Clean Air Act. This act names no fewer than 188 chemicals in the air that can cause cancer. Usually this boils down to the fact that our old friends the hapless rodents (§7.4) have had them smeared on their skins in great concentrations. The said act claims to set a standard of one extra cancer death per million. Let us remind ourselves that one per million is 1 inch in 16 miles or one minute in two years. Since about a quarter of us are going to die of cancer anyway, this requires a measurement precision of one part in 250,000 for it to be determined. The worst case in this study was Burbank with a claimed risk of 483 per million. Even if it were correct that would be an increase of less than 0.2% in cancer deaths. Now you may choose to worry about such a small number, but you sure as hell cannot measure it.

As always the report ends with a plug for the anti-smoking campaign – A one-pack-a-day smoker, the report said, is 250 times more likely to get lung cancer than a person who simply breathes bad air in L.A. That is going it some, even for the EPA; or perhaps LA air really does reduce the risk of lung cancer by an order of magnitude.

13.5 The extrapolation fallacy

As we have seen in numerous cases, the process that gives rise to most junk science is extrapolation; not only linear extrapolation, which was in our list of fallacies. An important case of this process is extrapolation across species, but the most egregious is extrapolation of concentration. Much of the experimentation upon which scares are based is on rodents. It is a major assumption to infer that any such results are applicable to humans. In the case of saccharin (q.v.) for example, it has been shown to be entirely specious.

The extrapolation of concentration, however, gives rise to most of the junk science and scares that we read about. As we discussed in relation to poisons, any substance is toxic in sufficient concentration (Vitamin D, table salt, oxygen, and water etc.) yet we would also die if deprived of them. This seems all so obvious that the frequency and sheer perversity of extrapolation from high to low concentration is hard to believe. The great Alar (q.v.) scare is just one case in point – hundreds of millions of dollars were lost by the apple industry because of an extrapolation so gross that the dose involved was equivalent to humans drinking nearly 4,000 gallons of apple juice per day for life.

Naturally, the SIFs and junk scientists abandon linear extrapolation when it does not suit their purpose. If they applied it to passive smokers, for example, who receive a maximum of the equivalent of one fifth of a cigarette per day, they would have to predict a lung cancer risk a small fraction of that of non-smokers.

13.6 The independence fallacy

In our discussion of fallacies the point was made that the probabilities of cause of death are not independent. Because we all die of something, they are constrained to add up to 100%. This is a point so important that it is worth re-emphasising.

Let us make an imaginary experiment. Someone invents a pill that is a miracle cure for Alzheimer's disease, call it Placebene.

Now, take some round figures for probabilities of causes of death

Alzheimer's	10%
Heart Disease	30%
Cancer	20%
All Others	40%

After the invention of Placebene the table for its adherents will change to

Alzheimer's	0%
Heart Disease	33.3%
Cancer	22.2%
All Others	44.4%

It does not take much imagination to come up with the ensuing headlines:

Harvard study shows that Placebene causes 11% rise in heart disease and cancer.

EPA calls for a world-wide ban on Placebene.

President declares Placebene to be the number one health problem

This is not a trivial point. Much of the bureaucratic interference in our lives has been justified by the putative increase in cancer rates. The main reason that they are increasing is that we are not dying of the other diseases that have inflicted man throughout his existence. Let's face it, the human body was not designed to work for more than about 75 years. Evolution does not require it. Modern scientific medicine has created a situation in which we are not prey to all the infectious diseases of the past. Our life expectancy is such that we are now likely to die of one of the diseases of old age (cancer, heart disease and Alzheimer's) which were once comparatively rare.

The prevalence of the independence fallacy means that every major improvement in public health can be presented as a disaster. The more lives we save from various diseases, the more we increase deaths from cancer and heart failure. Almost all people actually die of heart failure anyway, whatever the primary cause. When we have cured all diseases, including cancer, heart failure will be the only thing left to put on the death certificates. Even if the primary cause of death is a disease such as Alzheimer's, the chances are that it will be recorded as heart failure.

In fact, heart failure appears on death certificates far more often than is justified. In Britain it helps doctors to avoid the trauma of having to deal with the Coroner. The same constraints do no apply in some other countries; so we have a whole industry set up to explain why heart disease is more prevalent in Britain than in France, when the most likely explanation is the whim of the doctor signing the death certificate.

13.7 Lifestyle

Insisting on perfect safety is for people who don't have the balls to live in the real world.
Mary Shafer, NASA

The age of reason has given way to the age of panic. As a result of the pre-eminence of the social theory, it is one of the characteristics of our age that we are obsessed with the style of life that we adopt. We base our life choices on a bombardment of information from the media, much of it nonsense, as we have frequently observed in the earlier chapters. There is a limit to how much control we have. Wealth is a great help in presenting us with choice.

Perhaps the greatest risk factor in life is where you live. As I write the notes for this section I am sitting on a small Bronze Age tumulus on one of the last preserved Hampshire chalk downlands. Around me hundreds of butterflies (some of them quite rare, like the Chalk Hill Blue or the Duke of Burgundy Fritillary) flit between the cowslips, rockroses and orchids. In front of me lies one of the most beautiful valleys on earth and in it nestles the village in which I am privileged to live. I have not seen a human being for the last two hours. Down in the village pub the old boys will be lighting their pipes and sipping their first ale of the day. Most of them will die in their beds at an age of over eighty.

On the other hand I could have been sitting in a damp, overcrowded Glasgow tenement........No, on second thoughts forget that. I would probably be dead already.

I turned 60 just as I started drafting this book. This means that one of the greatest threats to my expectation of life, and certainly its quality, is Alzheimer's disease. I have now joined an age group in which 10% will fall prey to this dreadful condition. If I get to 80 it will be 20%. As a pipe smoker

I probably reduce this risk by half. A simple calculation suggests that the two thirds of non-smokers have to put up with a 12% risk in order to make up the 10%. Against this I have to trade a risk of getting lung cancer. There are few reliable statistics for pipes, but the risk is almost certainly considerably less than that for heavy inhalers of cigarettes.

It is a truism that the only thing we can expect in life is the unexpected. On April 3rd 1998, I was driving to the University, a journey I had made over 4,000 times. I had just had my car serviced and bought a new front lamp unit; it was running well after having been a bit unreliable. It was a beautiful spring day, all sunshine and emerging greenery. I had worked late the night before on this book and had made considerable progress. Life was good. Suddenly, I noticed that a white commercial van in front of me was sliding. I touched the brake and completely lost control. I was all over the road, which I now saw was white. I hit the bank on the far side of the road, then slewed across into the hedge on the near side. A small tree arrested my progress and the car spun round burying itself in the hedge. I clambered across the car and got out the passenger's side. I then realised that the road was covered with giant hailstones, many of them over 1 cm in diameter. Someone summoned the police and by the time they arrived twenty minutes later the road was completely clear of ice. The white van had disappeared. Fortunately for my story there was still a large residue of giant hailstones on the grass verge, otherwise I would have had no defence against a charge of dangerous driving. Only a month before I had written a piece for another part of this book about the AA, ending with the fact that I had not had to call them out for years.

Both the police and the AA man (who winched me out of the hedge) said I was lucky I was driving a Saab, otherwise I could have been seriously injured. If any vehicle had been coming the other way I would have been seriously dead. It turned out that several people had been injured in a nearby town in a similar incident. The only damage to my car was a few scratches, a slight dent and a smashed lamp unit, my new one. What is one to make of such an event? A superstitious person might have suggested that I had tempted the Fates (*Moirae* to the Greeks and *Parcae* to the Romans). However, it was just the result a random freak storm. I had read about giant hailstones, without quite believing it, but had never experienced anything like it. I could have spent the previous year leading an ascetic life, giving up my pipe, beer, red meat and many other pleasures, in the hope of prolonging my existence; all to no avail. The *a priori* probability of any individual dying of such a cause is tiny; not as small as catching CJD from eating beef on the bone, but far too small to worry about.

Many years ago I had a senior colleague who was an ultra careful driver. He contended that there was no such thing as an accident, and that anybody involved in one was culpable. One day he said to me "I had better tell you this, as it might be in the papers. I ran over a man and injured him". It turned out that the victim had been an epileptic and in a fit had thrown himself off the pavement into the path of my colleague's car.

The ways of injury, disease and death are so many and various that, though the probability of each may be small, the combined probability is significant. We all have to make our own judgements on minimising various risks, although the Nanny State tries to wrest that privilege away from us. I, for example, would not dream of riding a motor bike or climbing a mountain, though I indulge in other pleasures that are now frowned upon as unjustifiably risky. In the end life is controlled by a series of random events. We can tinker with the probabilities by taking appropriate precautions, but we cannot proscribe the operation of pure chance. In the end the change we make to the probabilities is pretty small. If all cancer were cured, average life expectancy would go up by only two years. If all vascular diseases were cured it would go up by two and a half years. Eradication of both diseases would condemn most of us to a lingering death of decrepitude and incontinence (Kealey in *What Risk*).

Professor Colin Blakemore, one of those who seek to impose their own ascetic life style on the rest of us cites his father, who was a heavy smoker had a coronary at 45 and died at the age of 63. My own father was a heavy smoker had a robust heart and died at 83. Neither statistic has any value. Blakemore also avoids the use of mobile phones – not the biggest risk in his case, as he is in the top ten of candidates for murder by animal rights SIFs.

Neither man nor nature has produced anything that last forever. The human heart is an extraordinarily robust organ. In my case, this lump of muscle has contracted over two billion times. One day soon it will come to a stop, as all things do. This is a fact of life, and nothing is achieved by my dwelling on it.

It is important to be clear that calculating the risks is not the same as predicting the outcome. By the time you read this I may well be dead from lung cancer. This would be a fact of no statistical significance, apart from the tiny contribution I make to mortality figures. Using single instances is one of the ways they lie to us. Dylan Thomas might have drunk himself to death, but Winston Churchill grossly abused alcohol all his life; yet at an age when most of us are retired or dead he was busy saving the free world from Fascism.

The world's oldest person, Jeanne Calment of Arles, happened to die while I was drafting this chapter, at the age of 122. She gave up smoking at the age of 120, because she could no longer see to light her cigarette and did not want to bother anyone else.

One of the greatest miscalculations of risk ever was by her lawyer, who had acquired her apartment cheaply in exchange for an income, which she enjoyed for over thirty years. He did not live long enough to realise his investment. What a cheering little story that is!

Let us say it again. We all die of something – a fact that continually seems to escape many of the pundits. The best advice I have been given is to live each day as though it might be your last. By all means wear a hair shirt if that is how you get your kicks, but do not expect it to extend your time on earth.

Chapter 14

A personal memoir

Myself when young did eagerly frequent
Doctor and Saint and heard great argument
About it and about: but evermore
Came out by the same Door as in I went
Fitzgerald - The Rubaiyat of Omar Khayyam

It was quite early in my research career that I became concerned about the abuse of measurement. I became convinced that in the field in which I worked a significant proportion of the published work was seriously wrong, and this is in a branch of physics, where there ought to be no confounding factors of human origin. On the contrary, it seemed to me that human factors were dominant in determining the results of many measurements. Not least of these is the mischievous ability of the human subconscious to generate the results it expects or desires. My reaction was to become one of the pioneers of computer controlled measurement, which for many years I was convinced was the solution. Now in towards the end of my career I am unable to believe even in this. Human beings still choose the experiments and write the programs. I appreciate that the details will be dull to the average reader and I have curtailed them as much as possible. As I describe below, I was inhibited as an insignificant young researcher from publishing my misgivings about the state of a particular research area. Indeed, it is probable that there is no way I could have published them. Now in my dotage I can do a little to redress the balance. One of the few advantages of growing old is that you can adopt the Rhett Butler principle and not give a damn.

I had an undistinguished undergraduate career. My overwhelming interest was in electronics, but at that time the only way to enter the profession was to take a general engineering degree. I had to learn to design girder bridges, earth dams and heat engines. The mathematical methods in those pre-computer days were crude and unsatisfying. I loathed it and did just enough work to scrape through. Meanwhile I taught myself some of the things I thought might be important, such as quantum mechanics and stochastic processes.

I emerged with a middling degree and, more in hope than expectation, enquired about the possibility of a research post. A man called Dr Harry House had just joined the Department as a Reader and was setting up a new research programme in the field of liquid dielectrics in a department that had little or no research tradition. To my surprise, after a five-minute interview he asked when I could start. Later Harry told me that he could not believe his luck in getting someone who had done an apprenticeship in instrumentation and had a working knowledge of quantum mechanics and stochastic processes. More by luck than judgement I had given myself exactly the right preparation.

The field I was assigned to work in was liquid dielectrics, the materials that are used as insulators in power transformers and cables. It was an area in which just a small improvement in performance could produce savings of billions of dollars around the world, and even get rid of those ugly pylons that straddle the countryside and are such a favourite target of the creators of panic. Yet little seemed to be achieved despite vast amounts of research effort.

I set about in the usual way of research students and began to read previous PhD theses and published papers in the field. I was in for a shock. I had previously immersed myself in the philosophy of science, and particularly the contribution of Popper (q.v.). Not one single solitary author applied the scientific method, as I understood it. Almost to a man they would adopt some scientific theory and then show how their results were consistent with it. I began to form the cynical view that all the subject was good for was generating PhDs.

The orthodoxy at the time was that there was such a thing as *intrinsic breakdown strength*. This was based on the idea that, if you could remove all the imperfections from your experiment, the liquid would break down at a voltage that was wholly determined by its own molecular properties. The inference from this was that, the higher the breakdown voltage and the lower the scatter you achieved, the better your results. In consequence values of breakdown voltage for a given thickness of material went up and up, while the scatter in the results went down. At least one research student failed to get his PhD because, however much he purified his liquid, he could not get the high results that the orthodoxy required. Then suddenly, one Andreas Sletten, who was a bit more persistent than most, proved that your could increase the breakdown strength of the liquid by adding an impurity, oxygen. The orthodoxy collapsed, but only to be replaced by another.

I was becoming convinced by this stage that the major factor in these breakdown tests was the experimenter himself. The method used was for the operator slowly to turn a knob that controlled a high voltage source, looking all the time at an electrostatic voltmeter that was monitoring the voltage. On breakdown, the voltage would suddenly collapse and the operator would write down what he remembered as the highest level obtained and them start the next trial. I decided to test my hypothesis on some undergraduate volunteers. I gave them a test rig and told them that the most skilled operators would achieve high breakdown voltages with low scatter. In the next room I had a chart recorder. They all reacted in the same way. For the first few trials, they would apply the voltage very tentatively, but as they began to learn where the breakdown voltage was likely to be, they would raise it rapidly to that point and then slow down.

I was subsequently able to show that, at any given level of voltage, there was a probability per unit time of breakdown occurring. This probability increased exponentially with voltage, but decreased with the amount of time a voltage had been applied. This meant that the experimenter could optimise the average and scatter of the results by means of his rate of voltage application. I then adopted the methods of analogue computing to design a high voltage supply that would automatically apply the voltage as a constant linear ramp. With this automatic system the distributions of breakdown voltage were not the low scatter, high average, normal distributions that had previously been observed, but another form that we have already met, the Gompertz distribution, which appeared in our discussions of life expectancy, and was in fact the only one that could logically apply. The averages were lower and the scatter much greater.

What had been happening was that the sub-consciences of previous experimenters had been learning how to achieve the results that were desired. I subsequently discovered that they had been discarding "freak" low results on the so-called 3σ rule, that anything three standard deviations from the mean can be discarded. It was not just a matter of the electrical test method, which I had wholly automated. I purified my liquid samples to a degree that had not been attempted before. To remove impurities, they were triple distilled in a system that had been baked under high vacuum at 400°C. The literature was full of portentous results in which breakdown strength and conductivity were plotted against such things as molecular weight. The problem I had was that the differences the experts were plotting between different materials were much smaller than what I was getting between nominally identical samples of the same material. I was a humble research assistant; who was I to call the most eminent international professors in the field liars? Nevertheless, the discovery that an impurity actually increased the breakdown strength was the death knell to the icon of intrinsic strength.

The orthodoxy was by then dead in the water. Blow me down, it was then immediately replaced by another one! The new orthodoxy went to the opposite extreme from intrinsic breakdown strength. It was based on the idea that all conduction and breakdown phenomena in the liquids were due to sub-microscopic particles. Thus I learned an early lesson that, as soon as you knock down one orthodoxy, another pops up in its place.

Now it is a fact that, however, much you purify and filter the liquid, there are always tiny solid particles present. You cannot see them by normal means and have to use a technique called the ultra microscope, in which they are shown up by scattered light when illuminated from a precise angle. The way this theory was developed was my first experience of the extrapolation fallacy.

The theorist had made an experiment with a small ball bearing between two electrodes. When a voltage was applied, it would bounce between the electrodes, being alternately charged with each polarity and attracted to the other. The charge carried was close to that predicted by a theory of Maxwell. These results were then extrapolated to tiny particles of less than a micrometer in diameter and it was "proved" that they could account for all the conduction and breakdown phenomena in the liquid. Now I knew from observation that the natural particles did not behave in this bouncy manner. They would dwell for a long time on the surface of each electrode before making a sudden transition to the other. I deduced from this that the charging process was a very inefficient one and that the particles carried very little charge at all, but I could prove nothing from what I had observed under the microscope.

By this time, however, the new orthodoxy had established itself and all papers submitted for publication in the field were going for refereeing to the institution that was promoting the theory. As a result in my first major paper, in order to achieve publication, I was obliged to mention a theory that I believed was wrong. We scientists like to pretend to objectivity, but I have to confess that I got bit between my teeth for reasons that were not entirely detached.

The proponents of the particle theory basked in the security of the knowledge that no one could possibly measure the charge carried by sub-microscopic particles moving at random. I determined that I was going to find a way to do it. The first problem was to acquire a sufficiently powerful computer. I had done some pioneering work with a retired general-purpose computer called Pegasus, and on the strength of this I applied for a research grant to obtain a powerful (for those days) on-line computer designed for military purposes. I then came up against another refereeing barrier, when I found that a group in another university had got themselves into an entrenched position where they could mount an attack to corner the market in computer-aided measurement. By this time I had developed a certain amount of political nous (not a lot). When I was summoned to explain myself I managed to convey that I was not serious competition as I was only interested in a rather abstruse topic of dielectric materials. So, after a lot of negotiation, I got my computer.

The next piece in the jigsaw was one of the few bits of outstanding luck that I have had in my career. An American company called Biomation launched onto the market a device called a transient recorder, a spin-off from the nuclear weapons testing programme that was orders of magnitude faster than had been available. Anyway, to cut a long story short, with the aid of a very bright research student I mounted what was one of the most elaborate on-line measurements of its time. While simultaneously monitoring the movement of the particles with a sensitive photo-multiplier, we monitored the tiny charge transients. We were able to show that the charge pulses correlated with the particle movements and that they were orders of magnitude smaller than required by the particle theory. A soon as the results were published in the journal *Nature*, the particle theory was also dead in the water.

Now you might think that all this is a sledgehammer to crack a nut and you would be right; but for two significant consequences. First, it was a demonstration that theorists could not hide behind a barrier of untestability. Second, there were important spin-offs and I found myself being consulted on a wide range of serious problems involving the observation of random events, such as the monitoring of the propagation of micro-cracks in high pressure gas vessels in remote places and the monitoring of brain waves. In the latter case we were able to make a major contribution, in conjunction with the famous Department of Clinical Neurophysiology at Bart's, to the monitoring of a precursor to epilepsy in the brain waves of children. This is all a potent illustration of the major flaw in modern bureaucratised science. That piece of research would almost certainly not be supported today. There were no customers for it and it was seemingly inconsequential; yet it turned out to have a major impact in different areas of health and safety. What we have now largely abandoned is the power of serendipity in science.

The consequence for me was that I began to move away from the study of dielectric liquids and into the field of more general digital instrumentation, eventually becoming one of the pioneers of microprocessor instrumentation. For a while, however, I also continued in my mission to knock down "untestable" theories. There were various features of test results that researchers were glibly ascribing to physical effects in the materials. I was able to show by analysis and modelling that such features were a product of the testing method and did not require any physical mechanism at all. I must, however, record the case of the breakthrough that never was.

One of the untestable theories I determined to tackle was the one that said that breakdown was initiated at crystal boundaries in the metal of the electrodes, as electrons could more easily escape into the dielectric from these areas. The reasoning was based on quantum mechanics and is not relevant here. Again it was considered untestable, but I devised a method of doing it. With the advice of a metallurgist colleague and the aid of another very bright research student I was able to create electrodes of brass with very large crystals. You could not see these until the material was etched, so we could conduct a number of breakdown tests which created small damage pits on the surface. After etching we could see whether there was any relationship between the crystal boundaries and the pits. We set out to test the null hypothesis that the distribution of the pits would be random. On looking at the first set of electrodes we got a shock. The correlation was so high it seemed that you could trace the outline of one crystal in the pits on the other electrode. This promised to be a famous result, the first ever in the field. We could have gone straight into print, which many would do today, but determined to prove that the experiment was repeatable. It was very expensive in terms of time and resources but we did it half a dozen times more and never got another significant result. The distribution of pits was thereafter wholly random. Had we somehow accidentally produced the conditions in the first test that brought out a genuine physical effect or was it a remarkable coincidence? We shall never know. Any way the research was never published apart from the PhD thesis of the research student. In those days we did not have the extreme publish-or-perish pressures that exist today. I would like to think that I would still resist the temptation, but I would not swear to it.

Looking back on this one narrow field of liquid dielectrics, millions of man-hours were wasted for zero achievement. The main reasons for this were failure to adopt the scientific method and the growth of orthodoxies. Above all, however, was the lack of appreciation of the implications of particular techniques of measurement. There was nothing unique in this. In 1905, for example, after considering the major conundrums of physics for ten years, Albert Einstein realised that the crux of the problem lay not in a theory of matter but in a theory of measurement. At the heart of his special theory of relativity was the realisation that all measurements of time and space depend on judgements as to whether two distant events occur simultaneously. It seems possible that I had chanced upon a particular field that was a strikingly bad example, but I am left to wonder how other fields would fare if they were subject to close examination.

In my subsequent career I was to come across many examples of inadequate measurement technique. In the field of process control, for example, which had many implications for human safety, the engineers quite properly took a conservative view and only used those sensors they knew to be reliable, trying to infer all other variables by a process of deduction. I gradually changed the direction of my research toward the development of new sensors that would measure the quantities that actually need to be known. Although it was all very fascinating to me, it is unlikely to be so for the general reader; so we shall pass on. I was fairly fortunate in my ensuing career, obtaining a chair in one of the world's leading electronics departments, but it all began to turn sour in 1982, as did so many things, and the intensity of my pleasure in my chosen métier diminished year after year. As I travelled around the universities, performing various duties, I found that the *esprit de corps* was simply dissolving away. It was like going back in time to my apprenticeship when I worked in various factory shops. The new managerialism had induced a sullen acceptance in place of the old fierce dedication. I was particularly distressed to hear some of the greatest scholars of my generation disparaged because they did not conform to the norms. In talking to people in other fields, such as the health service and the police force, I found that this was not a unique situation. While writing the section of this book that concerns universities, I came to the realisation that up with this I did not have to put, so I opted for early partial retirement to concentrate on writing about my concerns. If I had to summarise the results of my experience in one sentence it would be – **The greatest enemy of scientific progress is orthodoxy**.

Chapter 15

Reprise

In these pages we have ranged widely over the applications of measurement; occasionally straying from the point, but not too far. I have left out far more topics than I have included (breast implants, the hole in the ozone layer, PCBs, endocrine disrupters, rubber ducks, dowsing, cancerous air fresheners etc.). Lying with graphs is a whole topic in its own right, as was Margaret Thatcher's use of statistics at question time. By the summer of 1999 I began to feel that I should draw the process of collecting examples to a close. Frankly, I could not stand the thought of another silly season, collecting cuttings of unmitigated rubbish. If anything, the situation was getting worse than it had been when I started the project. Scares were appearing at a rate of almost one a day. The end of the world (according to followers of Nostradamus) came and went. Some themes, of which I had only been vaguely aware, had been recurrent, and it is to these that I would like to address a few final remarks.

15.1 1982 and all that

> Some men are born mediocre, some men achieve mediocrity,
> and some men have mediocrity thrust upon them.
> Joseph Heller, Catch-22

I have referred, in the introduction and throughout this book, to the fundamental dislocation that occurred in Western society in the early 1980s. I was beginning to have doubts that this might be just a bee in my own bonnet, when James Le Fanu came up with the exactly the same hypothesis from a different direction. This was a juncture in the most literal meaning of the term, a joining of a number of influences to create a critical moment in time. This is, of course, in the realms of social history, to which I can claim no expertise, and no doubt it will be analysed to death in subsequent decades. It is, however, useful just to name a few of the strands that contributed to the decline of real science.

Death of conservatism

Margaret Hilda Thatcher became British Prime Minister in 1979, while Ronald Wilson Reagan was elected 40th President of the United States in 1981. They both stood on a radical right wing platform that was a sharp deviation from the traditional conservative attitude, which favoured evolution over revolution and eschewed dogma. In Britain, the purge of "The Wets" in 1981 unleashed a period of undiluted market fundamentalism. Politics became polarised with dogma confronting dogma. The old consensus politics was blamed for all existing ills, including the rising tide of inflation that had been a unique feature of the start of the second half of the century. The effects on science were many and various and we have discussed just a few of them here. The fact is that science and dogma do no make easy bedfellows.

While the New Right had seized the heights of political power, the New Left was beavering away establishing its hold on institutions, especially universities. In Britain the Old Left had developed suicidal tendencies that were to keep it out of power for almost two decades. The eventual and inevitable swing of power was made all the more spectacular by its long postponement. By the late nineties the New Left was firmly in power and its own dogmas were applied with full force.

The end of optimism

Le Fanu calls the middle section of his book *The end of the age of optimism* and it is remarkable how the trends he describes for medicine are exactly mapped into the physical sciences. As in many human activities the moment of greatest success was followed by a decline. When Neil Armstrong stepped onto the surface of the moon on July 20th 1969 it marked the pinnacle of scientific and technological achievement, even though its motivation was largely political. The massive effort that had been launched by Kennedy eight years before had gripped a World that watched the culmination live on television. Although the Apollo missions continued for another three years, people never again identified with scientific achievement in the same way. The distant view of the Earth from space, however, had taken on a new symbolism. A month after the moon landing, the Woodstock Music and Art Fair took place. The fact that the Vietnam War was unwinnable was at last being officially accepted and President Nixon ordered the withdrawal of 25,000 troops, which had peaked at a total of half a million. The anti-war protest movement had become a powerful element in society

The New Age Movement was a hotchpotch of diverse spiritual, social, and political elements that promised the transformation of individuals and society through spiritual awareness. It was a utopian vision, offering an era of harmony and progress. In its wake there came spiritual leaders, feminists, ecologists, human-potential gurus and many other trendy types. By the early 1980s there was a huge world market for books, magazines, audio- and videotapes, workshops, retreats, and lectures on the subject, as well as for natural foods, crystals, meditation and healing aids. Real science was considered at best an irrelevance and at worst the enemy. Above all, the scientific requirement for evidence (i.e. measurement) was quietly dropped.

It is almost unbelievable that the interval of time between the Wright brothers' first take-off at Kitty Hawk and Neil Armstrong setting foot on the moon was a mere sixty six years, one life-time. Although the space shuttle and space station followed, the next thirty years were somewhat bathetic in comparison. The reasons were summed up by Apollo astronaut Walter Cunningham – "We developed the risk-avoidance society."

The decline of "hard" science

A world trend away from the physical sciences was already well underway in the 1970s. I was then writing articles in a physics journal with titles like *Decline and fall* and *Change and decay*. In Britain, the savage funding cuts of the early 1980s have caused people to forget that these had all begun in the previous decade. Science departments in universities began to go into decline because of the lack of candidates coming up from the schools. In desperation they began to reduce entry standards, which accelerated the vicious helix of descent. Science and scientists came to be treated with contempt by a majority of youngsters. Manpower planning policies such as the Shift to Science only made things worse. Physics departments, in particular, began to disappear or become transmogrified into something blander and more palatable. Of course, it was not only the sciences that suffered from the general decline in standards. Great chunks were removed, for example, from history syllabuses and experts were telling us that English grammar was no longer important and anything goes. The visual arts were adorned with piles of bricks and animal carcasses.

Rise of the computer

It is one of the ironies of this branch of history that one of the most monumental achievements of science and technology, the computer, was to accelerate their downfall. The almighty computer was the result of a brilliant piece of pure science, the abstruse study of the properties of matter in the solid state, which led to the transistor and the integrated circuit. The original computers were envisaged as scientific aids with possible business applications such as payroll calculations, but as soon as they became available startling new applications emerged at an accelerating rate. IBM had entered the commercial computer field in 1951, just three years after the first stored programme had been run, thanks largely to funding from the Atomic Energy Commission. It was highly innovative, particularly in the invention of the idea of a family of computers that could run common software. IBM dominated the market initially, but the emergence of the minicomputer in the early seventies were the first signs of a threat to this dominance. It was right at the crucial moment, however, in 1981 that IBM almost by accident launched the Personal Computer. It rapidly found that it had created a market that it could not defend and smaller more vigorous companies were responsible for the eventual dominance of this technology.

How could such a development possibly lead to the near demise of real science? There is no doubt that initially it was a great boon. Whole new areas of science, such as advanced crystallography, became possible only because of the huge computing power available. The computer, however, was intruding into new areas of human activity. At the moment when auditing became the icon of the new politics, the computer came along and made it possible to implement it to an undreamed of degree. The evolution of a world computing system had begun and science, which had begot it, began to take a back seat. The Internet had been created by Vinton Cerf in early 1973 as part of a project headed by Robert Kahn and conducted by the Advanced Research Projects Agency, part of the United States Department of Defense. It had been started as an idea to create a robust military computing system but in the early eighties it was turned over to the private sector and government agencies. Later the World Wide Web would be invented in 1989 by Tim Berners-Lee, a British computer scientist at the CERN research facility near Geneva, Switzerland, to allow information-sharing among internationally dispersed teams of high-energy physics researchers.

While scientists were in the vanguard in the exploitation of this new technology, it was rapidly taken up by other factions and was to become one of the main building blocks of the post-rational society. We have seen many examples of wrong numbers being propagated by the Web. Powerful computer packages were being created for use by people who had little understanding of their function. Bizarre theories could fly round the world instantly with no constraints such as peer review.

Ironically, it was computerised trading, by triggering automatic sell orders, that brought about Black Monday in October 1987 when stocks lost 22.5% of their value. This brought to an end the euphoric upward surge in business that had been a result of the powerful new political dogma.

The new business ethic

The sea change in politics brought about a corresponding change in business practice. Profit became the sole objective and the means of securing it were wide open. Manufacturing industry, which had been the backbone of the industrial revolution and the source of modern prosperity, was no longer regarded as the main agent for money generation. In Britain it was simply allowed to die, as a by-product of the current political numerical monomania based on inflation. The way to make money was moving other people's money around. Men in red braces were telling us that greed was good. Famous arbitrageurs, like Ivan Boesky, made billions and only a few of them ended up in gaol. There was no need for the West to make things; the Japanese economic miracle had occurred and the tiger economies were on their way. Manufacturing could be left to our little friends in the East. The creed was growth.

Typical is the case of Saatchi & Saatchi. This advertising agency achieved fame by being hired by the Conservative Party in 1978 and bringing the Thatcher Government to power in 1979. Almost immediately it became the biggest advertising agency in Britain and began a campaign of world-wide expansion, largely based on money borrowed from shareholders. It spread into consulting and research services and by successive take-overs became the largest agency in the world. The inevitable collapse did not occur until 1987, when many such burgeoning empires came to grief. While I was writing this book a new bubble, based on internet stocks, was beginning to grow.

What has all this to do with the progress of science and technology? Nothing, and that is the problem. These activities, which had been the powerhouse of prosperity, were suddenly irrelevant. In 1986, for example, when the so called Big Bang occurred following the massive deregulation imposed by the Financial Services Act, all four of my personal tutees, who graduated with honours degrees in electronics, found employment in the new financial conglomerates in the City of London (and at salaries several times my own). This Act, of course, brought with it a whole new tranche of auditing and regulatory bodies, but these were not enough to prevent a widespread miss-selling of financial products such as pensions. Despite huge amounts of money being later paid in compensation, the damage could not be undone.

Centralisation

One of the more annoying habits of politicians is that they say one thing and do the other. One of the promises made by the New Right when it came to power was that it would get government off the backs of the people; so of course it did exactly the opposite. In America this took the form of huge quasi government agencies disposing enormous sums of taxpayers' money. In Britain there were also many such quangos, but the overweening power was entrusted to the Civil Service. There were many disastrous aspects of this process, such as the decline of local government, but they are not relevant here. What is relevant is the centralisation of patronage. Science, which had largely pursued its own path of progress, suddenly found itself with a new set of bureaucratic masters with their own agenda. In Britain, the universities were knocked sideways by the massive financial squeeze of the early eighties and they were easy prey for the subsequent state take-over. There was no longer any unconstrained funding that allowed scientists to indulge in those little whims that usually lead to nothing but occasionally produce the great breakthrough. Control and auditing became the order of the day. When the New Left came to power in the nineties, it had been bequeathed all the tools it needed to indulge its own predilections, many of which were the antithesis of the search for scientific truth.

The dilution of talent

As we have seen, one of the prominent aspects of the 1980s was the haemorrhage of talent from the sciences. The brightest people were simply boycotting them. Meanwhile, governments were pursuing manpower policies that require the production of more scientists and technologists, albeit for considerably less money. University staff were on a progressive slide down the salary league that was to continue for a couple of decades. By the mid-nineties there were people calling themselves professor who had failed even to get a post in a university a decade before. Science and mediocrity simply do not go together. It might be anathematical to the New Left and Political Correctness, but it is a fact that scientific progress has never been brought about by dullards. The new mediocrats had to do something with their time, so they invented new debased forms of science that were not so demanding. Furthermore they were willing and eager to please their masters and so produce the results that policy required, regardless of the traditional tests of scientific truth. These pages have provided many examples. Under the new centralised patronage they prospered while real science withered.

15.2 PC

Don't you see that the whole aim of Newspeak is to narrow the range of thought? In the end we shall make thoughtcrime literally impossible, because there will be no words in which to express it.
George Orwell — Nineteen Eighty-Four

When an American Government official can lose his job for using an innocuous word like "Niggardly" it is a pretty good bet that numbers will not get a fair deal. It is not enough for zealots to play havoc with the grammar, syntax and vocabulary of our beautiful language. Just why the Land of the Free should be the origin of waves of intolerance is hard to understand. You would think that once they had got rid of McCarthyism they would appreciate the benefits of universal tolerance. Not a bit of it! Britain, of course, has to adopt the whole new prudery.

Now I have to admit that I am completely bemused by political correctness. When it is considered perfectly legal to sodomise a sixteen-year old boy, yet illegal to supply him with a cigarette, a glass of beer or a vote, it is like living on an alien planet to me. When racial minorities have unemployment inflicted on them, rather than expose them subjected to putative hazards of having industry on their doorstep, you begin to think with friends like that who needs enemies? The British Broadcasting Corporation puts a ban on the word "British" because it might offend the Scots and the Welsh. Why the latter in particular, who were the original Britons, would be offended is not explained. The England football manager is sacked, not because his results were mediocre or his bizarre beliefs were intruding on his work, but because he made a politically incorrect remark about the differently abled. It is characteristic that this petty dismissal followed intervention from the highest levels of Government, who might have been considered to have better things to think about.

PC has decreed the feminisation of education. In Britain socialist councils closed and sold off the sports fields because athletic competition was deemed to be inappropriate. The beautiful walled sports ground where I learned to play and love football, cricket and tennis is now a hypermarket. One of the things that the audits show is that the education of boys is suffering as a result. Rather than, as urged, getting in touch with their feminine side they are dropping out in increasing numbers. They turn to antisocial activities and crime. Meanwhile the British, who gave the world many of its major games, have become the world's duffers at sport, but the champions at hooliganism.

The principle effect of PC in creating wrong numbers is the way it sets the agenda. As we have seen in our discussion of the causes of wrong numbers, all that is required to guarantee the creation of a "significant" finding is for a sufficient number of people to perform the experiment.

PC ensures that large numbers of "scientists" are engaged in proving that all forms of "inappropriate" behaviour cause everything from athlete's foot to herpes zosta. Each time they hit the one-in-twenty jackpot in the statistical lottery they take their turn at publishing. They all read each other's papers and the large readership proves by bibliometry that they are important. Tobacco SIF, Professor Sir Kenneth Stuart, estimates that 70,000 scientific papers have spelled out the adverse consequences of smoking. This number tells me more about the "scientists" than it does about tobacco. We have looked at just a few of these effusions in these pages and found them to be dross.

Why, among all the other dangers faced by humanity, has PC picked out tobacco and alcohol for its especial displeasure? Why not mountaineering, marijuana or motorcycling? The only hypothesis I can come up with is that PC arose in the American new university departments. They rejected the former geniuses of academe (Dead White Males) and everything they stood for. These geniuses of the previous generation almost to a man (and I use the naughty word advisedly) were inveterate smokers. The likes of Bertrand Russel, Ernest Rutherford or Albert Einstein were rarely seen without a pipe and they all had the audacity to live to a grand old age. The Oxbridge colleges that consumed far more than their share of Nobel prizes were awash with alcohol. The idea of 21 units a week as the recommended maximum would have been greeted with hilarity at high table. It was to be tobacco, however, that would become the *cause célèbre* of PC, and its elimination the principal goal. The prime movers were in academe. As specious subjects, such as women's studies and black studies, took over what were once the arts faculties, so the social theory permitted junk to invade the science faculties.

15.3 EPA

No, no! said the Queen. Sentence first – verdict afterwards.
Lewis Carroll – Alice's Adventures in Wonderland

In any discussion of contemporary fraudulent science these three initials come up over and over again. I do not wish to be misunderstood in my judgement of the activities of the EPA. They are professional cheats and liars. They have committed multiple crimes against the integrity of science. They have debauched the statistical method. In the case of ETS alone they used a method (meta-analysis) that was, to say the least, dubious. When that did not produce the right result they reduced the statistical confidence limit to a level that has never been used in respectable science. After all that they produced a risk ratio that has never been regarded as significant in any previous statistical study. As for their claims of cause, even properly conducted statistics has nothing to say about causation. That is a total of four counts, each of which on its own would knock out the EPA's claims. Virtually every scientific group in the USA that has contributed to this farrago of lies is heavily in their pay. The Harvard School of Public Health, to take just one example, receives a donation of $3 million a year from the ever-generous taxpayers of the USA via the EPA. This school not only provides many of the bullets for the EPA guns, but its members also launch ferocious attacks on other scientists for daring to hold rational meetings to discuss the issues. On top of all this the EPA is intent on spreading its rot around the world. In one year the total of 106 foreign grants by the EPA was $27,806,509, including $1,200,000 to communist China. Good old American taxpayer! That's another ten cents to add to all the dollars that he pays to prop up junk science.

How did the EPA respond to the inevitable criticisms from real scientists? They issued a new set of guidelines. Not satisfied with moving the goalposts, they now wanted to redraw the playing field. The Junkman again:

> In its proposed cancer guidelines EPA specifically listed a number of criteria, but not statistical significance. Why? Was this an oversight? Hardly! With statistical significance out of the way, EPA's latitude in using epidemiologic studies to associate various substances and conditions with cancer has been significantly increased. Although included in the 1986 cancer risk assessment guidelines and, thus part of EPA's current epidemiologic criteria, the requirement of statistical significance has now been quietly deleted. Although EPA mentions that significance analyses should be conducted, achieving statistical significance is no longer an explicit requirement.

> This actually comes as no surprise. For years, epidemiologists have been trying to do away with the hurdle of statistical significance. Thanks to EPA, it appears that they are well on their way to victory.

> As proposed, the guidelines further enhance EPA's already virtually unfettered ability to label as cancer-causing whatever substance or condition it chooses. More important, however, given the public's acquired immunity to cancer fear-mongering, the proposed cancer risk assessment guidelines pave the way for EPA to take a new stranglehold on society through the future assessment of potential health risks from environmental estrogens.

It is sad that the Environmental Protection Agency, which ought to be a great force for good in the world, should have blown its credibility by publishing reports such as those on passive smoking or radon, riddled with pseudoscientific statistical fakery. There is no need for me to add more to the dozens of critical accounts by respectable scientists. For example, the independent pro-smoking pressure group, FOREST, naturally enough, will be only too pleased to provide you with a five page bibliography of scientific and journalistic articles on the matter. The EPA and its protégés, however, are completely oblivious to criticism, and continue to produce wave after wave of junk. Not only do such effusions put their publishers in the position of the boy who cried "Wolf!" but they also corrupt the scientific ethic itself. This politicisation of science is a serious matter indeed. We expect it under totalitarian regimes (Lysenko under Stalin or the eugenicists under Hitler) but when a Government agency in the world's greatest democracy lends itself to politically motivated trickery in the name of science the world has set out on a dangerous path. At the risk of being boring by repetition, science is either honest or it is nothing.

As for the suggested guidelines, if the reader is not aware what they mean, I could use them to prove anything carcinogenic. You want cancerous apple pie? You've got it. As for causality, I could use such methods to prove that a child's health depends on the number of pairs of shoes its mother has. I would be more sympathetic if I could convince myself that their motives were noble, but all the evidence points towards their being motivated by nothing but the lust for bureaucratic power. In all intolerant regimes such as Nazism, Bolshevism and Political Correctness, there are groups of people who seek to further their own interests by pandering to the official dogma. Sad to say, corrupt scientists are always among their number.

All Hail to a federal judge whose wisdom serves to underline the pusillanimity of the scientific establishment! He overturned the EPA's decision to classify what it calls "environmental tobacco smoke" as a known human carcinogen. In response to an industry lawsuit filed in 1993, U.S. District Judge William L. Osteen agreed that the "EPA was publicly committed to a conclusion before research had begun" and "adjusted established procedure and scientific norms to validate the Agency's public conclusion."

The details behind Osteen's decision are quite extraordinary. It emerged that the EPA actually started writing a policy guide recommending workplace smoking bans **four years** before it officially declared ETS a hazard. William Reilly, former EPA administrator, conceded that "beginning development of an Agency risk assessment after commencement of work on the draft policy guide gave the appearance of policy leading science."

This revelation brings the total number of unacceptable abuses in this one study to five, and confirms it as the all-time supreme exemplar of junk science. It is not, however, only the biggest lie in the annals of junk, it has also been the most effective, producing changes in social behaviour that would have been undreamed a decade before. Let it not be thought, however, that passive smoking is this agency's only essay into the realm of junk; far from it! You should see the stuff they and their *protégés* come up with on radon, all based on a meta-study, of course, to say nothing of a whole catalogue of "dangerous" chemicals.

There is, however, one thing of which the EPA cannot be accused – false modesty. During a speech at a conference sponsored by the State and Territorial Air Pollution Program Administrators and the Association of Local Air Pollution Control Officials , Mary Nichols, EPA's assistant administrator for air and radiation, claimed that the EPA's proposed air pollution standards for ozone and particulate matter would save (hang on to your hat!) 58 MILLION LIVES. You may wish to be reminded that 2 million Americans die every year from all causes. I stand to be corrected, but I think that this qualifies for the Guinness Book of Records for body counts. Move over Baron Münchausen.

The EPA plays a game of "heads I win, tails you lose" with US industry. The motor industry, for example, was obliged to install catalytic converters to break down compounds of nitrogen and oxygen from car exhaust that can combine with hydrocarbons under the action of sunlight into to form smog. Now the EPA has published a study suggesting that the converters form nitrous oxide, which they claim is a greenhouse gas more than 300 times more potent than carbon dioxide, the most common of the gases that are warming the atmosphere, according to "experts".

The EPA is even moving towards defining carbon dioxide itself, a substance vital to life on this planet, as a pollutant. A memorandum from EPA General Counsel Jonathan Cannon to Administrator Carol Browner says that CO_2 emissions are definitely within the scope of EPA's present Clean Air Act regulatory authority, and that if there is scientific evidence that CO_2 presents "a threat to human health, welfare, or the environment" then it falls into the same category as SO_2 or NO_x, and can be regulated as a criteria pollutant.

As we have previously mentioned, in 1991 an epidemic of cholera started in Peru and spread to the rest of Latin American. It arrived in the USA in 1992 via an outbreak among 75 commercial airline passengers from Peru. This epidemic is reported to have caused as many as 1 million cases of cholera and as many as 10,000 deaths. Incredibly, the Peruvian government had decided to stop chlorinating drinking water supplies. Its policy was based on EPA studies from the 1970s that associated drinking water chlorinated to 100 parts per billion with an increase in cancer risk for individuals of the order of 1 in 10,000. It was not until 1992 that EPA's Science Advisory Board and EPA staff finally acknowledged that the link between chlorinated drinking water and cancer was not scientifically supportable.

The EPA's chemical control division announced that they would screen 15,000 chemicals by the end of 1999 to develop a "suspect list" of chemicals that behave like oestrogen and other hormones that govern development of sexual traits. Once the EPA has a "suspect list," the chemicals will undergo more tests, costing about $200,000 each, to be paid for by the manufacturers, or more accurately by the consumer. A third round of tests on the chemicals' effects on rodents, fish, and other lab animals will cost $ 2 million each. According to Harvard's Centre for Risk Analysis, EPA regulations cost $7.6 million for each year of life saved, but that presupposes that you accept some of the EPA's own estimates of the benefits of its regulations.

It should not be thought that the cost of EPA is entirely borne by the good old American taxpayer. On September 10, 1997, EPA administrator Carol Browner blocked a request to build a polyvinyl chloride plant in an impoverished, predominantly black Louisiana town. She stated "It is essential the minority and low income communities not be disproportionately subject to environmental hazards". Without scientific evidence that the plant would cause any harm to the local community, Browner acted to ensure the community's continued health and economic poverty. Plant construction would have provided 2,000 jobs to community residents. Plant operation would provide 165 permanent jobs for which the average wage would be $45,000. The current average income in the area is $5,000.

Nor is the cost of the EPA borne equally by states. Ohio, Michigan, West Virginia and Indiana joined in a court action challenging the EPA's new smog-control rules. They are protesting the latest wave of regulations to hit the Midwest, where coal is the prime source of energy, harder than other states.

On the positive side the EPA are a boon to the economies of the rest of the world as their regulations shackle US industry and give a competitive advantage to everybody else. In the above I have used only a tiny fraction of the EPA junk stories I have collected. For hundreds of other examples of EPA lunacies see The Junk Science Home Page. The staggering level of regulation in the USA is hard to credit. It makes the EU look like hopeless beginners. Read, for example, the article **Rampant regulatory virus** by Clyde Wayne Crews, Jr. (*Washington Times*, June 1, 1999). Here are just a few of the points he makes:

> However controversial the $1.65 trillion federal budget, taxpayers know what Washington officially spends in the congressionally approved budget. That places some measure of voter accountability on Congress. But the money the public spends on Washington's environmental, safety and economic regulations doesn't appear in the federal budget. For these, Congress shrugs off accountability, often blaming agencies for excesses.

> Regulations are flourishing, and agencies don't mind the free rein. The 1998 Federal Register's 68,571 pages represent the highest count since the Carter presidency and a 6 percent jump over 1997. Contained within the Federal Register were 4,899 final rules, the second-highest count since 1984. Seventy of these new rules are "major," meaning they will cost at least $100 million each, compared with 60 such high-cost rules the year before.

Having now issued more than 21,000 final rules over the past five years, the 60 federal departments, agencies and commissions are now at work on 4,560 more. The Transportation Department and the Environmental Protection Agency, with 518 and 462 rules, respectively, lead the pack. Indeed, the five most active agencies account for 47 percent of all rules under consideration. Of the new rules, 937 are expected to affect small businesses, a 37 percent increase over the past five years.

What does all this regulation cost? Figures from the Rochester Institute of Technology's Thomas Hopkins pegs these regulatory compliance costs at $737 billion. For perspective, that's 44 percent of the level of federal spending of $1.65 trillion, 9 percent of GDP, the equal of all U.S. corporate pretax profits ($734 billion in 1998), and higher than Canada's gross national product of $542 billion in 1995. Bringing it home, the average family of four's $36,423 after-tax income in 1997 contained more than $7,000 of hidden regulatory costs - a 20 percent bite.

Let us be quite clear — no one is saying that a clean environment is unimportant. The improvement in air quality in London since I was a child there has been dramatic and welcome. I remember walking to school in a thick yellow fog in 1952, not being able to see a yard in front of me. It was reputed to have killed 12,000 people. What many real scientists are saying, however, is that the EPA way is, to say the least, counter-productive. As whistle blowing EPA employee David Lewis puts it "If we don't find a way to get science ahead of politics at EPA, the environment will suffer. What the public doesn't understand is that regulating with poor science puts the environment at risk."

The EPA likes to work in secret. It is involved in a running battle with critics to keep its data to itself. For example, to justify its draconian anti-smog regulations it cited a 1995 study which argued that reducing the emissions would theoretically save 2,400 lives a year. How was it able to produce this body count with such confidence? Well, that's EPA's little secret: It refuses release the data to the public, even though the public helped pay for the study with its tax dollars.

Above all, the worst thing about the EPA is that it kills people — Not just the few Challenger astronauts, or even the thousands of Peruvians. Its action against DDT has resulted in the death of millions from malaria. The withdrawal of DDT, as a result of a vigorous campaign orchestrated by the EPA, coincided with an abrupt reversal of the declining trend in this killer disease. See the article by Kelvin Klemm in *Environmental Health* (bibliography) for the details.

Why should the EPA have become so rapidly the world's gross polluter of science? Because it was founded on a big lie (that 90% of all cancers are environmental in origin). In order to sustain itself it had to sustain the lie and, as real science could not deliver, it bought bad science.

15.4 More Gore

Algorism — *the Arabic system of numeration: arithmetic.*
Chambers Twentieth Century Dictionary

When you are dealing with the subject of wrong numbers you just cannot get away from this guy. It is a frightening thought that a man with such bizarre beliefs could be a candidate for they job of most powerful man in the world. Among his weirder convictions is that he himself invented the Internet. He is most famous, of course, for his embracing of the Global Warming scam, attributing to this cause everything from floods in North Dakota to droughts in Texas and forest fires in Florida. Gore is convinced that "human civilisation is now the dominant cause of change in the global environment," conveniently forgetting little items like the sun, the oceans, volcanoes, and other natural phenomena. Gore's "strategic goal" is to "eliminate the internal combustion engine" by the year 2020. He has put his philosophy in a book called *The Earth in Balance*, an extraordinary progression from the works of Aristotle, Bacon and Decartes to the concept of environmental activists as "resistance fighters." He actually believes that modern environmental problems can be compared with Kristallnacht or the Holocaust. His arrogance is almost boundless and he knows better than most of the world's serious scientists.

Naturally, Gore's solution to the "environmental crisis" is more regulation, even down to controlling where people are allowed to live. All this on the grounds that "industrial civilisation is engaged in a terrible onslaught against the natural world" and the "cumulative impact of automobiles is posing a mortal threat to the security of every nation more deadly than that of any military enemy we are ever again likely to confront." Again, I have used a tiny fraction of the outpourings of this disturbed mind that I have come across. To use any more would make my account just as unbalanced.

15.5 Harvard

There are two very difficult things in the world.
One is to make a name for oneself and the other is to keep it.
Robert Schumann

In the annals of junk science the name of Harvard also comes up with extraordinary frequency. How can this be? After all it is one of the most revered names in all of academe and the oldest university in America, founded by the Calvinists in 1636. Among the many distinguished scientific groups in the university, however, is the Harvard School of Public Health (which was awarded the Junkman's Pennant for Junk Science, receiving twice as many points as Tulane University in second place). It is one of the most prolific publishers in the world. The list of junk contributions is impressive. Here are just a few examples:

Weight gain causes breast cancer (risk ratio 1.4)
Red meat causes bone fracture (risk ratio 1.23)
Selenium reduces prostate cancer risk (based on 35 cases)
Trans fats cause heart disease (risk ratio 1.5)
Coffee reduces suicide (ignoring the confounding factor that
depressives are advised to avoid it)
Fish intake reduces cardiac deaths (risk ratio 0.48)
Toenail levels of five trace elements (arsenic, chromium, copper, iron
and zinc) have no relation to breast cancer

(though nobody suggested they had, and I mistakenly thought that the relationship between toenails and cancer was a frivolous invention of my own.)

And on and on and on..........

A typical piece of Harvard junk was reported in the Boston Herald, 22 January, 1999:

> Maybe you should skip the bran muffin and have an extra cup of coffee instead.
>
> Now that it has been shown that eating a high-fiber diet does not protect against colon cancer, some are looking to java as a way to prevent the deadly disease.
>
> Dr. Edward Giovannucci of the Harvard School of Public Health published a study last year suggesting that the risk of colorectal cancer drops 24 percent among those who drink four or more cups of coffee a day.
>
> But before you go out and invest in a Starbucks franchise, take note. Giovannucci says the study is far from conclusive.
>
> "I wouldn't tell people to go out and start drinking coffee, although there isn't much harm in it," he said.
>
> Experts say the best ways to prevent colorectal cancer are still taking vitamins, staying in shape, taking an aspirin a day, avoiding red meat and getting regular screenings after age 50.

Oh yeah?

> Giovannucci's paper, which reviewed all the literature on the subject of coffee and colorectal cancer, appeared in the American Journal of Epidemiology. But he downplayed its importance.
>
> "I'm not sure the 24 percent reduction in risk is a cause and effect association," he said.
>
> "It would be important if it is real, but it is hard to say in an epidemiological study that there isn't a bias or other factor that is accounting for this.

Now, this is disarming honesty from such a source, but why would anyone publish a study that is far from conclusive (in fact, at a risk ratio of 1.24 our Headline Man (q.v.) did better than that) apart from adding to the precious publication list? Perhaps the next paragraph gives a clue:

> Giovannucci said the results were interesting enough to warrant further study, which is what Vanderbilt University in Nashville is planning to do. Vanderbilt is scheduled to open its Institute for Coffee Studies within the next six months, thanks to $6 million in funding from trade groups in leading coffee-producing nations.

The activities of the Harvard group gave rise to a law that was included in the appropriations bill that Congress approved as one of its final actions of 1998. This said that all data produced by researchers receiving federal grants can be obtained through the Freedom of Information Act, a federal law that gives citizens access to government documents. The measure arose from a complaint by industry groups that the Harvard School of Public Health refused to release data that the EPA relied on when they proposed tougher air-quality standards the previous year. Now this is a draconian law with high potential of destructive and unwanted side effects. Kevin Casey, spokesman for Harvard University said "We have grave concerns, This is a large problem, and the more we look into it, the more sirens go off." Other complainants included the National Academy of Sciences, the Massachusetts Institute of Technology, Boston University Medical Center, and the American Association of University Professors. They all have only themselves to blame. If scientists cannot practise self-regulation and allow these destructive and costly fatuities to occur they should not be surprised when someone else decides to regulate them.

This institution, however, is not all bad. For example when the EPA in a typical move to increase its powers claimed that "...the overall incidence rate of new cancers in children has increased "by about 12 percent from 1973 to 1994 in the U.S.] and naturally concluded that "The trends in some cancer types suggest the need for a closer examination of the underlying factors leading to [cancer] in children. This includes determining whether environmental contaminants play a role in causing the disease." A rebuttal was published by Harvard epidemiologist Dimitrious Trichopoulos who wrote that "Since the early 1960s, the incidence of childhood cancers, and in particular childhood leukaemia has remained relatively stable."

Harvard Nurses' Health Study

Let the *New York Times* (September 15, 1998) say it all:

> More than 20 years ago, a doctor who was curious about the effects of long-term oral contraceptive use sent questionnaires to 370,000 registered nurses. The answers he and colleagues received have turned into the largest and longest repeated follow-up study of a group of women, a fountain of information about health, in particular women's health.

> The project, known as the Harvard Nurses Health Study, has yielded more than 200 published findings, including these:

> * Hormone replacement therapy can increase the risk of breast cancer and can decrease the risk of heart disease and osteoporosis.

> * Margarine can increase the risk of heart disease.

> * Vitamin E can protect against heart disease.

> * One or two drinks a day can increase the risk of breast cancer while protecting against heart disease.

> These findings, and many more, have altered how people eat and drink and live their lives. Some scientists call the study the single greatest contributor to understanding women's health.

Some scientists call it the greatest single contribution to the proliferation of junk. Not the epidemiologists, however:

> "It was a brilliant idea, a unique idea," *said Dr. Leslie Bernstein, an epidemiologist at the University of Southern California.* "It's one of the largest studies ever to have been assembled. They were leaders, ahead of their time. Now everybody is trying to emulate what they've done."

The Harvard Group make our imaginary Headline Man look like a rank amateur, as the figure of 200 publications reveals. He only looked at one disease and made only four headlines (on the basis, remember, of no real effect at all). The Harvard group at regular intervals are able to leak out their findings, which are dutifully published by (to their eternal shame) journals such as the *BMJ* and then taken up with enthusiasm by the world's press. Now that research groups are audited for performance on the basis of bibliometry, the Harvard group must go down as the most successful research group of all time.

Occasionally a bit of light shows through the murk. The nurses health study actually demolished one well trailed falsehood – that a high fibre diet protects from colo-rectal cancer.

It is not only nurses who receive their attention. They have also made a study of middle aged men, producing such findings as the ten servings of tomatoes a week that reduce prostate cancer by a "dramatic" 45%. Do not underestimate the impact of these effusions – a web search of tomatoes AND prostate produced well over 6,000 hits. The news from Harvard is not all bad, however, in the Christmas edition of the *BMJ* (*The Times*, 24 Dec 1998) they report that eating sweets adds one year to the life expectancy of old men, while women who eat nuts have less heart disease.

I was devastated to discover that my own large tomato consumption was entirely without benefit, as I like them raw. Apparently, my digestive system is unable to extract the vital antioxidant lycopene without the assistance of a cook.

15.6 A State of Lunacy

California is a fine place to live – if you happen to be an orange.
Fred Allen

They tell me that if I want to see the future I should go to California. I would rather not, if you don't mind. I tried to adopt the attitude my mother had to had to importunate dogs – ignore it and it will go away. This was not a successful policy. The more I delved into the subject of this book, the more California intruded upon the scene. The credulity of Californians beggars belief. They swallow, hook line and sinker, every piece of junk that comes out of institutions such as the EPA. Californians are not allowed to smoke in bars (even cigar bars) because the Nanny State thinks it is bad for their health. The State is a Mecca for every guru, therapist, fakir, faker, junk scientist, pseudo-scientist, health freak and fanatic.

Is there anything that a Californian cannot be persuaded to believe? In a table of companies involved in technical fraud, the state comes easily at the top, as it does for the number of fraud victims. The real trouble with most Californians is that they have too much money (the poor ones don't count). They can buy anything except immortality (and they are not convinced of that). It was in California that junk science achieved its apotheosis with the notorious Proposition 65, which requires sellers of toxic substances known to cause cancer or reproductive toxicity to warn of risks associated with their use. As we have seen (§7.4) the weasel words " known to cause cancer" mean that they produce tumours when given in massive doses to hapless rodents bred to be highly cancer prone. This was not something foisted on an unwilling population by cranky politicians. It was passed by a voter initiative, receiving 63 percent of the vote, after being backed by Jane Fonda and a host of other Hollywood celebrities. By July 1988 no fewer than 216 substances were officially listed as carcinogens and 15 as reproductive toxins. California law requires the statement **This product contains a chemical known to the state of California to cause cancer** to be displayed, but the standards at which it operates mean that a life-time's consumption will produce a risk of only one in 100,000 of contracting the disease. You might just as well say **users of this product risk being struck by lightning**. Cunningly the legislators have added a catch 22 to the process. A group of builders were sued by the District Attorney for putting up warning notices just in case, when they did not know whether the substances in their houses were supposed to be toxic or not. This was claimed to dilute the "value" of such warnings.

The greatest sufferers from the effects of California's loony embracing of junk theories were its children. Thirty years ago, California's schools were of an acceptable standard. There were no state-mandated curriculum or graduation requirements a generation ago, and yet California's students were at or near the top of the league. Things began to change in the 1960s, as progressive ideas in education gained new currency in the education department and teachers' colleges began filtering into schools and became enshrined in law. The 1970s saw a downward slide in test scores. From 1970 to 1980, California's average SAT score fell 58 points, from 957 to 899. The average verbal score fell from 464 to 425, and the average math score from 493 to 474

Between 1983 and 1987 a modest reform programme had been implemented and standards began rising again throughout the state, but then the trendies really got hold of the system. New jargon entered the vocabulary: higher-order thinking skills, learning to learn skills, outcome-based curriculum and other abstract education theories. Most egregious of all was "whole math" in which students were supposed to develop their own methods of multiplying and dividing, ask questions of one another rather than of teachers, and learn that answers that are close to correct are good enough. Inevitably a long decline began. Scores in the Scholastic Achievement Test (SAT) at best stagnated, but in many places went into free fall. By 1994, in a survey, 63 percent of California employers said recent high school graduates applying for entry level jobs "lack a satisfactory education."

What was the bureaucrats' answer to all this? More auditing and central control, of course. The educational saga continues. Meanwhile all across the state economy regulation was piled upon regulation. State regulatory bodies burgeoned (Cal-EPA, Cal-OSHA, the South Coast Air Quality Management District etc.) and their tentacles probed into every corner of society.

What is the cost of all this excessive regulation? For a start, from 1989 to 1992 a third of US job losses occurred in California, a period in which it saw the biggest tax rises in its history. The severity of California's recession was blamed on the North American Free Trade Agreement, illegal immigrants, and violent criminals. But, according to a Cato Institute Policy report, the contributors to Regulation (1994, no. 3) say that the main problem with California's economy is burdensome regulations. Senior editor Edward L. Hudgins sums it up: "Just as New York has become a paradigm of what not to do with tax policy, California should be the model of which regulatory policies to avoid." One company, Rohr Industries, found the approval process for opening a new plant so trying that it gave up and moved to Arkansas. The permit, which would have cost $750,000 in California, cost only $750 in Arkansas.

Naturally the state's academics were not left behind in all this progress. In a 1997 study published in the journal Epidemiology (where else?) on diesel exhaust and lung cancer, researchers from the University of California (San Francisco) and the University of California (Berkeley) did a meta-analysis of 23 epidemiological studies of diesel exhaust and lung cancer. 7 other diesel exhaust/lung cancer studies were excluded from the meta-analysis, 6 of which did not support the researchers' ultimate conclusion. The results – a relative risk of 1.33 (95 percent confidence interval 1.24. - 1.44). Pure junk, of course.

According to the Los Angeles Times (Feb 22 1999), San Diego Police Department's vice squad has reduced its attack on pimps, hookers, johns and gamblers. Its major target is now the bar room smoker. Plain-clothes officers lurk about in bars and slap them with a ticket that can cost as much as $273. "San Diego is doing an excellent job," said Diane Kaiser, director of the California Smoke-free Bar Program, an offshoot of the American Lung Association. "We wish other cities would use the San Diego model, and we plan to bring it to their attention." In many cities the law has been virtually ignored, but in San Diego, where community-oriented policing is considered a religion, the vice squad has been prowling bars for months in response to complaints by bar patrons and employees that voluntary compliance is not working. The use of undercover, rather than uniformed, cops is also distinctly San Diegan. " The reality has got to settle in among the public," vice Detective James Jarrett said. "The law is here to stay and so are we. As long as there is a law, we'll enforce it." In 1998, 134 citations were written for bar smoking, a small number perhaps for a city of 1.2 million people but large enough, police hope, to send a message.

"What we want to do is create paranoia," Police Sgt. Sam Campbell said. "We want smokers to be paranoid about being cited for breaking the law. If paranoia gets compliance, I can live with it." On any given night, a bar room smoker in San Diego might light up and then be startled when that friendly fellow at the next bar stool discreetly flashes a badge and politely, quietly invites the smoker outside, where he receives a citation. Said one miscreant "You can't smoke in a bar, you can't talk to your friends. Is this still America? Not in San Diego." "Smoking enforcement is not popular with the detectives," Jarrett said. "We get into more confrontations than with anything else we do." According to Kate Nelson, president of the California Licensed Beverage Association and owner of the Hollywood Palace, a 1,500-seat theatre with six bars. "People simply have it in their minds that cigarette smoke is the deadliest legal substance available." It all goes to show the power of the big lie when told by a body like the EPA to a gullible population.

It all seems positively frivolous when you read on what actually goes on in the mean streets, down which a man must go who is not himself mean, who is neither tarnished or afraid. Crime and hard drug addiction are rife. Shootings are commonplace. The wealthy lock themselves behind walls and gates, pretending it is not happening. California is the home of the American film industry. It floods the world with the appalling graphic violence that it positively worships. Even in a country like Singapore, where it is illegal to possess a stick of chewing gum, you turn on the television nightly and see human bodies ripped apart by guns, cars and knives, blood and guts spurting out at regular intervals; all courtesy of Hollywood. And that is only the official industry. The state is also the world capital of hard porn, the directors of which are feted as successful citizens.

Having banned all the effective pesticides (because they cause cancer in mice in large concentrations) the state now finds that it faces an invasion of fire ants that threaten to wipe out many of the species that it is supposed to be protecting. The state budget is a disaster and promises years of economic chaos. For years they had it all too easy, living off the defence industry and regulating like mad. Nevertheless, the regulation goes on. The EPA is allowed to run riot; for example closing down 35 wells because they had tiny traces of trichloroethylene (TCE), which is also known to cause cancer in mice.

If California is the future, I feel more reconciled to the approach of death.

15.7 Cool Britannia

He that is mad, and sent to England..........T'will not be seen in him there; there men are as mad as he.
Shakespeare – Hamlet

Where California leads, America follows, with Britain and Europe not far behind. While I was writing this book, Britain elected a New Left Government that was virtually a clone of that in the USA. The presidential figure was a Cheshire Cat given to vacuous sound bites, while the vice presidential figure was an ambitious political animal with his colours firmly nailed to the mast of junk science. Ministers quickly establish their rights to the perks of power – fine homes, chauffeur-driven cars, luxurious foreign travel and endless parties attended by figures from the more banal reaches of the entertainment industry. The backbenchers were anonymous automata fit only to fill the voting lobbies on command. Parliament and the cabinet became ciphers and policy announcements were made from sofas in TV studios.

America is a huge and diverse country. It has the best and the worst of almost everything, but Britain seems intent on imitating only the worst. Thus over recent years we have adopted junk food, junk universities, self-assessment and no-win-no-fee lawyers who are escalating litigation out of all proportion and upping the cost of almost everything.

People trying to provide a public service are continuously reeling from the constant changes thrust upon them by radical politicians; not constructive changes, such as the introduction of new technologies, but destructive changes of organisation and auditing. They are harangued by the Prime Manager for being resistant to change. Still staggering under the burden of imposing the internal market, they are now required to dismantle it and replace it with another form of control and auditing. The destructive effect on services and morale is incalculable.

The sinister take-over by the party machine is accelerating. Policy is largely decided by what John Prescott calls "faceless wonders". These are over seventy young well-paid (up to £80,000 p.a.) officials, who have known no other trade than politics, and decide national policy in the complete absence of any regulatory mechanism. They all expect to get their turn at safe seats when they come up. Is it any wonder that each crazy effusion from the junk science lobbies is taken up with enthusiasm and becomes an engine of Government policy?

Is it an exaggeration to say that Britain has gone mad? If you went back twenty years and told people that they would one day have secret hoards of T-bone steaks and garden sprays, they would have put you away. These are just two of the results of the activities of MAFF, who implement senseless bans while encouraging such dangerous practices as the widespread abuse of antibiotics in farming. They have been completely out of control for years. The SIF organisations, dedicated to engineering panic, are now firmly in the driving seat. The Government lurches from one alarm to the next. Typically, it found itself Janus-like facing both ways when it was defending GM foods and attacking beef on the bone. Naturally, it backed down on the former under concerted SIF pressure.

The tragedy is that, as we enter the 2000s there is no effective opposition. The Conservative Party has gone into self-destruct. I watched it wither from the inside. It began to die from the roots through neglect in the early eighties, though the foliage did not begin to moulder until the late nineties. In the country and in Parliament, it has become an irrelevant right wing rump, without the first idea of how to re-establish contact with its traditional support. The British people are left subject to the Cunningham doctrine, that they are not fit to make their own decisions. The Government majority is so great that it is effectively a dictatorship, even ignoring protests from within its own ranks. The Government rules by diktat and exhortation (in the late nineties it became the country's largest customer for advertising).

Many traditional ways of British life are simply allowed to die away through neglect. They are of no interest to urban politicians and bureaucrats, for whom the countryside is just a place where one has one's second home (a freebee for senior ministers). The National federation of Women's Institutes reports a savage attrition of rural life, with the mass closure of post offices, pubs, banks, churches, surgeries etc. The village constable has gone and burglars ply their trade untrammelled. These losses do not affect the wealthy and influential, who barricade themselves in their country cottages at weekends and do not require services. Precious countryside is being built over at a high rate, while city centres decay, producing the doughnut effect that blights so many American towns.

British culture is dying of a surfeit of management. Time was when hospitals were run by matrons, universities by dons and the BBC by programme makers. They were the best in the world, but the finest techniques of modern management have now reduced them to mediocrity. A lesson I learned from my apprenticeship was that much of industry survives despite management, not because of it. Life for creative people is a constant battle to surmount the barriers created by administrators. The crux of the matter is the constant and overwhelming flow of numbers, mostly spurious.

The British must be on of the most put-upon people in the world. They pay more than other populations for almost everything, from cars to CDs. They work longer hours for less pay. SIF inspired duties on motoring, drink and tobacco are many times the average in other countries. They have to endure by far the highest crime rates in Europe (five times the burglary rate of Germany, Portugal or Spain, for example) and enjoy the lowest life expectancy. They also have the highest divorce, abortion and suicide rates. You can buy whole streets in Liverpool and Manchester for the price of one tiny house in London, but that is macro-economics for you. The Nanny State wrests from them the right to make their own lifestyle decisions. As we have seen in these pages, the phenomena are not unrelated. What kind of madness is it that causes a nation to dismantle its own manufacturing and farming industries, making itself a client state to the rest of the world? A small island, easily blockaded, is more at risk than most. If there ever really is a global natural disaster, such as a super-volcano, Britain has placed itself in a position to be the most disastrously affected country in the world. One of the cardinal errors of politicians and journalists is the assumption that thing will always be as they are now.

15.8 The Cancer Industry

I was wondering how to start this section when I heard the mail land on the doormat. One of the letters was in a large brown envelope prominently marked "You have been selected" – a standard ploy used by grifters down the ages; make the mark feel special. I was about to bin it without opening, assuming it was yet another draw from the *Readers Digest*, when I noticed that it was from the World Cancer Research Fund "Stopping Cancer before it starts" Registered Charity No 1000739. My curiosity was aroused. Why would a Research Fund use a typical scam opening that can be translated as "We bought your name and address from a data base of likely suckers"? The contents proved rewarding for my purpose. After asking my sex and date of birth the survey wanted to know about my diet (red meat, white meat, meat products, fish, salad, fruit). Was I a vegetarian? What was my consumption of alcohol? What was my use of cigarettes? A familiar list.

A sheet accompanying this impartial survey gave me guidelines for cancer prevention. Eat plenty of vegetables and fruit. Drink alcohol only in moderation, if at all. Select foods low in fat and salt. *And always remember* (their italics) do not smoke or use tobacco in any form.

Then came the scary bit. Cancer is the second largest cause of death in Britain today. It is a sad fact that one in three people in Britain will get cancer during their lifetime. In the following pitch three bits were underlined (my emphases):

> *But there is tremendous hope for the future – for cancer is a largely preventable disease.*
> *Now **there is hope** that ways to prevent cancer **may be** on the horizon.*
> *35% of all cancer deaths **have been estimated to be** related to diet.*

This was why it was important for me to fill out and return the survey. In return for my help they would be delighted to send me their free booklet "WCRF Dietary Guidelines to Lower Your Cancer Risk". There follows an extended blurb full of the usual weasel phrases, such as "research suggests that…"

Am I being a bit slow here? They are asking me to take part in a survey to which they already seem to know the answer. Almost the only things they are interested in are from the standard SIF hit list. What if cancer is caused by liquorice allsorts, potato crisps or a hundred other things that might be in my diet.

The sting, of course, appears on the last page of the survey, in which I can tick a box indicating the magnitude of my gift. A foot note says "Can you send £10 or more, The need is urgent."

The last thing I would wish to do is to dissuade people from contributing to research into this frightening disease. It scares the pants off me (almost as much as Alzheimer's) but as a regular reader of The Junkman I detect the malodorous tang of junk science. I have seen no convincing evidence to support their bald statement that cancer is a largely preventable disease, though I pray it may be so. If cures are to be found for the wide range of diseases we label "cancer", they will come from millions of hours of meticulous scientific research into the nature of cell division, not from the issuing of cranky diet sheets.

When President Nixon declared war on cancer the American people responded in the only way they know – they set up an industry. The rest of the world followed slavishly. America spent $22 billion on research in the twenty years following President Nixon's signature of the National Cancer Act. President Nixon created a monster that became known as the EPA in 1970, against a background of claims that "the environment causes 90 percent of cancer." There was never any truth in those claims. They were initiated by one John Bailar III, and must constitute one of the grossest examples of lying with numbers in human history.

The American Cancer Society alone is now a major industry. According to *The Tampa Tribune* (March 20, 1992) of the $367 million it spent in 1990-91, only 14 percent went to services for cancer patients. About 26 percent went to research or grants. But 23 percent of the Cancer Society's budget – some $85 million – went to administration and fund raising. In 1989, its chief executive made more than $200,000.

It would be wrong to be completely negative about the American approach to cancer. The survival rate (five years or more) in Britain rose from 25 to 30% in the 1980s, but in America it reached 40% (*The Times* June 19, 1998). Nevertheless, the incidence of the disease in America has risen 15 percent over the past 20 years and the death rates from cancers of the lung, prostate and breast remain almost unchanged.

The fact is that cancer, with a few tragic exceptions, is a disease of old age. An eighty-year-old faces a thousand times the risk of a teenager. The twenty-fold increase due to cigarette smoking is dwarfed in comparison.

One of the sickest examples of the exploitation of the fear of cancer was an advertisement for Florida orange juice I saw in the USA. A man is seen drinking orange juice at the breakfast table when a glass the size of a dustbin lands in the middle of it. The message was that drinking this would reduce the risk of cancer. This advertisement was endorsed by the American Cancer Association, which had apparently sold out for a million dollars. Ironically, according to the *American Journal of Epidemiology* (1997;146:833-841) consumption of fruit was associated with a "statistically significant" 76 percent increase in brain tumours. Furthermore, consumption of fruits rich in vitamin C was associated with a statistically significant 101 percent increase in brain tumours.

15.9 Smugglers' Joy

Brandy for the Parson
'Baccy for the Clerk

....

Watch the wall, my darling, while the Gentlemen go by!
Kipling – A Smuggler's Song

Who would have thought that smuggling would be restored to its position as one of Britain's major industries? The politicians, egged on by the SIFs, have managed to achieve this. The duty on beer, for example, is eight times higher in Dover than it is twenty two miles away in Calais. A P&O spokesman likened the Port of Dover to Chicago in prohibition times. Much of the traffic is, of course, quite legal. A large proportion of the population of the south of England go regularly on booze runs, which among other things are now a standard part of the preparations for a wedding. Pubs in Kent (which has taken on Cornwall's old *rôle*) are closing down because they cannot compete with the influx of cheap alcohol. A great deal of the traffic, however, is illegal in that it is not for the person's own consumption. Gangs are turning away from drugs to cigarettes because they are equally profitable and less risky. A British tobacco company had to increase its production of hand-rolling tobacco because of the demand from Belgium, from whence it is smuggled back into Britain. Customs and Excise estimate that 60% of such tobacco is smuggled. Every village has its local smuggler who can provide frowned-upon goods at knock down prices. I find this particularly annoying, as they do not deal with the goods that I consume. In his 1998 budget, the Chancellor, having put up duties yet again, proposed the solution of increasing resources to the policing authorities (i.e. more snoopers) but, as George Santayana remarked, those who do not remember history are condemned to repeat it.

The black market is a remarkable institution and a powerful illustration of the application of the Le Chatelier principle *(q.v.)* to ordinary life. As soon as taxation and regulation are deemed by general consent to be oppressive, the black market swings into operation to provide a corrective force. In some cases, such as taxes on windows and motor fuel, it is of course impractical for such forces to operate, but in many cases they are very effective. When really destructive ideologues gain power, such as Chancellors Healey and Howe in Britain, the black market regenerates itself to mitigate the effects of their disastrous policies. There is a sad aftermath in that the most honest nation on earth became corrupted.

15.10 The persistence of lies

The amazing thing about the many fabrications we have discussed is that, however often they are authoritatively refuted, they simply bounce back. This, of course, is the great strength of the SIFs and the junk peddlers. As long as they can get their thrust in first, it will make a lasting impact, no matter how often it is debunked.

On June 11th 1999 I was on the road much of a day during the great Belgian dioxin scare. I must have heard on the car radio the phrase "cancer-causing dioxins" at least two dozen times. When you think that no one has ever produced a single iota of evidence that dioxins are human carcinogens, it all takes on a dream-like quality. I got home and opened *The Times* and there was a letter quoting the decline of raptors due to DDT as only one example of the effect of pollution, yet raptors actually increased in numbers in the USA during the period for which DDT was in use.

In a television debate on GM foods the Chairman, Jonathan Miller, contrasted the uncertainties of the subject with the well-known fact that eating butter causes coronary thrombosis.

One of the factors that make these fabrications so robust is the frequency with which they are slipped into articles to which they have little relevance. A two-page article (*The Times* January 16 1999) on erosion of the British coastline, for example, contains the paragraph –

> Studies by the climatic research unit at the University of East Anglia show how sea levels have begun to increase sharply with the increase in concentration of carbon dioxide and other greenhouse gases.

It is like water wearing away a rock. The constant drip drip of propaganda has people bemused into accepting as established fact claims that, at the very best, are unproven.

15.11 Return of The Magnificent Seven

While I was trying to put an end to the research for this book in June 1999, a welter of scares appeared in the media. There was about one a day on teletext. One that got a big splash was a story that heavy drinking (more than 35 units a week) caused strokes. The source was a BMJ paper from Glasgow University. Great play was made of the fact that this was based on a long-term study of a large cohort of men (5766), which made it all sound very convincing. I began to wonder just how many men actually were heavy drinkers who died of strokes. I broke my rule about sticking to media stories and looked at the original text of the paper. It turned out that just 17 out of 503 in the heavy drinking category died of strokes. How many could we expect? Well, 38 out of the 1833 non-drinkers also died of strokes, i.e. about 2%. On this basis we would expect about 10.4 out of the 503, so the excess number of men was under 7. I make this a risk ratio of 1.63, while the authors published 1.74 (95% confidence level 1.47-2.06); good enough for epidemiology but not acceptable for real science. By the time it got into the press it had developed into a real scare; e.g. The Times, June 25 1999 –

Drink Danger

A long term study of 5,766 working men has found no support for the idea that drinking alcohol in moderation is good for you. Those drinking more that 35 units a week – the recommended maximum is 22 – are twice as likely to die from a stroke, the researchers from Glasgow University report in the British Medical Journal today.

So the whole scare was based on just seven men, the same number of smoking schoolboys who were motor racing fans and caused *The Lancet* to call for ministerial resignations (§.2). This is an example of one of our Trojan numbers *(q.v.)*. The large number 5,766 gives credence to the story, but only about 0.12% of this number actually contributed to the scare, which gave an opportunity to slip in yet another reference to the recommended maximum. As for the figure of 35 units a week, a colleague brought up in Glasgow tells me that would put any man in the Jessie class.

15.12 What shall we tell the children?

One of the great problems for individuals and society is the question of how we inform children, particularly about the dangers they will face. We used to use what teachers called the method of diminishing deception, starting off with Santa Claus and fairies and gradually progressing to the awful truth about adult life. It is perhaps a sad thing that childhood and innocence have largely been eliminated in modern society. Children are more and more treated as miniature adults. The process began in Britain in 1955 with the introduction of commercial television. Children stopped being children and became consumers. As communication increased in power and presence, children obtained access to all the information there was. There is no point in dissembling. There is no choice. **You have to tell children the absolute truth**. The dangers they face seem so much more terrifying than those we did. Dangerous addictive drugs, for example, are freely available to them and they make their own life choices at a relatively early age. Guidance gets more difficult as they grow into adolescents. Rebellion is one of their jobs in life, but the political scene has changed so much that even this is problematic. The fashionable permanent revolution has highjacked much of the natural right of youth to rebellion and it finds other outlets. Yet, even more than adults, they are subjected to all sorts of coercion by interested parties. It is, however, in the nature of young people that the more you hector them the more they are likely to do the other thing.

The SIFs think they are the solution, when they are in fact a major part of the problem. The vulnerable young, to whom death seems such a long way off, are largely unimpressed, for example, by the threat of lung cancer, which they rightly perceive as a disease of the elderly. A teen-ager can spot a lie at a hundred paces. In their desperation the anti-smoking SIFs come up with such scams as "smoking causes impotence" (risk ratio 1.5) which produce nothing but mirth. The more tobacco and alcohol become forbidden fruits, the more they adopt them. Savage price-hiking and legal bans have little effect or even an adverse one. These commodities simply move out of the normal market into the black market. The use of tobacco and alcohol among the young, despite all the propaganda is actually on the increase.

If you are a parent it is impossible not to worry. Dangerous addictive drugs, like heroin and crack-cocaine, are freely available to schoolchildren. Marijuana is even more a freely available commodity. Ecstasy is widely used by young people at their raves. Despite the few highly publicised deaths that have occurred, Ecstacy would seem to be a relatively safe drug. I am not advocating these drugs. I have no personal experience of them. Despite working in universities all my life, I do not even know what marijuana smells like. I do recognise, however, that there is a world of difference between the so-called social drugs and the likes of heroin and crack, which corrode the individual and society. Apart from the destruction of the lives of individuals, heroin is one of the major causes of the current crime wave. Grouping it with other drugs that are disapproved of or are politically incorrect is plain stupid. The scatter-gun, ban-everything approach is stupid, wasteful and ineffective. Massive effort is wasted tracking down errant traders who are selling tobacco and alcohol to young adults, when it could be devoted to a savage attack on the heroin dealers.

Repression does not work on the young; nor does over-protection. I have been personal tutor to hundreds of young people in my time. The ones most likely to go off the rails are those brought up in a strict teetotal household. I am grateful that my father introduced me to the moderate use of alcohol at an early age.

I have never known a time when the young were more alienated, boys in particular. Their mentors purport to be so sympathetic and understanding, yet they subject them to unprecedented stress. Boys, conditioned by evolution to be competitive, physical and obstreperous, are forced into the feminised straight jacket dictated by political correctness. They grow up into a world for which nature has not prepared them. Suicide rates among young men (15-24) rose by 80% between 1980 and 1992. Over 1000 of them take their own lives every year. Many more drop out and turn to petty crime. Their rebellion does not receive the constructive opposition it needs. Wayward youngsters terrorise whole estates with impunity. If an adult tries to correct them he is the one who lands up in court. The old sureties of family, community and career have dissolved away.

From the age of three children become slaves of the audit. Whether they are suited to examinations or not, they have to conform to the testing routine. Before they can even communicate effectively they are required to contribute to the attainment of norms. They do not know the reasons why, but their antennae pick up the vibrations and the pressure. In young adulthood they find a world in which insecurity has been in-built as a tool of social engineering. Stress is the common factor. Mankind has always been subjected to stress and is conditioned to combat it, but now it is different in nature and inhuman in operation. More people die by their own hand than in road accidents. Yet which receives the greater publicity? According to the Samaritans, the UK has the highest rate of suicide attempts in Europe and attempts among young men have doubled since the eighties. It is fairly typical that the state piles on the pressure and a voluntary organisation picks up the pieces.

I was lucky to be an infant when the only thing to worry about was the bombs that were dropping on us. It is so much harder and more stressful today. The only thing you can tell young people is as much of the truth as you think you have grasp of. This is rather difficult when you are yourself being systematically lied to on a grand scale. They will find a world that we have cocked up for them. They might do better. Who knows?

15.13 The onset of scare fatigue?

As I began to bring the writing of this book to a conclusion I seemed to detect the seeds of a change in the climate. Perhaps it was just an uncharacteristic outbreak of optimism. Ordinary people (but not their masters) were beginning to treat scares as part of the entertainment industry rather than something they should be panicked by. Even while the mobile phone hysteria was at its peak, one of the devices was being sold in Britain every four seconds. When I asked the denizens of the village pub what they thought of the Glasgow alcohol and strokes scare, none of them had noticed it, yet it had appeared in all their papers that day. Even more importantly, influential journalists were beginning to join the resistance movement. Simon Jenkins (**Panic is now the plague: science committees now obfuscate and leave politicians running scared**, *The Times*, June 6 1999) found his last straw in the order of Frank Dobson, the Health Secretary, that all trial contact lenses should be destroyed after one use. This latest manifestation of the CJD panic made the notorious beef-on-the-bone ban look like the Wisdom of Solomon. Jenkins quite rightly points out that this sort of action is a symptom of mad scientist disease. The Spongiform Encephalopathy Advisory Committee (SEAC) had finally gone completely off its rocker. Over the ten-year period of its prominence nCJD had killed about the same number of Britons as lightning. It would be some sort of miracle if this measure saved a single life; yet it put up the cost of this important visual aid by about £50. As Jenkins asserts, this sort of panic risk aversion is enslaving Britain under the dictatorship of health and safety regulation.

I was trying hard to cut off the collection of examples in the summer of 1999, having set the end of June as a deadline, but they were coming thick and fast. I just had to make a stop, so I will leave the last one as……..

15.14 An exercise for the reader

From *The Times* July 14 1999;

> **VDU radiation making office workers sick**
> **New device cuts symptoms ranging from runny nose to backache, reports Ian Murray**
>
> *Office workers involved in a trial on the effects of radiation from computer screens were found to be suffering in total from 19 symptoms of ill health. They ranged from runny noses, itchy eyes and tiredness to back pain, short-term memory loss and depression.*
>
> *When the screens were fitted with a device that neutralises the low-level radiation, the office staff, who on average had been suffering from seven of the symptoms each, improved dramatically.*
>
> *In the trial involving the 100 staff at the Southampton Area Health Authority head office, the VDUs of half them were fitted with a device made up of two 9in aluminium tubes with crystals inside.*
>
> *The maker, TecnoAo of Swindon, Wiltshire, claims that they provide protection against low-level radiation. The other half of the staff were provided with dummy look-alike devices. Nobody, including the researchers, knew who had which device.*
>
> *A month later, the staff were questioned again about the 19 symptoms. There was no significant difference among those who had the dummy devices but the number of symptoms reported by those with the real ones fell by between 27 per cent and 44 per cent.*
>
> *The largest reduction was in neck and backache symptoms. TecnoAo, which in part funded the research, said that was probably because aches and pains of this sort are*

caused by the build-up of lactic acid in the muscles and low-level radiation fields interfere with the body's ability to rectify the situation.

Derek Clements-Croome, of Reading University, who led the research, said that normal brain rhythms during the working day functioned at between 7 and 14 hertz, which is similar to the range of the electromagnetic waves coming from a VDU. This meant that the VDU waves interreacted with the brain rhythms, causing it to work too hard and triggering different symptoms in the body.

John Jukes, of the consultants Optimum Workplace Environments, who collaborated in the research, said there was no longer any doubt that magnetic fields affected the way the human body and the brain functioned. The average office was full of such fields from cables, photocopiers and VDUs, which emitted waves effective up to two metres away. The crystals in the TecnoAo devices resonate when they are struck by the low frequency radiation and send out their own signal, which the manufacturer says increases the brain's resistance, preventing it from being overactivated.

The National Radiological Protection Board, which sets standards for microwave emissions, has said there is no danger from the radiations if they are not strong enough to heat the body.

But Milton Silverman, of the London law firm Streathers of Piccadilly, said that employers who did nothing to protect workers could face criminal charges if they exposed them to such dangers. Because of mounting evidence of the dangers of VDU and mobile telephone radiation, the EU was looking at the question and there could one day be a directive to force all employers to make screens safe.

Bibliography

Dewdney, A K, *Yes we have no Neutrons* (Wiley, 1997)

Dewdney, A K, *20% of nothing* (Wiley, 1993)

Bate R, Editor, *What Risk?* (Butterworth Heinemann, 1997)

Cohen, J and Stewart, I, *The Collapse of Chaos* (Viking 1994)

Eastham, R and Wyndham, J *Why do buses come in threes: the hidden mathematics of everyday life* (Robson, 1998)

Furedi, F, *Courting Mistrust: the hidden growth of a culture of litigation in Britain* (Centre for Policy Studies, 1999)

Furedi, F, *Culture of Fear: Risk-taking and the morality of low expectation* (Cassell, 1997)

Le Fanu, J *The rise & fall of modern medicine*, Little Brown, 1999.

Lock, S, and Wells, F, Editors, *Fraud and Misconduct in Medical Research* (BMJ Publishing Group, 1996)

McLeish, J, *Number* (Bloomsbury, 1991)

McTaggart, L, *What doctors don't tell you: the truth about the dangers of modern medicine* (Thorsons, 1996)

Mooney, L and Bate, R, Editors, *Environmental Health: Third World Problems – First World Preoccupations* (Butterworth Heinemann, 1999)

Power, M, *The Audit Society: Rituals of Verification* (Oxford, 1997)

Stewart, I., *The Magical Maze* (Weidenfield and Nicolson, 1997)

Webography

Because of the instability of many of the URLs involved, the webography is now stored and maintained at a web site – http://www.numberwatch.co.uk

Index